MARVEL CINEMATIC UNIVERSE GUIDEBOOK:
THE GOOD, THE BAD, THE GUARDIANS

MARVEL CINEMATIC UNIVERSE GUIDEBOOK:
THE GOOD, THE BAD, THE GUARDIANS

CONTENTS

Marvel's *Captain America: The Winter Soldier* — 3
Marvel's *Ant-Man* — 21
Marvel's *Guardians of the Galaxy* — 35
Marvel's *Avengers: Age of Ultron* — 67
Marvel's *Captain America: Civil War* — 99
Marvel's *Doctor Strange* — 131
Marvel's *Guardians of the Galaxy Vol. 2* — 163

COVER ART BY **STEPHANIE HANS**

HEAD WRITER/COORDINATOR: **MIKE O'SULLIVAN**

EDITOR: **SARAH BRUNSTAD**

ASSOCIATE MANAGER, DIGITAL ASSETS: **JOE HOCHSTEIN**

ASSISTANT EDITOR: **CAITLIN O'CONNELL**

ASSOCIATE MANAGING EDITOR: **KATERI WOODY**

EDITOR, SPECIAL PROJECTS: **MARK D. BEAZLEY**

SENIOR EDITOR, SPECIAL PROJECTS: **JENNIFER GRÜNWALD**

VP PRODUCTION & SPECIAL PROJECTS: **JEFF YOUNGQUIST**

BOOK DESIGNER: **JAY BOWEN**

COLLECTION INTERIOR DESIGNER: **SALENA JOHNSON**

SPECIAL THANKS TO GEORGE BELIARD, SHAWN "KEEBLER" BYERS, ERIKA DENTON, JOE FRONTIRRE, ELISSA HUNTER, AVIA PEREZ, JACQUE PORTE, AND RYAN POTTER.

SVP PRINT, SALES & MARKETING: **DAVID GABRIEL**

EDITOR IN CHIEF: **AXEL ALONSO**

CHIEF CREATIVE OFFICER: **JOE QUESADA**

PRESIDENT: **DAN BUCKLEY**

EXECUTIVE PRODUCER: **ALAN FINE**

FOR MARVEL STUDIOS

CREATIVE DIRECTOR, RESEARCH: **WILL CORONA PILGRIM**

DIRECTOR OF DEVELOPMENT: **ERIC HAUSERMAN CARROLL**

VP PRODUCTION & DEVELOPMENT: **BRAD WINDERBAUM**

SVP PRODUCTION & DEVELOPMENT: **STEPHEN BROUSSARD**

SVP PRODUCTION & DEVELOPMENT: **JEREMY LATCHAM**

PRESIDENT: **KEVIN FEIGE**

MARVEL CINEMATIC UNIVERSE GUIDEBOOK: THE GOOD, THE BAD, THE GUARDIANS. Contains material originally published in magazine form as GUIDEBOOK TO THE MARVEL CINEMATIC UNIVERSE — MARVEL'S CAPTAIN AMERICA: THE WINTER SOLDIER, MARVEL'S ANT-MAN, MARVEL'S GUARDIANS OF THE GALAXY, MARVEL'S AVENGERS: AGE OF ULTRON, MARVEL'S CAPTAIN AMERICA: CIVIL WAR, and MARVEL'S DOCTOR STRANGE. First printing 2017. ISBN# 978-1-302-90240-7. Published by MARVEL WORLDWIDE, INC., a subsidiary of MARVEL ENTERTAINMENT, LLC. OFFICE OF PUBLICATION: 135 West 50th Street, New York, NY 10020. Copyright © 2017 MARVEL No similarity between any of the names, characters, persons, and/or institutions in this magazine with those of any living or dead person or institution is intended, and any such similarity which may exist is purely coincidental. **Printed in China.** DAN BUCKLEY, President, Marvel Entertainment; JOE QUESADA, Chief Creative Officer; TOM BREVOORT, SVP of Publishing; DAVID BOGART, SVP of Business Affairs & Operations, Publishing & Partnership; C.B. CEBULSKI, VP of Brand Management & Development, Asia; DAVID GABRIEL, SVP of Sales & Marketing, Publishing; JEFF YOUNGQUIST, VP of Production & Special Projects; DAN CARR, Executive Director of Publishing Technology; ALEX MORALES, Director of Publishing Operations; SUSAN CRESPI, Production Manager; STAN LEE, Chairman Emeritus. For information regarding advertising in Marvel Comics or on Marvel.com, please contact Vit DeBellis, Integrated Sales Manager, at vdebellis@marvel.com. For Marvel subscription inquiries, please call 888-511-5480. **Manufactured between 8/11/2017 and 10/23/2017 by R.R. DONNELLEY ASIA PRINTING SOLUTIONS, CHINA.**

10 9 8 7 6 5 4 3 2 1

GUIDEBOOK TO THE MARVEL CINEMATIC UNIVERSE

MARVEL

CAPTAIN AMERICA
THE WINTER SOLDIER

MARVEL STUDIOS PRESENTS CHRIS EVANS "CAPTAIN AMERICA: THE WINTER SOLDIER" SCARLETT JOHANSSON SEBASTIAN STAN ANTHONY MACKIE COBIE SMULDERS FRANK GRILLO EMILY VANCAMP HAYLEY ATWELL WITH ROBERT REDFORD AS ALEXANDER PIERCE AND SAMUEL L. JACKSON AS NICK FURY CASTING BY SARAH HALLEY FINN, C.S.A. MUSIC BY HENRY JACKMAN MUSIC SUPERVISOR DAVE JORDAN VISUAL EFFECTS SUPERVISOR DAN DELEEUW VISUAL EFFECTS AND ANIMATION BY INDUSTRIAL LIGHT & MAGIC COSTUME DESIGNER JUDIANNA MAKOVSKY EDITOR JEFFREY FORD, A.C.E. PRODUCTION DESIGNER PETER WENHAM DIRECTOR OF PHOTOGRAPHY TRENT OPALOCH CO-PRODUCER NATE MOORE EXECUTIVE PRODUCER VICTORIA ALONSO MICHAEL GRILLO STAN LEE EXECUTIVE PRODUCER ALAN FINE EXECUTIVE PRODUCER LOUIS D'ESPOSITO PRODUCED BY KEVIN FEIGE, p.g.a. SCREENPLAY BY CHRISTOPHER MARKUS & STEPHEN McFEELY
#CaptainAmerica Facebook.com/CaptainAmerica
DIRECTED BY ANTHONY AND JOE RUSSO

Collecting information from Marvel's *Captain America: The Winter Soldier* (2014) and *Marvel's Captain America: The Winter Soldier Infinite Comic #1* (2014).

HEAD WRITER/COORDINATOR: **MIKE O'SULLIVAN**

COORDINATION: **DARON JENSEN**

WRITERS: **PATRICK DUKE, DARON JENSEN, ROB LONDON, CHRIS MCCARVER, JACOB ROUGEMONT,** AND **KEVIN WASSER**

ARTISTS: **MARK BRIGHT, JAMES CARSON, STEFANO CASELLI, GENE COLAN, KIERON DWYER, STEVE EPTING, PASQUAL FERRY, TIM FLATTERY, RYAN MEINERDING, DAVID MOREAU, JOSH NIZZI, GERMÁN PERALTA,** AND **JAMIE RAMA**

COVER ARTIST: **MIKE DEL MUNDO**

SPECIAL THANKS TO DAVE ALTHOFF, SHAWN "KEEBLER" BYERS, JEFF CHRISTIANSEN, MATT DELMANOWSKI, ERIKA DENTON, TIM DILLON, PERCIVAL LANUZA, AMANDA NALLEY, AVIA PEREZ, JACQUE PORTE, AND RYAN POTTER.

THIS ISSUE IS DEDICATED TO GARRY SHANDLING

CAPTAIN AMERICA CREATED BY JOE SIMON AND JACK KIRBY

AGENT 13

FIRST APPEARANCE:
Captain America: The Winter Soldier [2014]

Agent 13 of S.H.I.E.L.D.'s Special Service was secretly assigned by S.H.I.E.L.D. Director Nick Fury to protect Steve Rogers, a.k.a. Captain America. Posing as a nurse named Kate, Agent 13 resided in the apartment next door to Cap's, and maintained a friendly, sometimes flirtatious, relationship with him. One evening, while Cap and Agent 13 conversed outside of their apartments, she noticed that Cap's stereo was on at high volume. Inside, Cap found Fury, who was seriously injured after an attack by the Winter Soldier. As Fury warned Cap that S.H.I.E.L.D. had been compromised, Fury was shot by the Winter Soldier. Hearing the noise, Agent 13 burst into Cap's apartment, identified herself as a S.H.I.E.L.D. agent, and reported Fury's shooting to S.H.I.E.L.D. as Cap left to pursue the Winter Soldier. After being debriefed by World Security Council Secretary Alexander Pierce at the S.H.I.E.L.D. Triskelion about the events of the night before, Agent 13 and Cap passed each other in the adjoining corridor, where Cap made no secret of his displeasure with her deception. After Cap refused to reveal Fury's apparently final words, Pierce ordered Cap's arrest; Agent 13 was the first to question the resulting manhunt.

Later, as S.H.I.E.L.D. prepared to launch the three Project: Insight Helicarriers, Agent 13, in the launch control center, heard Cap reveal over S.H.I.E.L.D. communications channels that S.H.I.E.L.D. had been infiltrated by the terrorist organization Hydra. Agent Brock Rumlow and his S.T.R.I.K.E. team commandos—all Hydra agents—commandeered the control center and ordered the technicians at gunpoint to launch the Helicarriers. Though Agent 13 drew her own weapon, Rumlow disarmed her, launched the Helicarriers, and escaped. After the revelation of Pierce's Hydra loyalties, the destruction of the Triskelion and the Helicarriers, and the dissolution of S.H.I.E.L.D. itself, Agent 13 joined the CIA. ✪

FACT SHEET

▶ BEFORE THEY VISITED OUTSIDE THEIR APARTMENTS, CAP FOUND AGENT 13 SPEAKING ON THE PHONE; SHE CLAIMED TO BE SPEAKING TO HER AUNT, WHO SHE SAID WAS AN INSOMNIAC.

▶ AGENT 13 POLITELY REFUSED CAP'S INVITATION TO USE HIS WASHING MACHINE, CLAIMING THAT SHE HAD JUST COMPLETED ORIENTATION IN INFECTIOUS DISEASES AND WAS WORRIED HER SCRUBS WERE CONTAMINATED.

▶ AGENT 13'S PERSONAL SIDEARM WAS A LASER SIGHT-EQUIPPED FABRIQUE-NATIONALE FNP-45 TACTICAL.

▶ BLACK WIDOW REPEATEDLY ENCOURAGED CAP TO ASK AGENT 13 OUT ON A DATE.

▶ BLACK WIDOW EVENTUALLY REVEALED TO CAP THAT AGENT 13'S NAME WAS SHARON.

BLACK WIDOW
UPDATE

FIRST APPEARANCE: *Iron Man 2 [2010]*

Director of S.H.I.E.L.D. Nick Fury assigned Agent Natasha Romanoff, a.k.a. Black Widow, to help Captain America and Brock Rumlow's S.T.R.I.K.E. team rescue the crew of the S.H.I.E.L.D. satellite launch vessel *Lemurian Star* from pirates, but gave her a secret secondary objective: to download data from the *Lemurian Star*'s computers onto a flash drive to confirm his suspicions that S.H.I.E.L.D. had been compromised. Widow completed her objective, but Cap was angered when he learned of her secondary mission.

After Fury was shot and gave Cap the flash drive, Widow met Cap and Deputy Director Maria Hill at the hospital where Fury was being treated. From Cap's recounting, Widow recognized Fury's assailant as the Winter Soldier, a ruthless assassin she had encountered before. When Fury apparently died and World Security Council (WSC) Secretary Alexander Pierce summoned Cap for questioning, Widow, though distraught, still recovered the *Lemurian Star* flash drive, which Cap had hidden inside a vending machine.

After Pierce branded Cap a fugitive for withholding information Fury may have given him, Cap and Widow traced the *Lemurian Star* data to Camp Lehigh, New Jersey—where Cap had been selected to take the Super-Soldier Serum decades before. In a bunker beneath the camp, the digitized consciousness of World War II-era scientist Arnim Zola revealed to them that Hydra, the Nazis' deep science cabal, had vastly infiltrated S.H.I.E.L.D.; Widow was greatly disturbed by this, feeling she'd just traded the KGB for Hydra. After barely surviving a S.H.I.E.L.D. airstrike, Cap, Widow, and Cap's friend, pararescueman Sam Wilson (a.k.a. Falcon), abducted Hydra infiltrator Jasper Sitwell, who revealed under intimidation that S.H.I.E.L.D.'s Project: Insight Helicarriers were intended to proactively eliminate millions of Hydra's potential enemies across the globe in one fell swoop. The Winter Soldier and a Hydra team attacked the trio en route to the S.H.I.E.L.D. Triskelion, and Widow was shot in the melee. The S.T.R.I.K.E. team abducted all three, but Hill, impersonating a S.T.R.I.K.E. agent, rescued them and brought them

to a deep-cover base commanded by Fury, who had faked his death. Fury armed them with technology capable of reprogramming the Project: Insight Helicarriers.

Disguised as WSC Councilwoman Hawley, Widow confronted Pierce while Cap and Falcon attempted to disable the Helicarriers. After defeating Pierce's guards and revealing herself, Widow made S.H.I.E.L.D.'s records available online—revealing Hydra to the world. Pierce killed the other council members with booby-trapped access badges and threatened to do the same to Widow unless she helped him escape, but Widow used her Widow Sting weapon on herself, disabling the badge and allowing Fury to fatally shoot Pierce. After the Triskelion and Helicarriers were destroyed, Widow testified before a government inquest into S.H.I.E.L.D.'s corruption, then, after providing Cap and Wilson a file on the Winter Soldier, left to find a new purpose. ✷

CAPTAIN AMERICA UPDATE

FIRST APPEARANCE: *Captain America: The First Avenger [2011]*

After relocating to Washington, D.C., Steve Rogers began to acclimate to the modern era. He befriended Air Force veteran Sam Wilson, flirted with his neighbor "Kate" (secretly S.H.I.E.L.D. Agent 13, assigned to protect him), and reconnected with an elderly Peggy Carter. As Captain America, he served as one of S.H.I.E.L.D.'s top operatives, often working alongside his fellow Avenger, Black Widow, and Brock Rumlow's S.T.R.I.K.E. team. With them, he recovered the Zodiac weapon from terrorists in Chicago, and rescued the crew of the *Lemurian Star*, a S.H.I.E.L.D. launch vessel, from Georges Batroc and his mercenaries. During the mission, Cap learned Widow was operating under dual orders from Nick Fury to backup the ship's hard drive, which caused him to question S.H.I.E.L.D.'s priorities. Cap met with Fury, who showed him the Project: Insight Helicarriers, designed to preemptively neutralize threats; Cap disagreed with the nature of the program, believing punishment should be meted after a crime—not before. Unbeknownst to both men, Project: Insight was the brainchild of Hydra, which had secretly survived its defeat in World War II and grew as a subversive cabal within S.H.I.E.L.D. Fury's suspicions that S.H.I.E.L.D. had been compromised marked him for death by Hydra. Upon being shot by the assassin Winter Soldier, Fury gave Cap the USB device with the *Star*'s data. Soon, Fury apparently died from his wounds.

Afterward, Cap met with World Security Council Secretary Alexander Pierce (secretly a Hydra commander) who questioned Cap about Fury. Concluding that the uncooperative Cap was a threat, Pierce ordered Rumlow and S.T.R.I.K.E., (also secretly Hydra agents) to attack him; Cap defeated them and escaped the S.H.I.E.L.D. Triskelion, making him a fugitive. With Widow's help, Cap traced the conspiracy to his old Army base Camp Lehigh. There, they found the stored consciousness of long-dead Hydra scientist Arnim Zola, which survived in a vast, but antiquated, computer network inside a hidden bunker. Zola bragged of Hydra's infiltration of S.H.I.E.L.D. over the previous 70 years, stalling Cap and Widow until a Hydra missile strike destroyed the bunker.

Escaping, Cap and Widow went to Sam Wilson, who offered his help. With Wilson (now outfitted in his winged Air Force flight gear as Falcon), they extracted more information from secret Hydra operative Jasper Sitwell, but were ambushed by the Winter Soldier, who killed Sitwell. During the battle, Cap unmasked the Winter Soldier and immediately recognized him as his childhood friend James "Bucky" Barnes, who Cap had believed died during WWII. Rumlow and his men captured Cap and his allies, but the trio was rescued by Deputy Director Maria Hill and a team of S.H.I.E.L.D. agents still loyal to Fury, who had faked his death to go deep underground. Armed with technology designed to turn the Project: Insight Helicarriers against each other, Cap, Widow, and Falcon set out for the Triskelion.

Cap used S.H.I.E.L.D.'s communication systems to broadcast Hydra's plans to all S.H.I.E.L.D. agents present, both loyal and Hydra. In the ensuing chaos, Cap and his allies reprogrammed two of the Helicarriers, but when on board the third, he was confronted by Winter Soldier. After an intense battle during which Barnes shot Cap repeatedly before being pinned down by falling rubble, Cap reprogrammed the final Helicarrier and gave the order to open fire on each other, despite still being in danger. Cap freed Barnes from the rubble, but the still brainwashed Barnes attacked and beat him brutally, despite Cap's refusal to fight back. When more falling debris caused Cap to fall through a broken window into the Potomac River, Barnes saved him from drowning, and then disappeared—his Hydra programming apparently weakened by Cap's loyalty to him. After Cap recovered, he and Sam set out to find Barnes with the help of Soviet files provided by Widow, who warned Cap to be careful in his search. ✪

FALCON
SAM WILSON

FIRST APPEARANCE:
Captain America:
The Winter Soldier [2014]

As a Pararescue officer with the Air Force's 58th Rescue Squadron, Sam Wilson was a test pilot of the EXO-7 Falcon, a backpack that afforded its wearer self-sustained flight using miniature jet engines and flexible metallic wings that could retract when not in use. After losing his friend and fellow test pilot Riley on a mission, Wilson left the military and joined the Department of Veterans Affairs, counseling veterans suffering from post-traumatic stress.

Wilson met Steve Rogers, a.k.a. Avenger and S.H.I.E.L.D. Agent Captain America, while jogging around Washington, D.C.'s National Mall. Though annoyed that Cap continually outpaced him thanks to Super-Soldier serum enhancements, Wilson bonded with him through friendly teasing. Cap later accepted Wilson's invitation to come by the V.A., and their friendship was solidified when they shared their experiences of service and loss.

Wilson gave refuge to Cap and fellow S.H.I.E.L.D. agent Natasha Romanoff (a.k.a. Black Widow) after the pair learned S.H.I.E.L.D. had been infiltrated by Hydra—a

decades-old deep science terrorist enclave that Cap believed he had helped defeat in World War II. As Cap and Black Widow planned the abduction and interrogation of Hydra infiltrator Jasper Sitwell concerning Hydra's plans, Wilson offered his help and revealed to them his service record in order to convince them of his battle merits. Wilson, Cap, and Widow procured the sole remaining Falcon pack from military storage, and captured Sitwell, who revealed a plan dubbed Project: Insight, in which Hydra would use three advanced Helicarriers to kill millions of potential threats to Hydra's plans of global conquest. On the way to the S.H.I.E.L.D. Triskelion to stop the Helicarriers from launching, Hydra assassin the Winter Soldier attacked the trio, allowing Hydra agent Brock Rumlow and his S.T.R.I.K.E. team to capture them, but the trio was rescued by S.H.I.E.L.D. deputy director Maria Hill. Cap was shocked to learn the Winter Soldier was his brainwashed childhood friend, James "Bucky" Barnes.

After gaining access to the Triskelion, Cap revealed Hydra's infiltration scheme over S.H.I.E.L.D. communications channels; he and Wilson, now "Falcon," set off to disable the three Insight Helicarriers. Though Falcon and Cap succeeded in reprogramming two of the Helicarriers, the Winter Soldier destroyed Falcon's flight pack, forcing him to parachute to the Triskelion's roof, leaving Cap to battle the Winter Soldier, and complete their mission without backup. Inside the Triskelion, Falcon battled Rumlow until the final Helicarrier crashed into the facility; Falcon escaped by leaping from the devastated high-rise into a waiting helicopter piloted by fugitive S.H.I.E.L.D. Director Nick Fury, and Black Widow. In the aftermath of the battle—and S.H.I.E.L.D.'s subsequent decommissioning, Falcon sat at the hospital bedside of the severely injured Cap, waiting for him to recover. After Cap recovered, Falcon turned down Fury's offer to become a spy and resolved to help Cap track down Barnes. ✪

NICK FURY UPDATE

FIRST APPEARANCE: *Iron Man [2008]*

After S.H.I.E.L.D. initiated Project: Insight to proactively target potential insurgents with specialized Helicarriers, Director Nick Fury began to suspect certain information was being hidden from him. Anonymously hiring the mercenary Georges Batroc to hijack the *Lemurian Star* as a cover, Fury sent Captain America to rescue the hostages aboard the ship while Black Widow stole Insight information from its computers. Discovering Widow's secret mission, Cap later confronted Fury, who explained that compartmentalization was necessary for security purposes. No one person knew the whole picture—save Fury himself.

To earn Cap's trust, Fury showed him the Insight Helicarriers. Feeling punishment should not precede a crime, and that the project would engender a state of fear, Cap objected to the program. Fury countered that the world had become a dangerous and unpredictable place, and a stronger stance was needed to keep people safe. Cap rejected the argument, unwilling to forgo freedom and liberty for security.

Fury soon realized he'd been locked out of the *Star*'s data, and was perplexed to learn he supposedly gave the order himself. Suspicious,

Fury asked his old friend, World Security Council Secretary Alexander Pierce, to delay the Project: Insight launch—unaware Pierce was the leader of Hydra and mastermind of a plot to use the program to further the terrorist organization's own agenda. Before he could act, Fury was attacked by Hydra agents and the Winter Soldier assassin, and barely escaped to Cap's apartment. Moments before being shot by Winter Soldier, Fury told Cap that S.H.I.E.L.D. had been compromised. He entrusted Cap with a data drive containing the information from the *Star* before faking his death with the help of Deputy Director Maria Hill.

After Pierce ordered S.H.I.E.L.D. to capture Cap, Fury arranged for Hill to rescue him. Revealing his survival, Fury told Cap his plan for disabling the Project: Insight program and saving S.H.I.E.L.D. Cap objected, declaring that the corrupt S.H.I.E.L.D. needed to be destroyed. Realizing Hydra's corruption was too thorough, Fury reluctantly agreed. As Fury confronted Pierce, Cap and his ally, Falcon, reprogrammed the Helicarriers to destroy each other. Pierce murdered the gathered WSC members, but Fury killed his former friend before he could slay Widow. Later, with S.H.I.E.L.D. dismantled and all its secrets made public, Fury went underground in Europe, letting the world continue to believe he was dead. ✪

FURY'S S.U.V.

HYDRA UPDATE

FIRST APPEARANCE:
Captain America: The First Avenger [2011]

After the Strategic Scientific Reserve defeated Nazi rogue science division Hydra in 1945, the United States recruited several leading Hydra researchers—including the Red Skull's top scientist, Arnim Zola—granting them amnesty for SSR service. But as the SSR grew into S.H.I.E.L.D., Hydra secretly festered within as like-minded agents were recruited. The terminally ill Zola preserved his consciousness in a massive computer bank; according to the scientist, Hydra had learned its lesson in the wake of its earlier defeat. Instead of taking humanity's freedoms by force, Hydra now intended to do so by sowing so much chaos and fear that humanity would surrender its liberties willingly. To this end, Hydra fomented revolutions, financial crises, and wars, frequently by employing the Winter Soldier—the brainwashed and cybernetically enhanced James "Bucky" Barnes, one of Zola's World War II test subjects. By the modern day, Hydra had infiltrated every echelon of S.H.I.E.L.D., and counted several top operatives among the peacekeeping organization's members—including Brock Rumlow, Jasper Sitwell, and one of its leaders, World Security Council Secretary Alexander Pierce. Eventually, Hydra's goal was within reach: S.H.I.E.L.D.'s three Project: Insight Helicarriers would proactively eliminate millions of potential threats, as identified by a Zola-created algorithm.

Growing suspicious, S.H.I.E.L.D. Director Nick Fury began investigating Insight and anonymously hired mercenary Georges Batroc to hijack a S.H.I.E.L.D. ship carrying project data so Black Widow would have a cover for stealing the information. Learning of his suspicions, Hydra marked him for death. Though Fury escaped the initial assassination attempt, the Winter Soldier succeeded in shooting him after he fled to Captain America's apartment. Fury was able to pass Cap a thumbrive with the Insight data before faking his own death. Captain America was also targeted, but evaded the assassins; with Widow's aid, he began investigating the conspiracy while staying one step ahead of Rumlow's S.T.R.I.K.E. team. Hydra tracked Cap and Widow to the abandoned Camp Lehigh, where Zola's consciousness was housed, but the heroes survived a missile strike to Zola's bunker.

Captain America, Black Widow, and Falcon captured and interrogated Sitwell, who revealed details of Project: Insight, but the Winter Soldier and S.T.R.I.K.E. attacked the group while in transit and killed Sitwell. After a firefight in which Cap learned the Winter Soldier was Barnes, believed killed in action in World War II, a shocked Cap and his allies surrendered. Rumlow ordered that they be taken to a remote location and murdered. They escaped with the aid of a Fury loyalist, Deputy Director Maria Hill, then infiltrated the Triskelion headquarters to disrupt the Insight Helicarriers' launch. Cap took control of the Triskelion's communications system to reveal Hydra's infiltration, and a battle broke out between Hydra operatives and S.H.I.E.L.D. agents. In the midst of the chaos, Rumlow launched the Helicarriers. In the ensuing action, Cap and his allies reprogrammed the Helicarriers to shoot each other out of the sky, Black Widow released all of S.H.I.E.L.D. and Hydra's secrets to the public, and Fury shot and killed Pierce. During the battle, Cap weakened Hydra's brainwashing of the Winter Soldier, who saved him from drowning before disappearing. Despite its defeat, remnants of Hydra remained elsewhere— including a European faction led by Baron Strucker, who had acquired Loki's mind-controlling staff, and twins Wanda and Pietro Maximoff, the only survivors of experiments performed to create enhanced humans. ✪

FACT SHEET

- ▶ HYDRA ORCHESTRATED HOWARD AND MARIA STARK'S DEATHS IN A 1991 CAR ACCIDENT.

- ▶ PROJECT: INSIGHT'S TARGETS INCLUDED BRUCE BANNER, TONY STARK, AND STEPHEN STRANGE.

- ▶ U.S. SENATOR STERN WAS ALSO A MEMBER OF HYDRA.

- ▶ HYDRA MEMBERS ACKNOWLEDGED EACH OTHER SECRETLY WITH A WHISPERED "HAIL HYDRA."

BROCK RUMLOW

FIRST APPEARANCE:
Captain America: The Winter Soldier [2014]

Leader of S.T.R.I.K.E., S.H.I.E.L.D.'s counterterrorist unit, Brock Rumlow was secretly a member of Hydra, as were all his men. During a mission to Chicago with Captain America and Black Widow to retrieve the Zodiac weapon, Rumlow saved Cap's life. A subsequent operation to rescue a hijacked S.H.I.E.L.D. freighter started a chain of events that led to Cap's discovery that S.H.I.E.L.D. had been compromised. Rumlow and his men cornered Captain America in an elevator in S.H.I.E.L.D.'s Triskelion, but Cap defeated them all and escaped. With Widow's help, he repeatedly evaded Rumlow and his men.

Aided by the Winter Soldier, Rumlow and S.T.R.I.K.E. finally captured Captain America, Black Widow, and Falcon—but with the media present, Rumlow ordered his men to take the prisoners to a remote location to be executed. After being freed by loyal S.H.I.E.L.D. Agent Maria Hill, Cap and his allies infiltrated the Triskelion to stop Hydra's plans to assassinate millions they deemed a threat. As Captain America broadcast the truth to the entire base, Rumlow outfought S.H.I.E.L.D. loyalist Agent 13 and launched three Helicarriers to carry out the assassinations. He was then summoned to assist Hydra leader Alexander Pierce, but Falcon ambushed Rumlow en route. Rumlow was the superior combatant, but was unable to outrun a crashing Helicarrier. Rumlow survived, however, and was taken to a hospital for treatment for his critical injuries. ✪

TRISKELION

S.H.I.E.L.D. UPDATE

FIRST APPEARANCE: *Iron Man [2008]*

When S.H.I.E.L.D.'s satellite launch platform, the *Lemurian Star*, was taken hostage by Georges Batroc and his pirates, S.H.I.E.L.D. task force S.T.R.I.K.E. and Agents Captain America and Black Widow were sent to rescue hostages, including technicians and Senior Agent Jasper Sitwell. S.T.R.I.K.E. and Captain America defeated the pirates and Batroc, and rescued the hostages while Widow completed a secret secondary mission of downloading the *Star*'s data files. Back at the Triskelion, S.H.I.E.L.D.'s massive new high-rise headquarters on the Potomac River, Director Nick Fury showed Captain America Project: Insight, three next-generation Helicarriers linked to targeting satellites, which could use advanced algorithms to predict potential threats, track their DNA, and eliminate them anywhere on the globe.

Suspecting possible corruption in the agency, Fury requested that World Security Council Secretary Alexander Pierce delay the project. Pierce, secretly a leader of Hydra, sent the Winter Soldier to assassinate Fury. While Fury survived the initial assault and warned Cap of S.H.I.E.L.D.'s corruption, the Winter Soldier subsequently shot and apparently killed him. Before dying, Fury was able to give Cap a device containing the *Star*'s data.

Pierce debriefed Cap and informed him that Fury hired Batroc to hijack the *Lemurian Star*. Despite this, Cap refused to tell Pierce anything Fury had told him. Classifying Cap a threat, Pierce called for his arrest. S.T.R.I.K.E. operatives attacked Cap in an elevator, but Cap defeated them and fled; S.H.I.E.L.D. subsequently labeled him a fugitive, confusing many true S.H.I.E.L.D. agents. While on the run, Cap and his allies discovered that Hydra infiltrated S.H.I.E.L.D. after World War II and had grown to massive proportions within it. Later, following a prolonged battle with the Winter Soldier, S.T.R.I.K.E., and Hydra agents, Cap, Widow, and their ally, Falcon, were captured, but S.T.R.I.K.E. commander Brock Rumlow delayed executing them because news helicopters were nearby. Before they could be killed, Cap and his allies were rescued by Fury loyalist Maria Hill. With Project: Insight prepared for launch and Hydra poised to assume control of Earth, Cap and his allies infiltrated the Triskelion and exposed Hydra via S.H.I.E.L.D.'s communication systems, resulting in an agency-wide civil war, during which the Helicarriers were launched. While Cap and Falcon replaced targeting codes in the three Helicarriers to shut down Project: Insight, Widow, with the help of a returned Fury, uploaded S.H.I.E.L.D. and Hydra's records onto the internet to reveal Hydra to the world. Pierce assassinated the Council and threatened to kill Widow, but Fury killed him. Once the Helicarriers were reprogrammed, Hill directed them to destroy each other and crash into the Triskelion. Following these events S.H.I.E.L.D. was effectively decommissioned. ✪

INSIGHT HELICARRIERS

IN THE COMICS

ED BRUBAKER · STEVE EPTING
CAPTAIN AMERICA

BELIEVED DEAD, JAMES "BUCKY" Barnes was secretly recovered by the Soviet Navy and brainwashed into an emotionless covert operative, the Winter Soldier, who committed multiple assassinations and espionage missions for Russia, and was cryogenically frozen between missions. Upon encountering Captain America (Steve Rogers) in modern times, Barnes eventually regained his memory. Barnes served as Captain America for a time, but returned to his Winter Soldier identity once Rogers reclaimed the Cap role; the Winter Soldier continues to seek redemption for his actions.

FIRST APPEARANCE (AS THE WINTER SOLDIER): *CAPTAIN AMERICA #1 (2005)*

THE WINTER SOLDIER (BUCKY BARNES) UPDATE

FIRST APPEARANCE: *Captain America: The First Avenger [2011]*

Believed killed by a massive fall in 1945, Sgt. James Buchanan "Bucky" Barnes barely survived thanks to experiments performed on him by Hydra scientist Arnim Zola. Hydra replaced his severed left arm with an advanced robotic prosthesis, and he was brainwashed into an emotionless killing machine called the Winter Soldier. His mind was routinely and painfully erased to prevent empathy, and he was cryogenically frozen between missions, which, coupled with Zola's experiments, slowed physical aging. On one mission, the Winter Soldier killed a target by shooting through his protector, the future Avenger Black Widow.

To prevent S.H.I.E.L.D. Director Nick Fury from investigating corruption within the agency, World Security Council Secretary and Hydra infiltrator Alexander Pierce assigned the Winter Soldier to assassinate him; Fury secretly survived, working against Hydra in secret. After Cap and Widow uncovered Hydra's infiltration of S.H.I.E.L.D., Pierce ordered the Winter Soldier to kill them. As they traveled to the S.H.I.E.L.D. Triskelion, the Winter Soldier attacked, killing captured Hydra agent Jasper Sitwell. During the ensuing battle, the Winter Soldier was unmasked as Barnes, who dismissed a shocked Cap's recognition. Later, as Hydra scientists repaired the damage to his arm, the Winter Soldier told Pierce he remembered Cap, prompting Pierce to have his mind erased.

Later, during Cap's assault on the Triskelion, the Winter Soldier slaughtered dozens of S.H.I.E.L.D. agents, defeated Falcon in combat and fought Cap, shooting him multiple times. However, he could not stop Cap from reprogramming Hydra's Helicarriers, stopping their plans to murder millions of potential Hydra enemies. During their battle, Cap appealed to the Winter Soldier's memories, which caused the Winter Soldier's brainwashing to weaken. However, falling debris caused Cap to fall from the Helicarrier into the Potomac river; the Winter Soldier saved Cap from drowning before disappearing. Barnes later visited the Smithsonian Institute's Captain America exhibit and saw his own memorial. ✪

PROSTHETIC ARM

COUNCILMAN SINGH

COUNCILMAN ROCKWELL

COUNCILMAN YEN

COUNCILWOMAN HAWLEY

WORLD SECURITY COUNCIL UPDATE

FIRST APPEARANCE: *Marvel's The Avengers [2012]*

After the Chitauri invasion of New York, S.H.I.E.L.D. Director Nick Fury convinced the World Security Council that a quantum increase in threat analysis was crucial; this led to S.H.I.E.L.D.'s Project: Insight, a security measure using three Helicarriers that could assassinate thousands at a time. Sometime later, after beginning to suspect S.H.I.E.L.D. had been compromised, Fury secretly hired the mercenary Batroc to hijack the S.H.I.E.L.D.'s *Lemurian Star* to cover an undercover inquest. Displeased by the hijacking, the Council convened via digital projections to discuss it. Fury asked WSC Secretary Alexander Pierce (secretly a high-ranking Hydra agent) to ask the Council to delay Project: Insight while he investigated. After Fury was believed assassinated, the WSC reinstated Project: Insight, believing Fury had delayed the project to cover up his own illegal activities, thanks to Pierce's deceptions. When the WSC members arrived at S.H.I.E.L.D. headquarters to watch the Helicarriers' deployment, Captain America broadcast news of Hydra's infiltration of S.H.I.E.L.D. over the communications system.

Hydra agents held the shocked WSC at gunpoint while Pierce completed the launch. However, Black Widow, who had impersonated Councilwoman Hawley, defeated the gunmen and uploaded Hydra's secrets onto the Internet. A still-alive Fury arrived to take down Pierce, but was too late to stop him from murdering the Council with booby-trapped security badges. ✪

FACT SHEET

▶ KNOWN COUNCIL MEMBERS INCLUDE YEN, SINGH, ROCKWELL, AND HAWLEY; THE LATTER'S WHEREABOUTS ARE UNREVEALED.

WSC CHAMBER

BATROC

FIRST APPEARANCE:
*Captain America:
The Winter Soldier [2014]*

Demobilized by French intelligence after gaining a reputation for maximum casualties, Algerian-born mercenary Georges Batroc was anonymously hired by S.H.I.E.L.D. Director Nick Fury to hijack S.H.I.E.L.D.'s *Lemurian Star* launch ship as part of Fury's secret investigation into S.H.I.E.L.D. corruption. Seizing the *Lemurian Star* with the aid of a mercenary group, Batroc demanded $1.5 billion for the hostages. Awaiting S.H.I.E.L.D.'s response, Batroc was confronted by Captain America, who—unaware of Fury's plans—had mounted a hostage rescue. After goading Cap into fighting without his helmet or shield, Batroc was still defeated. However, upon recovery, Batroc used a grenade to cover his escape. S.H.I.E.L.D. later captured Batroc at a safe house in Algiers and interrogated him. ✪

FRENCH FOREIGN LEGION
member-turned-mercenary Georges Batroc was nicknamed "Batroc the Leaper" due to his mastery of savate kickboxing. He also led the mercenary team Batroc's Brigade. Despite being a recurring foe of Captain America (Steve Rogers), Batroc occasionally aids heroes and considers himself an honorable man.

FIRST APPEARANCE:
TALES OF SUSPENSE #75 (1966)

FACT SHEET

▶ BATROC WAS AT THE TOP OF INTERPOL'S RED NOTICE, AND WAS FORMERLY PART OF THE FRENCH DGSE'S ACTION DIVISION, WHERE HE COMPLETED 36 KILL MISSIONS.

▶ FOR HIS ATTACK ON THE *LEMURIAN STAR*, BATROC WAS CONTACTED VIA EMAIL AND PAID BY WIRE TRANSFER USING MONEY THAT RAN THROUGH 17 FICTITIOUS ACCOUNTS.

PEGGY CARTER
UPDATE

FIRST APPEARANCE:
*Captain America:
The First Avenger [2011]*

Agent of the Strategic Scientific Reserve during and after World War II, and later a founder of S.H.I.E.L.D., Peggy Carter married a man who was one of the thousands saved during WWII by Carter's wartime ally and would-be paramour Captain America. In 1953, Carter filmed an interview about Cap that was shown decades later at the Smithsonian Institute's Captain America exhibit. In modern times, an elderly Carter had become physically debilitated and was suffering from dementia. When a revived Cap visited her, Carter told him her only regret was that as she had lived her life, he never got the chance to live his. Cap shared doubts about the modern world with her; she replied that the world had changed, and all they could do was their best. After this advice, her lucidity escaped her, and she reacted with shock when, thanks to her dementia, Carter learned Cap was alive all over again. Though disturbed at seeing his former love in this state, Cap gently resumed the conversation where Carter's dementia had taken it. ✪

FACT SHEET

▶ CAPTAIN AMERICA TOLD CARTER THAT HALF THE REASON HE HAD REMAINED WITH S.H.I.E.L.D. WAS HIS KNOWLEDGE THAT SHE HELPED FOUND IT.

▶ PICTURES AT HER BEDSIDE INDICATE PEGGY AND HER HUSBAND HAD AT LEAST ONE SON AND A DAUGHTER.

▶ IN HER 1953 INTERVIEW, PEGGY REVEALED THAT DURING WWII, CAP HAD SAVED THE LIFE OF THE MAN WHO WOULD LATER BECOME HER HUSBAND.

MARIA HILL
UPDATE

FIRST APPEARANCE:
Marvel's The Avengers [2012]

Becoming suspicious that S.H.I.E.L.D. was compromised, Director Nick Fury contacted Deputy Director Maria Hill and ordered her to rendezvous with him in Washington, D.C., under "deep shadow conditions" just before he was gravely wounded by Hydra agents and Winter Soldier. At the hospital, Tetrodotoxine B was used to slow Fury's heart rate enough to mimic death. With S.H.I.E.L.D. believing Fury gone, Hill secretly transported him to a safe house.

When Hydra operatives captured Captain America, Black Widow, and Falcon, Hill posed as a Hydra agent to rescue them from the back of a prisoner transport; she took them to Fury's safe house, revealing he was still alive. Hill and Fury laid out their plan to destroy the Project: Insight Helicarriers, which Hydra intended to use to eliminate potential threats—20 million at a time. During the discussion, Hill agreed with Cap that S.H.I.E.L.D. needed to be destroyed due to Hydra's corruption.

Hill, Falcon, and Cap infiltrated S.H.I.E.L.D.'s Triskelion, and Hill took command of the communications center. After Cap and Falcon reprogrammed the Helicarriers, Hill redirected them to fire on one another—dropping them out of the sky. Later, with Hydra exposed and S.H.I.E.L.D. dissolved, Hill interviewed for a job at Stark Industries. ✪

FACT SHEET

▶ DESPITE THE HIGH STRESS OF THE BATTLE AGAINST HYDRA, HILL REMAINED CALM AND BUSINESSLIKE AT ALL TIMES.

▶ HILL IS A MARKSMAN OF GREAT SKILL, ABLE TO HIT MOVING TARGETS WITH GREAT ACCURACY, EVEN WHILE MOBILE.

SENATOR STERN
UPDATE

FIRST APPEARANCE: *Iron Man 2 [2010]*

Senator Stern, chairman of the Senate Armed Forces Committee, was secretly a Hydra loyalist. Stern had lunch with S.H.I.E.L.D. Agent Jasper Sitwell, and while leaving the building, Stern told Sitwell he needed to fly to his home state that night to deal with a "constituency problem." Stern confided in Sitwell that the "problem" was actually a "kinda hot" 23-year-old he thought wanted to become a reporter. As he was leaving, Stern hugged Sitwell goodbye and whispered "Hail Hydra" in his ear. After Captain America and his allies thwarted Hydra's plan to murder 20 million potential threats to its plans of world domination, Hydra's continued existence was revealed to the world when Black Widow released S.H.I.E.L.D. records online. Stern was arrested for his role in the terrorist organization as he exited the Department of Homeland Security. ✪

FACT SHEET

▶ STERN SAID HE SUFFERED FROM BACK PAIN, WHICH HE ALLUDED TO BEING CAUSED BY RELATIONS WITH THE 23-YEAR-OLD CONSTITUENT. HE MELODRAMATICALLY PLAYED UP HIS BACK PROBLEMS WHILE WALKING DOWN THE STAIRS.

▶ STERN WAS DISMISSIVE OF HIS YOUNG CONSTITUENT, TELLING SITWELL HE NEVER REALLY LISTENED TO WHAT SHE SAID.

▶ WHILE SPEAKING OUTSIDE, STERN AND SITWELL WERE GUARDED BY NUMEROUS MEN, AT LEAST FOUR OF WHOM LEFT WITH STERN.

▶ WHEN STERN NOTICED THE S.H.I.E.L.D. PIN ON SITWELL'S LAPEL, STERN SARCASTICALLY TOLD SITWELL HE ADMIRED IT.

JASPER SITWELL
UPDATE

FIRST APPEARANCE: *Thor [2011]*

An undercover Hydra agent within S.H.I.E.L.D., Jasper Sitwell was taken hostage by mercenary Georges Batroc aboard S.H.I.E.L.D.'s *Lemurian Star* as part of S.H.I.E.L.D. Director Nick Fury's covert investigation into corruption within the agency. After the hostages were rescued and Nick Fury was apparently killed, Sitwell ordered the S.T.R.I.K.E. unit (all secretly Hydra) to attack Captain America under orders from undercover Hydra commander Alexander Pierce. When Rogers escaped, Jasper directed S.H.I.E.L.D. agents to stage a manhunt for him. Later, having deduced Sitwell's true loyalties, Cap, Black Widow, and their ally, Falcon, located Sitwell following a lunch with secret Hydra loyalist Senator Stern and threatened him into revealing Hydra's true goal of killing millions of Hydra's potential enemies. Hoping to use him to get through security, the heroes forced Sitwell to accompany them to S.H.I.E.L.D. headquarters, but they were attacked by the Winter Soldier, who hurled Sitwell from the moving vehicle to his death. ✪

FACT SHEET

▶ WHEN THREATENED BY CAPTAIN AMERICA, JASPER SCOFFED, BELIEVING CAP WOULD NOT THROW HIM FROM A ROOFTOP. AFTER BLACK WIDOW KICKED HIM OFF, REQUIRING THE FLYING FALCON TO STOP HIM FROM HITTING THE GROUND, SITWELL BEGAN TALKING.

ARNIM ZOLA UPDATE

FIRST APPEARANCE:
Captain America: The First Avenger [2011]

Following World War II, Dr. Arnim Zola was imprisoned by the Strategic Scientific Reserve for his involvement with the Nazi science division Hydra. He met Johann Fennhoff in prison and expressed interest in Fennhoff's work on matters of the human mind. Sometime later, Zola was recruited to work for the new peacekeeping organization S.H.I.E.L.D. in exchange for amnesty. His S.H.I.E.L.D. handlers remained unaware that Zola also continued to secretly work for Hydra.

Realizing that humanity wouldn't willingly give up freedom, Zola and Hydra secretly used S.H.I.E.L.D. resources to foment chaos in the ensuing decades to prime the populace to willingly relinquish liberty for security, occasionally utilizing the brainwashed Winter Soldier to assassinate people who stood in their way. When Zola received a terminal diagnosis in 1972, he transferred his consciousness into a massive S.H.I.E.L.D. computer system, where he continued to covertly coordinate Hydra operations.

In modern times, Captain America and Black Widow found Zola's computer system and reactivated him. In an attempt to delay them until Hydra could kill them, Zola explained that S.H.I.E.L.D.'s Project: Insight program was an algorithm Zola wrote to predict and target potential adversaries to Hydra's goals. A Hydra missile strike destroyed Zola's bunker and computer system, but Cap and Widow survived. ✪

FACT SHEET

▶ ZOLA TOLD FENNHOFF TO BE GRATEFUL THEY WERE IN AN AMERICAN PRISON, AS AMERICA WAS THE "LAND OF OPPORTUNITY."

▶ ZOLA WAS RECRUITED AS PART OF OPERATION PAPERCLIP, A S.H.I.E.L.D. PROGRAM THAT ENLISTED WARTIME ENEMIES OF STRATEGIC VALUE TO WORK FOR AMERICA.

▶ ZOLA'S CONSCIOUSNESS WAS HOUSED IN 200,000 FEET OF DATABANKS BENEATH CAMP LEHIGH IN WHEATON, N.J.—CAP'S WWII TRAINING GROUND.

▶ ZOLA'S ALGORITHM INVESTIGATED PEOPLE'S PASTS TO PREDICT THEIR FUTURES TO DETERMINE IF THEY WOULD BE THREATS TO HYDRA'S CAUSE.

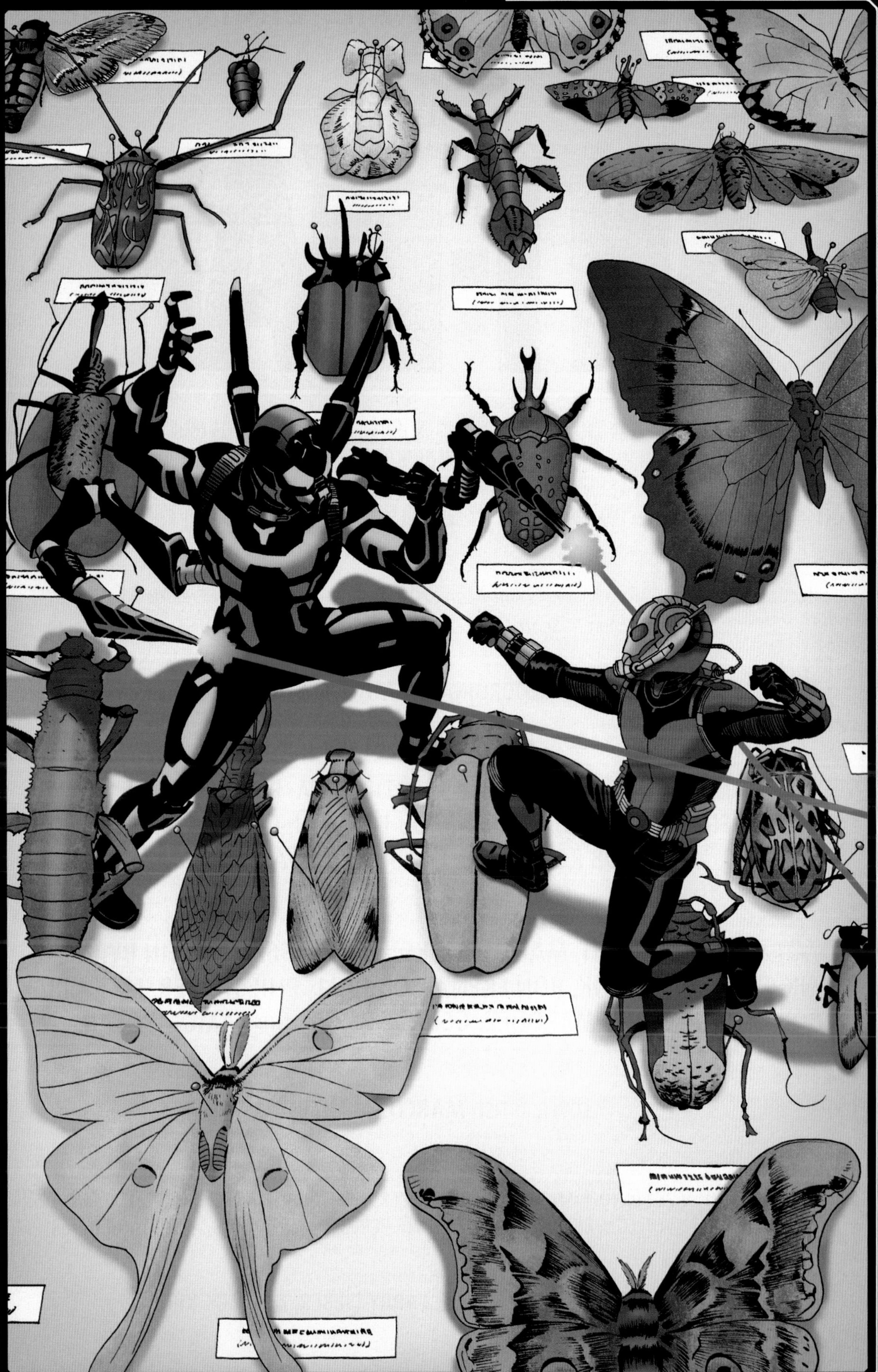

GUIDEBOOK TO THE MARVEL CINEMATIC UNIVERSE

MARVEL

ANT-MAN

MARVEL STUDIOS PRESENTS PAUL RUDD "ANT-MAN" EVANGELINE LILLY COREY STOLL BOBBY CANNAVALE MICHAEL PEÑA TIP "T.I." HARRIS WOOD HARRIS JUDY GREER DAVID DASTMALCHIAN AND MICHAEL DOUGLAS AS DR. HANK PYM CASTING BY SARAH HALLEY FINN, C.S.A. MUSIC SUPERVISOR DAVE JORDAN MUSIC BY CHRISTOPHE BECK HEAD OF VISUAL DEVELOPMENT CHARLIE WEN RYAN MEINERDING VISUAL EFFECTS SUPERVISOR JAKE MORRISON COSTUME DESIGNER SAMMY SHELDON EDITED BY DAN LEBENTAL, ACE COLBY PARKER, JR., ACE PRODUCTION DESIGNER SHEPHERD FRANKEL DIRECTOR OF PHOTOGRAPHY RUSSELL CARPENTER, ASC CO-PRODUCERS BRAD WINDERBAUM DAVID J. GRANT EXECUTIVE PRODUCERS STAN LEE EDGAR WRIGHT EXECUTIVE PRODUCERS VICTORIA ALONSO MICHAEL GRILLO EXECUTIVE PRODUCER ALAN FINE EXECUTIVE PRODUCER LOUIS D'ESPOSITO PRODUCED BY KEVIN FEIGE, p.g.a. STORY BY EDGAR WRIGHT & JOE CORNISH SCREENPLAY BY EDGAR WRIGHT & JOE CORNISH AND ADAM McKAY & PAUL RUDD DIRECTED BY PEYTON REED

Collecting information from Marvel's *Ant-Man* (2015), Marvel's *Ant-Man Prelude #1-2* (2015), and *Ant-Man — Scott Lang: Small Time Infinite Comic* (2015).

HEAD WRITER/COORDINATOR: **MIKE O'SULLIVAN**

COORDINATION: **DARON JENSEN**

WRITERS: **ROB BOCK, ANTHONY COTILLETTA, PATRICK DUKE, MIKE FICHERA, DARON JENSEN, ROB LONDON, CHRIS MCCARVER, JACOB ROUGEMONT,** AND **KEVIN WASSER**

ARTISTS: **MARK BRIGHT, MARK BROOKS, JOHN BUSCEMA, JOHN BYRNE, FRANK CHO, GARY FRANK, RON FRENZ, BOB HALL, PHIL HESTER, JACK KIRBY, BOB LAYTON, DAVID MARQUEZ, GEORGE PÉREZ,** AND **RAMON ROSANAS**

COVER ARTIST: **MARCOS MARTIN**

SPECIAL THANKS TO DAVE ALTHOFF, SHAWN "KEEBLER" BYERS, JEFF CHRISTIANSEN, MATT DELMANOWSKI, ERIKA DENTON, TIM DILLON, PERCIVAL LANUZA, AVIA PEREZ, JACQUE PORTE, AND RYAN POTTER.

ANT-MAN CREATED BY STAN LEE, LARRY LIEBER, AND JACK KIRBY

ANT-MAN
SCOTT LANG
FIRST APPEARANCE: *Ant-Man [2015]*

Released after a three-year jail sentence for burglary, electrical engineer Scott Lang sought to rebuild his life and re-establish ties with his daughter, Cassie. Unable to hold a job due to his criminal record and refused contact with Cassie by his ex-wife, Maggie, and her fiancé, San Francisco Police Detective Jim Paxton, due to his inability to pay child support, Lang reluctantly accepted an offer from former cellmate Luis to burglarize the home of Pym Technologies founder Hank Pym. Lang was unaware Pym himself had spread word of his home's vulnerabilities to test Lang's skills.

Lang infiltrated Pym's house with help from Luis, along with cohorts Dave and Kurt, but found only an odd jumpsuit and helmet in the safe; he took them nonetheless. Later, a curious Lang put on the suit. Pressing a button on one of the gloves, he shrank to the height of an insect. Pym coached him through the experience, communicating via the helmet. Shaken, Lang returned the suit to Pym's home—but was arrested on his way out after Pym's daughter, Hope Van Dyne, called police. Pym offered Lang a second chance in life while posing as his lawyer, and a group of ants under Pym's influence smuggled the suit into Lang's cell. Lang donned the suit, shrank himself, and allowed an armada of winged carpenter ants to transport him to freedom.

At Pym's home, Pym told Lang of his corrupt ex-protégé, Darren Cross, and his attempts to re-create the Ant-Man technology, asking Lang to steal Cross's Yellowjacket suit and research. After Lang agreed, Pym and Van Dyne trained him in hand-to-hand combat and taught him how to use the Ant-Man tech. Though Van Dyne initially appeared hostile due to her desire to don the suit and carry out the plan herself, Lang began to earn her trust when he convinced her Pym had selected him because he was expendable. Late in Lang's training, Pym sent him to steal a prototype signal decoy needed for the plan from a Stark Industries warehouse—unaware it had been converted into the Avengers' head-quarters. To Pym and Hope's sur-prise, Ant-Man bested the Avenger Falcon in combat and completed the mission.

When a suspicious Cross tripled security around the Yellowjacket tech, Lang recruited Luis, Dave, and Kurt's assistance, and gained entry into Cross's vault as Cross was selling the suit to the terrorist organization Hydra. Ant-Man was captured, but quickly escaped and pursued the fleeing Cross. After watching his building and research destroyed by Lang's sabotage, Cross donned the Yellowjacket suit, battled Lang, and threatened Cassie. During the resulting fight, Lang disabled his suit's regulator and shrank to subatomic size so he could enter and destroy the Yellowjacket suit, defeating Cross. Uncontrollably shrinking into the Quantum Realm, a quick-thinking Lang jury-rigged his regulator and returned to human size.

Lang and Van Dyne thereafter took the first steps toward romance, and—grateful he saved Cassie—Maggie and Paxton welcomed Lang into their home for a family dinner. Later, Lang was was dismayed to learn from Luis that Falcon was looking for Ant-Man.

ENGINEER AND FORMER THIEF

Scott Lang returned to crime when he burglarized founding Avenger Henry Pym's home in hopes of funding the care of his critically ill daughter, Cassie; he found Pym's size-changing Ant-Man suit instead. When corrupt industrialist Darren Cross kidnapped the surgeon who could save Cassie's life, Lang used the suit to rescue the surgeon, who successfully treated Cassie. An impressed Pym allowed Lang to keep the suit so long as he gave up crime. Though proficient as a costumed hero, Lang's activities eventually cost him custody of Cassie, and he was killed during an attack by a corrupted Scarlet Witch (Wanda Maximoff). Cassie, now the size-changing Stature, later rescued him by time-traveling to moments before his death. Lang has established Ant-Man Security Solutions in his new home of Miami.

FIRST APPEARANCE:
(LANG) *AVENGERS* #181 (1979);
(ANT-MAN) *MARVEL PREMIERE* #47 (1979)

FACT SHEET

▶ LANG BURGLARIZED HIS FORMER EMPLOYERS AT VISTA CORP AFTER THEY FIRED HIM FOR DISCOVERING THEY WERE OVERCHARGING THEIR CUSTOMERS. HE HACKED VISTA'S SYSTEMS, PAID BACK ITS CUSTOMERS, AND DROVE THE CEO'S CAR INTO A SWIMMING POOL.

▶ THOUGH THE ANT-MAN SUIT WAS UNARMED, PYM SUPPLIED LANG WITH PYM PARTICLE DISCS—RED DISCS THAT SHRANK OBJECTS AND BLUE DISCS THAT ENLARGED THEM.

▶ AN ACCOMPLISHED ENGINEER, LANG BROKE INTO PYM'S SAFE BY USING LIQUID NITROGEN AND WATER TO EXPAND THE DOOR FROM WITHIN.

▶ AFTER LYING ABOUT HIS CRIMINAL RECORD, LANG LEARNED THE HARD WAY: BASKIN-ROBBINS ALWAYS FINDS OUT.

SHRINKING AND ENLARGING DISCS

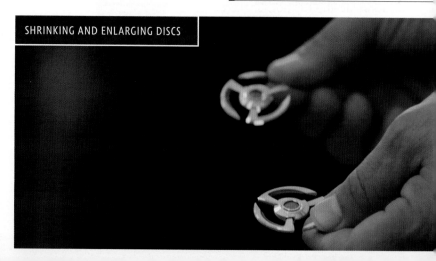

ANT-MAN'S ANTS

FIRST APPEARANCE: *Ant-Man [2015]*

As Ant-Man, Hank Pym allied himself with an army of loyal ants, later training Scott Lang to do the same. Using an earpiece to stimulate the insects' olfactory nerve centers, Ant-Man can command ants to perform a variety of tasks. For the ants to obey, the transmitted thoughts must be clear and focused. Ants used by Pym and Lang on their missions have included:

Crazy ants (*Paratrechina longicornis*): Named for their erratic and fast movements, the electricity-conducting crazy ants are the smallest members of Ant-Man's army. Lang deployed the crazy ants to short out the electronics in the Pym Technologies server room with devices strapped to their backs, thereby disabling the laser grid protecting the Yellowjacket pod.

Fire ants (*Solenopsis mandibularis*): The reddish fire ants are known primarily for their painful sting. However, fire ants are also the hive-like architects and engineers of Ant-Man's tiny team, capable of building remarkable structures with their bodies. Lang used fire ants as a raft to travel through the PymTech water main; they then created a riser to lift him up to pipe access vents.

Carpenter ants (*Camponotus pennsylvanicus*): These common insects are either wingless worker ants, excellent for ground transport, or longer-bodied flying ants, which serve as steeds for Ant-Man. Lang rode his first such steed, which he named "Ant-Thony," while escaping jail, and later during his theft of a prototype signal decoy from

CRAZY ANT

FIRE ANTS

CARPENTER ANT

BULLET ANT

IN THE COMICS

BOTH HANK PYM AND HIS successor, Scott Lang, have used a cybernetic helmet to communicate with ants, often employing them for surveillance, reconnaissance, and transportation. Both have also occasionally named the ants they rode.

FIRST APPEARANCE:
TALES TO ASTONISH #27 (1962)

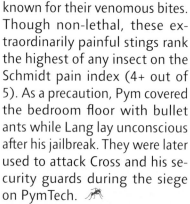

the Avengers' headquarters. When Cross shot and killed Ant-Thony, Lang was devastated. Lang summoned worker carpenter ants from the garden outside his ex-wife's home during Ant-Man's final battle against Yellowjacket.

Bullet ants (*Paraponera clavata*): The largest and most threatening members of Ant-Man's army, giant tropical bullet ants are known for their venomous bites. Though non-lethal, these extraordinarily painful stings rank the highest of any insect on the Schmidt pain index (4+ out of 5). As a precaution, Pym covered the bedroom floor with bullet ants while Lang lay unconscious after his jailbreak. They were later used to attack Cross and his security guards during the siege on PymTech.

FACT SHEET

▶ TO RIDE A CARPENTER ANT, PYM INSTRUCTED LANG TO PUT HIS FOOT ON THE CENTRAL NODE— BETWEEN THE MIDDLE THORAX AND LOWER ABDOMEN—AND MOUNT THE THORAX.

▶ CASSIE KEPT A CARPENTER ANT AS A PET AFTER IT WAS ACCIDENTALLY ENLARGED TO THE SIZE OF A GREAT DANE.

▶ THE PAIN OF A BULLET ANT STING WAS DESCRIBED BY ENTOMOLOGIST DR. JUSTIN SCHMIDT AS AKIN TO "FIRE-WALKING OVER FLAMING CHARCOAL WITH A THREE-INCH RUSTY NAIL IN YOUR HEEL."

LUIS

DAVE

KURT

ANT-MAN'S CREW

FIRST APPEARANCE: *Ant-Man [2015]*

Chatty, personable thief Luis was Scott Lang's cellmate at San Quentin Prison. Upon his release, Luis suffered a number of personal setbacks but maintained his relentlessly cheerful demeanor. When Lang was released a year later, he stayed with Luis at San Francisco's Milgrom Hotel. Luis hoped Lang would resume his criminal career in partnership with him and two new associates, Eastern European computer hacker Kurt and getaway driver Dave. Lang initially resisted, hoping to go straight, but eventually accepted their offer out of desperation. They planned a heist based on a tip Luis received about a "super-legit, big-ass" safe in retired scientist Hank Pym's basement. Unbeknownst to them, Pym himself had planted the tip, hoping to

recruit Lang into his plot to destroy Darren Cross's Yellowjacket battlesuit. With the group's help, Lang broke into Pym's safe, finding only Pym's size-changing Ant-Man suit. The disappointed Lang took the suit, not realizing what it was; after being contacted by Pym, Lang agreed to help him.

When Pym, Lang, and Pym's daughter, Hope Van Dyne, planned to break into Pym Technologies to steal the suit and destroy Cross's research, complications forced them to seek help. Much to Pym's displeasure, Lang recruited Luis, Kurt, and Dave. They eagerly accepted the job—but when Lang demonstrated Pym's shrinking technology, they were so terrified they needed a sedative and a lengthy science lecture from Pym to calm down. Luis infiltrated Pym

Technologies as a security guard, lowering the building's water pressure to allow Lang—as Ant-Man—to enter via the water main while Kurt and Dave waited in their van outside. To help Pym avoid suspicious police, Dave stole the officers' car, distracting them. However, the officers tracked down Dave and Kurt when Dave accidentally honked the van's distinctive horn. Moments before they were arrested, Kurt was able to complete his remote shutdown of the laser grid protecting the Yellowjacket suit. Inside, Luis saved Lang from Cross's guards, then fled the building before the bombs Lang planted destroyed it. Still disguised as a guard, Luis escaped the ensuing chaos with Dave and Kurt. Later, Luis learned that Falcon, whom Lang had encountered while stealing a prototype signal decoy from Avengers headquarters, was looking for Ant-Man. Luis passed on the tip to Lang.

LUIS WITH HIS VAN

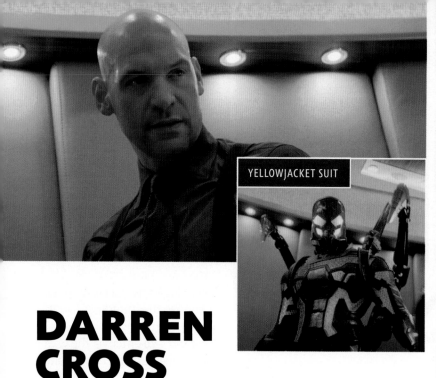

YELLOWJACKET SUIT

DARREN CROSS

FIRST APPEARANCE: *Ant-Man [2015]*

As a lab assistant to Dr. Hank Pym at Pym Technologies, Darren Cross harbored powerful ambitions. Cross sought to learn more about the size-altering particle Pym allegedly had invented and used as the costumed Ant-Man, but Pym denied its existence. Increasingly alienated from his mentor, Cross rose up through the ranks. He joined forces with Pym's estranged daughter, Hope Van Dyne, to force Pym out of the company, and eventually re-created Pym's size-changing formula, which he incorporated into the miniature Yellowjacket battlesuit. Cross had yet to perfect the technology—he was unable to shrink living tissue without killing the subject—but showed it off to a group of investors nonetheless. When a Pym Technologies executive expressed doubts, Cross secretly murdered him. Before long, Cross succeeded in shrinking a living subject, and prepared to sell the Yellowjacket suit to Mitchell Carson, an associate of the terrorist group Hydra.

On the day of Cross's sale to Carson, the reconciled Pym and Van Dyne sent a new Ant-Man, ex-con Scott Lang, to infiltrate Pym Technologies to destroy the Yellowjacket suit and all of Cross's research. Having anticipated treachery, Cross captured Lang, planning to sell his suit as well. Lang soon freed himself; in the resulting chaos, Cross shot Pym and fled to a waiting helicopter with the Yellowjacket suit. Lang followed close behind. Cross was horrified when the Pym Technologies building imploded thanks to bombs Lang planted. Cross donned the Yellowjacket armor and battled Lang; the fight ended when Lang swatted Cross into a bug zapper. Cross survived, but unshielded exposure to Pym Particles had damaged his mind. He headed for Lang's ex-wife's home to take their daughter, Cassie, hostage to draw out Lang. Cross and Lang battled in her bedroom; to save Cassie, Lang shrank to subatomic size to fit between the armored panels of the Yellowjacket suit. Lang damaged the suit's internal mechanisms, apparently causing Cross to shrink into oblivion. 🐜

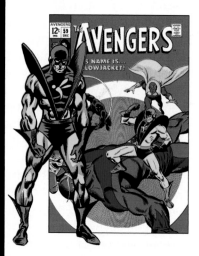
FACT SHEET

► CROSS USED LAMBS AS TEST SUBJECTS FOR HIS PYM PARTICLES.

► CROSS HAD BEGUN TO REBRAND PYM TECHNOLOGIES AS CROSS TECHNOLOGIES.

► THE TITANIUM-ARMORED YELLOWJACKET ARMOR COULD FLY AND FIRE ENERGY BLASTS FROM EXTRA "LIMBS" PROTRUDING FROM ITS BACK.

JIM PAXTON

FIRST APPEARANCE: *Ant-Man [2015]*

San Francisco Detective Jim Paxton shared a tense relationship with ex-con Scott Lang, his fiancé Maggie Lang's ex-husband. When Lang crashed his daughter Cassie's birthday party, Paxton restrained his anger. Later, Paxton relayed Maggie and Cassie's disappointment to Lang after he was arrested for breaking into scientist Hank Pym's house. When Lang escaped his holding cell—with Pym's help—Paxton led Lang's manhunt. Paxton's partner, Gale, later recognized Scott's "lawyer" as Pym. The detectives staked out Pym Technologies and attempted to arrest Pym as he arrived, but were distracted when Dave, Lang's criminal cohort, stole their unmarked police car.

When Paxton recognized a nearby van as being a vehicle he had seen Lang driving earlier, he and Gale investigated. They found Dave and hacker Kurt inside, unaware they were providing remote assistance to Lang, now the size-changing Ant-Man, in his efforts to sabotage corrupt Pym Technologies CEO Darren Cross.

When alarms began sounding, thanks to Ant-Man, Paxton attempted to keep Pym Tech's evacuation orderly until choosing to pursue a fleeing helicopter. They followed it, locating and arresting Lang in his Ant-Man

When Lang escaped his holding cell—with Pym's help—Paxton led Lang's manhunt.

suit. However, while transporting Lang to the police station, a police alert referenced Paxton's home address. Rushing there, the men learned that Cross, now wearing a similar size-changing Yellowjacket battlesuit, was threatening Cassie to draw out Lang.

Paxton protected Cassie while Ant-Man defeated Yellowjacket. Grateful that Cassie was safe, he allowed Lang to leave the scene. Later, Paxton helped clear Lang of the charges against him, and the two began making amends, bonding over their mutual love for Cassie. 🐜

FACT SHEET

▶ PAXTON DISAPPROVED OF SCOTT'S CRIMINAL HISTORY AND HIS INABILITY TO PAY CHILD SUPPORT.

▶ PAXTON LIVES WITH MAGGIE AND CASSIE AT 840 WINTER STREET.

▶ PAXTON WAS NOT SURPRISED FOR LONG WHEN ANT-MAN REVEALED HIMSELF AS LANG; PAXTON QUICKLY KNOCKED HIM OUT WITH A STUN GUN, THEN LATER ANGRILY DISMISSED HIM AS DELUSIONAL.

HANK PYM

FIRST APPEARANCE: *Ant-Man [2015]*

AFTER DISCOVERING SIZE-ALTERING particles he named Pym Particles, scientist Hank Pym became the super hero Ant-Man and co-founded the Avengers. Over the years, the mentally unstable Pym took numerous super-hero identities, such as Giant-Man and Yellowjacket. While trying to create artificial intelligence, Pym unintentionally created Ultron, a genocidal sentient robot; to stop Ultron's plan to eliminate all biological life, Pym bonded himself with the robot to become a single, hopefully benevolent being.

FIRST APPEARANCE:
TALES TO ASTONISH #27 (1962)

Scientist Henry "Hank" Pym discovered particles that could shorten the distance between an object's molecules, reducing its size while retaining its mass; dubbing these particles "Pym Particles," Pym created the size-changing Ant-Man suit and the ant-communicating EMP Communication Device. When a group of radicals in Soviet-controlled East Berlin stole Hydra technology, S.H.I.E.L.D.'s Howard Stark requested Pym hand over his technology so S.H.I.E.L.D. could use it to stop them. Pym refused, believing Pym Particles were too dangerous for any government to control, but S.H.I.E.L.D. Agent Peggy Carter convinced Pym to defeat the radicals as Ant-Man on S.H.I.E.L.D.'s behalf. Successfully completing the mission, Pym continued working with S.H.I.E.L.D. as a field agent, partnering with his wife, Janet Van Dyne, the Pym Particle-empowered Wasp. On a mission in 1987, the Wasp shrunk to subatomic levels to stop a nuclear bomb, vanishing into the Quantum Realm. Grief-stricken over the Wasp's apparent death, Pym sent their 7-year-old daughter, Hope Van Dyne, to boarding school and dedicated himself to researching the Quantum Realm, but he could not find the Wasp. When Pym discovered S.H.I.E.L.D.'s efforts to replicate his Pym Particle formula, he quit the agency in protest and retired as Ant-Man.

To fund his Quantum Realm research, Pym created Pym Technologies, but years later was ousted from the company by his protégé Darren Cross and estranged daughter Hope Van Dyne. The reclusive Pym was later horrified to learn that Cross was preparing to publicly sell a duplicate Pym Particle formula. Secretly working with Van Dyne, Pym constructed a plan to steal Cross's formula. Fearing for his daughter's safety, Pym refused to let her use the Ant-Man suit, instead opting to recruit and train thief Scott Lang to become the new Ant-Man; Pym and Van Dyne finally reconciled when Pym told her the truth of Wasp's disappearance. Though shot in the process, Pym helped halt Cross's plan by working with Ant-Man to destroy Pym Technologies. Pym later learned Ant-Man had successfully entered and escaped from the Quantum Realm while battling an unstable, size-changing Cross, making Pym wonder if Wasp could still be alive. Later, Pym at long last presented Van Dyne with a new Wasp suit.

MENTORING LANG

▶ PYM COMMUNICATED WITH ANTS BY STIMULATING THEIR OLFACTORY NERVE CENTERS WITH ELECTROMAGNETIC WAVES; HE FOUND BULLET ANTS THE MOST DIFFICULT TO CONTROL.

▶ PYM BUILT A REGULATOR FOR THE ANT-MAN SUIT WHICH STOPPED THE USER FROM SHRINKING TOO SMALL; THIS REDUCED THE RISK OF BECOMING LOST IN THE QUANTUM REALM.

▶ PYM KEPT A SHRUNKEN TANK ON HIS KEYCHAIN THAT HE COULD RE-ENLARGE FOR EMERGENCIES.

HOPE VAN DYNE

FIRST APPEARANCE: *Ant·Man [2015]*

The daughter of Pym Technologies founder Hank Pym, Hope Van Dyne resented her father for his refusal to discuss the details of the death of her mother, Janet Van Dyne, and for sending her away to boarding school afterward. As Pym Tech's board chairperson, she backed the takeover of Pym Tech by Pym's former protégé Darren Cross and cast the deciding vote that ousted Pym. When Van Dyne learned Cross had developed the Yellowjacket, a combat suit recreating Pym's size-altering technology, which Cross intended to make publicly available, she conspired with Pym to steal the Yellowjacket suit and destroy Cross's research. Though Van Dyne sought to use Pym's size-changing Ant-Man suit to commit the theft, she bristled when Pym recruited paroled burglar Scott Lang.

Van Dyne reluctantly helped prepare Lang for the heist by training him in unarmed combat. The strain in Pym and Van Dyne's relationship affected Lang's progress until Lang convinced Van Dyne that Pym selected him over her because he was expendable. Van Dyne then learned from Pym that her mother, who worked with Pym as the similarly equipped Wasp, was lost in a subatomic realm while stopping a nuclear missile from hitting the U.S., and that he had been searching for her ever since. Her relationship with Pym beginning to heal, Van Dyne completed Lang's training and was present at Pym Tech during Cross's attempted sale of the Yellowjacket suit to the terrorist Hydra organization. Despite Lang's capture by Cross and Pym suffering a gunshot in the melee, Lang ultimately defeated Cross. Van Dyne thereafter began a romance with Lang, and Pym showed her an in-progress redesign of her mother's Wasp suit intended for her.

FACT SHEET

▶ VAN DYNE PRETENDED TO DESPISE HER FATHER MORE VEHEMENTLY IN CROSS'S PRESENCE IN ORDER TO GAIN CROSS'S TRUST.

▶ VAN DYNE CALLED HER FATHER "HANK" AS A REMINDER OF THEIR STRAINED RELATIONSHIP BUT BEGAN CALLING HIM "DAD" AFTER PYM WAS SHOT BY CROSS.

▶ VAN DYNE BEGAN STUDYING MARTIAL ARTS SHORTLY AFTER HER MOTHER'S DEATH.

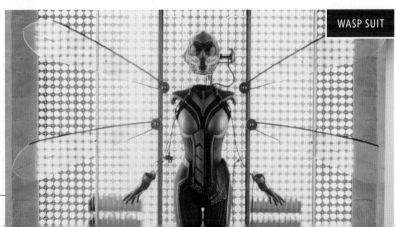

WASP SUIT

MITCHELL CARSON

FIRST APPEARANCE: *Ant-Man [2015]*

In 1989, S.H.I.E.L.D. Head of Defense Mitchell Carson served on a council that met with Hank Pym, who resigned after learning of S.H.I.E.L.D.'s attempts to recreate his size-altering Pym Particles. After Carson insinuated that Pym's deceased wife might still be alive if Pym had protected her as much as he did the Particles, Pym slammed Carson's face into the table. Carson insisted that Pym be detained so S.H.I.E.L.D. could obtain Pym's work, but council members Howard Stark and Peggy Carter prevented this. Years later, after Carson had secretly allied with the terrorist group Hydra, he attended the unveiling of Pym's protégé Darren Cross's size-changing Yellowjacket armor, for which Mitchell offered 20 percent above asking price. Two weeks after Cross accepted Carson's deal, Carson met with Cross, who had decided to sell Carson the suit, but keep the size-altering formula for himself. When Pym's hand-picked successor Scott Lang used the size-changing Ant-Man suit to attack Cross, Carson absconded with the Pym Particle serum.

ANT-THONY

FIRST APPEARANCE: *Ant-Man [2015]*

While recruiting the criminal Scott Lang to take over as the size-changing Ant-Man, scientist Hank Pym mentally orchestrated ants to facilitate Lang's jailbreak. Pym had the winged carpenter ant he dubbed "247" carry Lang safely past the authorities' five-block perimeter. Lang became nauseous and disoriented, falling off 247 in mid-air, but 247 caught and delivered him to Pym's home unharmed. Later reunited with 247, Lang renamed him Ant-Thony, and a bond soon formed between them. Later, Ant-Thony assisted Lang in infiltrating the Avengers' upstate New York headquarters to reclaim a prototype signal decoy of Pym's design. During an operation to prevent scientist Darren Cross from selling his miniaturized Yellowjacket suit to the terrorist organization Hydra, Lang led a flying ant swarm to attack Cross, but Ant-Thony was killed by a bullet fired from Cross's gun. Angered, Lang promised retribution.

FACT SHEET

- ► ANT-THONY WAS FITTED WITH A SADDLE FOR LANG.
- ► PYM BELIEVED CARPENTER ANTS LIKE ANT-THONY WERE IDEAL FOR GROUND AND AIR TRANSPORT.

FACT SHEET

- ► REUNITED YEARS LATER, CARSON SNIDELY ASKED PYM HOW RETIREMENT WAS GOING, TO WHICH PYM REPLIED, "HOW'S YOUR FACE?" CARSON SILENTLY TURNED AND WALKED AWAY.
- ► AFTER ANT-MAN SUCCESSFULLY INFILTRATED AN AVENGERS FACILITY, CARSON INCREASED HIS 20 PERCENT OFFER AND PAID CROSS TWICE THE ASKING PRICE FOR THE YELLOWJACKET SUIT.

IN THE COMICS

ANT-MAN (SCOTT LANG) FREQUENTLY befriends and uses flying ants during missions, occasionally needing them to get into tough-to-reach places. Lang names the ants to let them know they're valued, claiming they respond well to positive reinforcement. Some of his flying steeds include Chuck Barris, Indy, Prince, Silver, Silver Streak, and Whitmore.

FIRST APPEARANCE:
TALES TO ASTONISH #27 (1962)

IN THE COMICS

HAVING SECRETLY KILLED HIS father at age 15, Mitchell Carson joined S.H.I.E.L.D. and was assigned to wear Hank Pym's Ant-Man suit before it was taken by Eric O'Grady. While trying to recover the suit, Carson's face was burned battling Ant-Man. Eventually capturing and torturing O'Grady, Carson gloated about his earlier crimes and was arrested by Iron Man (Tony Stark).

FIRST APPEARANCE:
MARVEL TEAM-UP #21 (2006)

PEGGY CARTER
UPDATE

FIRST APPEARANCE:
Captain America: The First Avenger [2011]

Years ago, S.H.I.E.L.D. research consultant Hank Pym refused to relinquish his size-altering Ant-Man suit for a covert mission, fearing its misuse. When Pym insisted on carrying out the mission himself, Agent Peggy Carter tested his readiness by firing a gun at him; Pym reflexively shrunk in time to avoid the bullets, convincing Carter he was prepared; Pym successfully completed his mission. In 1989, Carter was still a high-ranking member of S.H.I.E.L.D., and was present at S.H.I.E.L.D. headquarters when an angry Pym arrived to confront Carter, Mitchell Carson, and Howard Stark about S.H.I.E.L.D.'s attempt to replicate the Pym Particle serum that powered the Ant-Man suit. Carter was upset to learn of Carson and Stark's actions. When Carson insulted Pym by implying that Pym should have been as dedicated to protecting his deceased wife as he was the serum, Pym slammed Carson's face into a table. Carter quickly restrained Pym, ending the assault. As Pym left, Carson suggested they stop him, but Carter chastised him and Stark for lying to Pym and warned them not to antagonize him further. 🐜

FACT SHEET

- ▶ CARTER'S HAIR WAS NOW STARTING TO GO GRAY, REFLECTIVE OF HER AGE IN THE LATE 1980s.
- ▶ CARTER'S QUICK REACTION IN RESTRAINING PYM SUGGESTS THAT EVEN IN HER ADVANCED AGE, SHE WAS STILL A SKILLED COMBATANT.

FALCON UPDATE

FIRST APPEARANCE:
Captain America: The Winter Soldier [2014]

When something tripped a sensor on the rooftop of the Avengers' new upstate New York headquarters, Falcon investigated. He initially believed it was a false alarm, but after scanning the area with his goggles' enhanced optics, Falcon spotted a miniaturized Ant-Man (Scott Lang). Lang was attempting to steal a prototype signal decoy that his predecessor and employer, Hank Pym, had created during his tenure with S.H.I.E.L.D. Ant-Man enlarged and introduced himself, then asked Falcon if he could borrow the item, promising to return it after saving the world. Distrustful of Ant-Man's intentions, Falcon attempted to detain him, but Ant-Man resisted, using his size-changing abilities to battle Falcon. Although Falcon landed several blows, Ant-Man successfully entered the Avengers' compound and retrieved the device. Falcon pursued Ant-Man into the warehouse, but Ant-Man compromised Falcon's flight pack from within, destroying several internal components. Grounded, Falcon was unable to thwart Ant-Man's escape; he requested that the present Avengers personnel keep Captain America from learning about the embarrassing incident. Later, when Falcon and Cap located the Winter Soldier, Cap wanted to contact Iron Man (Tony Stark), but both men worried Stark wouldn't believe their current situation or even be permitted by "the Accords" to assist them. When Cap stated that they were on their own, Falcon replied he knew someone who could potentially help. 🐜

FACT SHEET

- ▶ ANT-MAN STATED HE WAS A FAN, BUT FALCON REMAINED UNFAZED DESPITE CLAIMING TO APPRECIATE THE SENTIMENT.
- ▶ AMUSED BY THE CODENAME ANT-MAN, FALCON SMIRKED UPON HEARING IT.

CASSIE LANG

FIRST APPEARANCE: *Ant-Man [2015]*

Cassie Lang loved her father, Scott, and thought of him as a hero despite the years he spent in prison for burglary. When an uninvited Lang attended Cassie's birthday party at ex-wife Maggie Lang's house, Cassie was thrilled to see him and loved the hideous stuffed animal he gave her. Maggie cut the reunion short, reminding Lang he must pay child support before he could visit again.

Needing an ally to stop the corrupt Darren Cross' activities, scientist Hank Pym recruited Lang to be the size-changing Ant-Man. In response, Cross donned his size-changing Yellowjacket battlesuit and threatened Cassie. To destroy Cross's suit, Lang had to shrink to dangerously subatomic size. However, Cassie's voice inspired Lang to jury-rig his suit's regulator to return to normal size; a grateful Maggie started welcoming Lang's visits. 🐜

FACT SHEET

- ▶ SCOTT'S NICKNAME FOR CASSIE IS "PEANUT."
- ▶ CASSIE KEPT AN ANT THAT WAS ACCIDENTALLY ENLARGED DURING SCOTT'S BATTLE WITH CROSS AS A PET.
- ▶ CASSIE IS ALSO FOND OF HER MOTHER'S FIANCÉ, DETECTIVE JIM PAXTON.

IN THE COMICS

WHEN CASSIE LANG WAS DIAGNOSED with a heart condition that could only be cured by Dr. Erica Sondheim, Scott Lang stole the size-changing Ant-Man suit to rescue Dr. Sondheim from corrupt Darren Cross so she could save his daughter. Years later, Cassie developed size-changing powers as the Young Avengers' Stature.

FIRST APPEARANCE:
MARVEL PREMIERE #47 (1979)

MAGGIE LANG

FIRST APPEARANCE: *Ant-Man [2015]*

Electrical engineer Scott Lang promised his wife Maggie that he would refrain from criminal activities after the birth of their daughter Cassie, but when Lang discovered that his employer Vista Corp was illegally overcharging its customers, he felt compelled to intervene. Disregarding Maggie's advice to leave things alone, Scott was arrested for stealing funds from Vista Corp and returning them to customers. He was sentenced to three years in prison, leaving Maggie to care for Cassie alone. Maggie divorced Scott and later became engaged to Detective Jim Paxton. After his release, Scott attended Cassie's birthday party, despite not having an invitation. Maggie sent Scott away, promising that he could see Cassie only after he paid child support and had a steady job and an apartment. Later, after Scott became the size-changing hero Ant-Man, he saved Cassie from the criminal Darren Cross. A grateful Maggie and Paxton allowed Scott to be involved in Cassie's life, welcoming him as part of the family. 🐜

FACT SHEET

- ▶ MAGGIE WAS SO SURPRISED TO HEAR THAT SCOTT WAS CRASHING CASSIE'S BIRTHDAY PARTY THAT SHE CHOKED ON HER DRINK.
- ▶ AFTER HIS RELEASE, MAGGIE BELIEVED THAT KEEPING SCOTT FROM VISITING THEIR DAUGHTER WAS BEST FOR THE FAMILY'S WELFARE.

IN THE COMICS

PEGGY RAE DIVORCED SCOTT LANG IN the early years of their daughter Cassie's life and eventually married police officer Blake Burdick. Fearing for Cassie's safety due to Lang's exploits as the super hero Ant-Man, Peggy successfully applied for custody of Cassie. However, Cassie soon adopted a super-hero identity of her own for a time.

FIRST APPEARANCE:
AVENGERS #62 (2003)

HOWARD STARK
UPDATE

FIRST APPEARANCE: *Iron Man [2008] [photo];*
Iron Man 2 [2010] [full appearance]

Howard Stark requested that scientist Hank Pym hand over his size-altering technology to S.H.I.E.L.D. for a covert mission. Refusing the request, Pym insisted on conducting the mission himself. In 1989, at S.H.I.E.L.D.'s Washington, D.C.-adjacent Triskelion headquarters (under construction at the time), top S.H.I.E.L.D. administrator Howard Stark was surprised by the sudden return of Pym, who was supposedly in Moscow. Infuriated, Pym confronted Stark, Peggy Carter, and Head of Defense Mitchell Carson after discovering the S.H.I.E.L.D. defense lab was attempting to replicate Pym's formula for the Pym Particle serum that enabled him to shrink and grow as Ant-Man. Insisting on keeping the formula to himself lest it be misused, Pym resigned from S.H.I.E.L.D., though Stark rejected his resignation. When Carson insulted Pym by suggesting Pym's wife might still be alive had he protected her as much as he did the serum, Pym slammed Carson's face into the desk; Stark refused to come to Carson's defense. Though Carson admonished Stark for letting Pym leave, Stark retorted that he had known Pym a long time and knew he was no security risk.

FACT SHEET

▶ THOUGH STARK WAS A BRILLIANT SCIENTIST AND INVENTOR, NEITHER HE NOR ANY OTHER S.H.I.E.L.D. SCIENTIST HAD COME CLOSE TO REPLICATING PYM PARTICLES.

▶ IN THE PRESENT DAY, PYM COMPLAINED HE SPENT HIS LIFE KEEPING HIS TECHNOLOGY OUT OF THE HANDS OF THE STARKS, REFERRING TO BOTH HOWARD AND HIS GENIUS SON, TONY.

WASP
JANET VAN DYNE

FIRST APPEARANCE: *Ant-Man [2015]*

Janet Van Dyne and husband, scientist Hank Pym, had a daughter, Hope. After Pym discovered size-altering particles and became the shrinking super hero and S.H.I.E.L.D. agent Ant-Man, she quickly convinced him to build a size-changing suit for her. Partnering with Ant-Man, Van Dyne became the Wasp.

In 1987, separatists hijacked a Soviet missile silo in Kursk and launched an ICBM at the U.S.; Ant-Man and Wasp were sent to deactivate it, but Ant-Man's size-controlling regulator was damaged. Willing to sacrifice herself for millions, the Wasp deactivated her own regulator and shrunk to subatomic size, enabling her to move between molecules so that she could get inside the missile and deactivate it. However, the regulator-less Wasp continued shrinking into the Quantum Realm and was believed dead; Pym spent years unsuccessfully searching for her.

FACT SHEET

▶ PYM FELT VAN DYNE WAS BORN TO BE THE WASP.

▶ UNLIKE ANT-MAN, THE WASP HAD WINGS WHICH ENABLED HER TO FLY; THE SOURCE OF THESE WINGS IS UNREVEALED.

IN THE COMICS

SOCIALITE AND EVENTUAL FASHION designer Janet Van Dyne became the crime fighter Wasp when her romantic interest Ant-Man (Hank Pym) empowered her with his size-altering Pym Particles. Alongside Iron Man (Tony Stark), Hulk (Bruce Banner), and Thor, the pair co-founded a super-hero team, which the Wasp named the Avengers. The Wasp has served with the Avengers ever since, even as one of their most effective leaders.

FIRST APPEARANCE:
TALES TO ASTONISH #44 (1963)

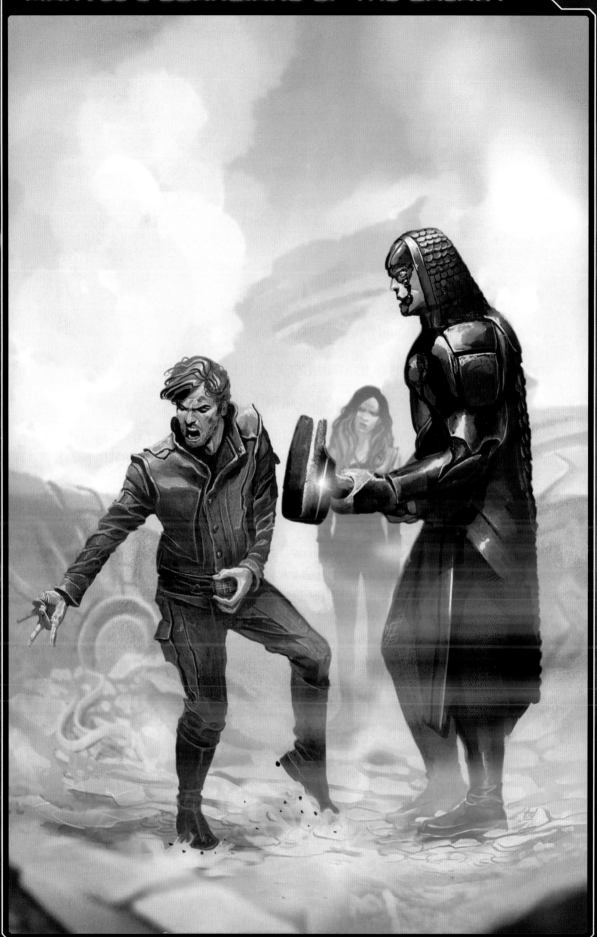

GUIDEBOOK TO THE MARVEL CINEMATIC UNIVERSE

MARVEL
GUARDIANS OF THE GALAXY

MARVEL STUDIOS PRESENTS A JAMES GUNN FILM "GUARDIANS OF THE GALAXY" CHRIS PRATT ZOE SALDANA DAVE BAUTISTA FEATURING VIN DIESEL AS GROOT BRADLEY COOPER AS ROCKET LEE PACE MICHAEL ROOKER KAREN GILLAN DJIMON HOUNSOU WITH JOHN C. REILLY WITH GLENN CLOSE AS NOVA PRIME AND BENICIO DEL TORO AS THE COLLECTOR CASTING BY SARAH HALLEY FINN, C.S.A. MUSIC SUPERVISOR DAVE JORDAN MUSIC BY TYLER BATES HEAD OF VISUAL DEVELOPMENT CHARLIE WEN CO-HEAD OF VISUAL DEVELOPMENT RYAN MEINERDING VISUAL EFFECTS SUPERVISOR STEPHANE CERETTI COSTUME DESIGNER ALEXANDRA BYRNE EDITED BY FRED RASKIN, A.C.E. CRAIG WOOD, A.C.E. HUGHES WINBORNE, A.C.E. PRODUCTION DESIGN CHARLES WOOD DIRECTOR OF PHOTOGRAPHY BEN DAVIS, BSC CO-PRODUCERS DAVID J. GRANT JONATHAN SCHWARTZ EXECUTIVE PRODUCERS NIK KORDA STAN LEE EXECUTIVE PRODUCERS VICTORIA ALONSO JEREMY LATCHAM EXECUTIVE PRODUCER ALAN FINE EXECUTIVE PRODUCER LOUIS D'ESPOSITO PRODUCED BY KEVIN FEIGE, p.g.a. WRITTEN BY JAMES GUNN AND NICOLE PERLMAN DIRECTED BY JAMES GUNN

Collecting information from Marvel's *Guardians of the Galaxy* (2014), Marvel's *Guardians of the Galaxy Infinite Comic #1* (2014), and *Marvel's Guardians of the Galaxy Prelude #1-2* (2014).

HEAD WRITER/COORDINATOR: **MIKE O'SULLIVAN**

COORDINATION: **DARON JENSEN**

WRITERS: **ROB BOCK, ANTHONY COTILLETTA, PAT DUKE, MIKE FICHERA, DARON JENSEN, ROB LONDON, CHRIS MCCARVER, JACOB ROUGEMONT,** AND **STUART VANDAL**

ARTISTS: **WELLINTON ALVES, SIMONE BIANCHI, NICK BRADSHAW, SAL BUSCEMA, JOHN BYRNE, ROBERTO FERNANDEZ CASTRO, PAUL CATLING, JIM CHEUNG, GENE COLAN, GABRIELE DELL'OTTO, STEVE DITKO, ANDREA DIVITO, JACK DUDMAN, ANTHONY FRANCISCO, JAVIER GARRÓN, ADI GRANOV, BOB HALL, SCOTT HEPBURN, DAVE JOHNSON, GIL KANE, JACK KIRBY, NIC KLEIN, JOSÉ LADRÖNN, BOB LARKIN, AARON LOPRESTI, JORGE LUCAS, CHRIS MARRINAN, FRANCESCO MATTINA, MIKE MAYHEW, STEVE MCNIVEN, GRAY MORROW, RUDY NEBRES, ARIEL OLIVETTI, PAUL PELLETIER, GEORGE PÉREZ, KEITH POLLARD, OLIVIER PRON, JOE QUINONES, HUMBERTO RAMOS, VALERIO SCHITI, JIM STARLIN, GUS VAZQUEZ,** AND **PATRICK ZIRCHER**

COVER ARTIST: **MIKE DEL MUNDO**

SPECIAL THANKS TO DAVE ALTHOFF, SHAWN "KEEBLER" BYERS, JEFF CHRISTIANSEN, STEVE COTTON, MATT DELMANOWSKI, ERIKA DENTON, TIM DILLON, HUNTER HARRINGTON, PERCIVAL LANUZA, AVIA PEREZ, JACQUE PORTE, AND RYAN POTTER

COLLECTOR'S COLLECTION

FIRST APPEARANCE: *Thor: The Dark World [2013]*

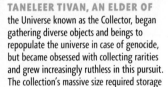

TANELEER TIVAN, AN ELDER OF the Universe known as the Collector, began gathering diverse objects and beings to repopulate the universe in case of genocide, but became obsessed with collecting rarities and grew increasingly ruthless in this pursuit. The collection's massive size required storage across several worlds and spacecraft.

FIRST APPEARANCE:
AVENGERS #28 (1966)

Deep within the mining colony of Knowhere, an extraordinary museum houses the galaxy's most unique artifacts, objects, plants, animals, and creatures. This gathering's curator, the enigmatic Taneleer Tivan, known as the Collector, was assisted by his attendant slave, Carina. The collection included many captured sentient beings, such as a Dark Elf, a cosmic cocoon, a Chitauri soldier, a cosmonaut dog named Cosmo, and Howard, a humanoid duck. Carina's predecessor was also bound and imprisoned as part of the collection for failing Tivan in unknown circumstances.

Asgardians Sif and Volstagg delivered the Aether, one of the massively powerful Infinity Stones in fluid form, to Tivan for safekeeping after it was recovered from the Dark Elf Malekith and deemed too dangerous to keep in the royal vault alongside the Tesseract, another Stone. Tivan later hired Gamora to obtain the Orb containing another Infinity Stone. When Gamora and her new allies delivered it, Tivan took particular interest in the tree-like humanoid Groot, offering payment for his carcass upon his eventual death. Explaining the origin of the Infinity Stones, Tivan exposed the Infinity Stone within the Orb. When Carina, desiring freedom from servitude, grabbed the Stone, its power consumed her and explosively destroyed much of the Collection.

FACT SHEET

▶ UPON RECEIVING THE AETHER, THE COLLECTOR MUTTERED UNDER HIS BREATH, "ONE DOWN, FIVE TO GO."

CHITAURI

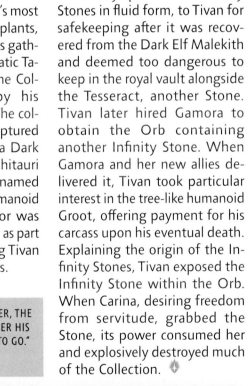

DARK ELF

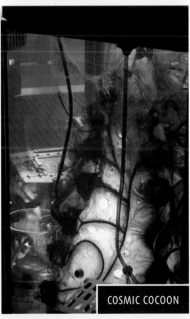

COSMIC COCOON

DRAX

FIRST APPEARANCE:
Guardians of the Galaxy [2014]

D rax was a humanoid warrior seeking vengeance for the murder of his wife Ovette and daughter Camaria by Kree warlord Ronan the Accuser. After claiming many lives in his quest, Drax, a.k.a. "the Destroyer," was imprisoned in the Kyln penal facility. Upon learning that the assassin Gamora, a former associate of Ronan's, had also been incarcerated, Drax planned to kill her until inmate Peter Quill convinced him to spare her since she could ultimately lead him to Ronan. When Gamora and Quill escaped alongside mercenaries Rocket and Groot and fled to Quill's ship the *Milano*, Drax joined their partnership, but only in hopes of using Gamora to find Ronan.

The five traveled to the mining outpost Knowhere to sell an Orb—stolen by Quill and sought by Ronan and his Sakaaran soldiers—to the Collector, unaware the Orb contained a vastly powerful Infinity Stone. While awaiting the Collector's representative, they enjoyed brief revelry at a nearby bar until Drax inadvertently insulted Rocket. Though Quill defused hostilities, an infuriated and inebriated Drax

---

Drax united with his allies to share the Stone's power and turn it against Ronan.

---

left their company and impulsively transmitted a challenge to Ronan, revealing their location. Upon arriving, Ronan easily defeated Drax and left him to drown, but Groot saved Drax' life.

After Ronan purloined the Orb and Quill and Gamora were captured by the Ravagers, a pirate crew Quill had previously betrayed, Groot and the repentant Drax convinced a reluctant Rocket to help rescue Quill and Gamora. Confronting the Ravagers, the trio threatened to destroy the pirates' ship with Rocket's Hadron Enforcer weapon, but stood down upon learning Quill and Gamora had struck a deal, promising the Ravagers the Stone in exchange for help stopping Ronan from destroying the planet Xandar.

Boarding Ronan's ship, the *Dark Aster*, Drax, Groot, Gamora, and Quill fought Ronan's minions, including his lieutenant, Korath, whom Drax personally slew. Upon confronting Ronan, Drax was again overpowered but was saved by Rocket, who flew into Ronan with a Ravager ship. The damaged *Dark Aster* crashed on Xandar, but Groot saved Drax and the others by forming a protective nest around them, apparently sacrificing his own life.

REAL ESTATE AGENT ARTHUR

Douglas and his family were attacked by Titan warlord Thanos when they inadvertently witnessed his landing on Earth. Though Douglas and his wife were killed, Mentor, an elder Eternal and Thanos' father, transferred Douglas' consciousness to an artificial body, remaking him into Drax the Destroyer, a super-strong behemoth with no memory of his past and an insatiable desire to kill Thanos. Drax subsequently regained his memories, and eventually joined the Guardians of the Galaxy on their mission to free the Kree homeworld from the techno-organic Phalanx. He has remained with the team during several interstellar conflicts.

FIRST APPEARANCE:
IRON MAN #55 (1973)

Surviving the crash, Ronan again attacked Quill and his allies, but Drax and Rocket used the Enforcer to dislodge the Stone from Ronan's Cosmi-Rod, and Drax united with his allies to share the Stone's power and turn it against Ronan, destroying him. Drax then comforted the grieving Rocket over Groot's death by petting his head. Gamora reassured Drax that he had avenged his family, but Drax remarked that Ronan's master, the mad nihilist Thanos, was his next target. With their criminal records expunged and their damaged ship rebuilt, Drax and his allies, calling themselves the Guardians of the Galaxy, left Xandar in search of new adventures. As Drax sharpened his knives aboard the *Milano*, a remnant sprout of Groot, saved and potted by Rocket, began dancing to a mixtape belonging to Quill, but froze when Drax glanced his way. ⚑

FACT SHEET

▶ DRAX IS A SUPERHUMANLY STRONG HAND-TO-HAND COMBATANT, INCREDIBLY RESISTANT TO INJURY, AND SKILLED IN THE USE OF HIS PAIRED KNIVES.

▶ UNABLE TO COMPREHEND METAPHORS, DRAX'S PEOPLE TYPICALLY INTERPRET COLORFUL EXPRESSIONS AND GESTURES LITERALLY.

▶ DRAX' BODY IS COVERED IN ORNAMENTAL SCARS—SIMILAR TO EARTH TATTOOS—THAT DETAIL SIGNIFICANT EVENTS OF HIS LIFE AND CULTURE.

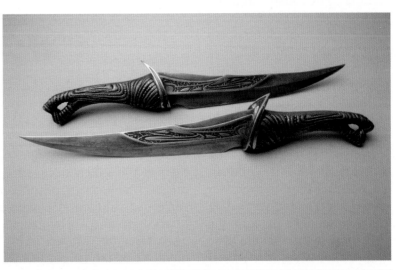

GAMORA

FIRST APPEARANCE:
Guardians of the Galaxy [2014]

After the galactic tyrant Thanos wiped out the Zehoberei species, he took in their last survivor, Gamora, and raised her as his daughter. She was trained to be a warrior and assassin alongside Thanos' other "children," including the Luphomoid Nebula, who would come to be Gamora's fierce rival; their exercises often left Nebula grievously injured, prompting Thanos to repair her injuries with cybernetics; over time, Gamora sought to be free from her abusive "father." When Thanos allied with Kree extremist Ronan the Accuser to seek the Orb, an artifact containing a powerful Infinity Stone, Gamora contacted the Collector, a curator of exotic antiquities, and arranged to sell the Orb to him for safekeeping. After persuading Ronan to send her to locate the Orb instead of Nebula, she tracked it to Xandar, where it was in the possession of the human outlaw Peter Quill. She tried to steal it from him, but found herself also fighting bounty hunters Rocket and Groot, who were attempting to capture Quill. Eventually, the Nova Corps arrested all four of them and sent

> ## Having seen the Stone's power for herself, Gamora decided to instead turn it over to the Nova Corps.

them to the Kyln, a deep-space prison. Many of the prisoners there had suffered at Thanos' hands, and burned for retribution against Gamora. She was nearly murdered by the vengeful Drax, whose family had been killed by Ronan, but Quill convinced him to relent; Drax decided to use her to find Ronan instead. Working together, Gamora, Rocket, Groot, Drax, and Quill masterminded a daring escape from the Kyln.

Taking her allies to Knowhere to deliver the Orb, Gamora flirted with Quill while waiting to see the Collector, but cut the romance short, mistakenly suspecting Quill was manipulating her. Upon their arrival at the Collector's museum, the Collector's assistant, Carina, grabbed the Infinity Stone in an attempt to gain its power and free herself from her oppressive master; the Stone proved too potent, however, resulting in Carina's death and the destruction of the Collection. Having seen the Stone's power for herself, Gamora decided to instead turn it over to the Nova Corps, but that plan was forestalled by Drax, who had drunkenly alerted Ronan to their location to provoke a duel. Gamora tried to escape with the Stone, but was left to die in space when

WHEN HER SPECIES WAS MASSACRED by the Universal Church of Truth, Gamora was rescued by the mad Titan Thanos, who raised her to become an assassin. Sent to kill Adam Warlock, she instead became his ally and turned on Thanos. She was eventually entrusted with one of the Infinity Gems as part of Warlock's Infinity Watch, and later joined the Guardians of the Galaxy, led by Star-Lord (Peter Quill).

FIRST APPEARANCE:
STRANGE TALES #180 (1975)

Nebula destroyed her craft and claimed the Stone; Quill almost died saving her, but they were both captured by the Ravagers, Quill's old pirate crew. Quill convinced the Ravagers to help stop Ronan's impending attack on the planet Xandar.

Gamora and the others infiltrated Ronan's flagship, the *Dark Aster*, where she dueled with Nebula. Eventually, Nebula decided that both Gamora and Thanos were insane, and fled. With the way cleared, Gamora and her allies confronted the Infinity Stone-empowered Ronan. They crashed the *Dark Aster* on Xandar, but Ronan survived, and prepared to destroy the planet. When Quill distracted Ronan and grabbed the Stone, Gamora, Drax, and Rocket joined together to share its power, allowing them to survive and destroy Ronan. Her criminal record cleared by the grateful Nova Corps, Gamora joined Quill and their allies—now dubbed the Guardians of the Galaxy—to set out on new adventures. ⬥

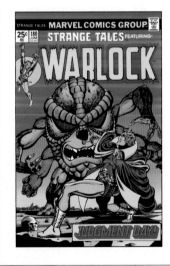

GROOT

FIRST APPEARANCE:
Guardians of the Galaxy [2014]

A plant-like Flora colossus from Planet X, Groot and his mercenary companion Rocket were hired by crimelord Zade Scraggot to procure a consignment of sentient Scalluscs; they reneged upon learning Scraggot wished to deshell the creatures, potentially fatally, for bathroom decorations. On Xandar, the pair hunted human pirate Peter Quill for a 40,000-unit, live-capture bounty. The pair's pursuit was interrupted by the assassin Gamora, who sought the Orb artifact in Quill's possession; Xandar's Nova Corps arrested all four and incarcerated them in the Kyln prison. Recognizing a common need, the four conspired to escape and sell the Orb, splitting the huge profits. When Rocket began listing items he would need for the escape, Groot immediately retrieved one—the guard tower's quarnyx battery—in full view of the guards, unaware Rocket had

wanted to covertly gather the other items first. Despite being forced to assemble the remaining gear within minutes while under fire from the guards thanks to Groot's presumption, the group escaped, recruiting fellow inmate Drax along the way, and fled the Kyln aboard Quill's spacecraft, the *Milano*.

> ## Groot grew a flower from his hand and gave it to a young girl in the crowd.

They visited the mining station Knowhere, where Gamora had arranged the Orb's sale to the eccentric Collector. Accosted by a group of beggars, Groot grew a

flower from his hand and gave it to a young girl in the crowd. While awaiting the Collector's emissary at a bar, Groot intervened in a brawl between Rocket and Drax after Rocket took offense to a comment made by Drax. Later, during their meeting, the Collector offered Groot money for the rights to his corpse upon his death. When Gamora's employer Ronan arrived seeking the vastly powerful Infinity Stone inside the Orb, Groot could only watch as Rocket, Quill, and Gamora combatted Ronan's forces using

FACT SHEET

▶ GROOT CAN EXTEND THE LENGTH OF HIS LIMBS AND REGROW THEM IF SEVERED. HE CAN ALSO GROW COLORFUL BLOOMS AND EXPEL PHOSPHORESCENT SEEDPODS THAT ILLUMINATE DARKENED AREAS.

▶ GROOT'S LANGUAGE CONSISTS PRIMARILY OF SUBTLE VARIATIONS OF THE PHRASE "I AM GROOT."

▶ THOUGH FEARSOME IN COMBAT, GROOT HAS AN INNATELY KIND HEART, AND OFTEN HAD TO CONVINCE ROCKET TO TAKE ACTIONS NOT SOLELY AIMED TOWARDS PROFIT OR SELF-PRESERVATION.

A MEMBER OF PLANET X'S indigenous tree-like species, Groot was exiled due to social activism and wandered the galaxy until he met and befriended galactic adventurer Rocket Raccoon in a Kree prison. The pair joined a team assembled to free the Kree homeworld Hala from the techno-organic Phalanx. Groot was seemingly destroyed multiple times during their exploits, but survived through cuttings that retained his consciousness and eventually attained his full-grown form. After Hala's liberation, Groot remained with the team, who named themselves the Guardians of the Galaxy.

FIRST APPEARANCE:
TALES TO ASTONISH #13 (1960)

mining pods, for which Groot was too large. After Ronan left with the Stone and Quill and Gamora were captured by Quill's former associates the Ravagers, Groot saved Drax from drowning after he was defeated in combat with Ronan, and urged a reluctant Rocket to rescue Quill and Gamora.

After threatening to destroy the Ravagers' ship, Groot, Drax, and Rocket learned Quill and Gamora had enlisted the Ravagers' aid against Ronan in exchange for the Stone. Reaching Xandar with the Ravagers, Groot, Drax, Quill, and Gamora boarded Ronan's warship, the *Dark Aster*, and battled Ronan and his Sakaaran soldiers; Groot speared several soldiers, viciously smashing them into the walls, while boyishly seeking his peers' approval. As the damaged *Dark Aster* plummeted to Xandar's surface, Groot formed a protective nest around his allies, replying to Rocket's pleas not to sacrifice himself with an atypical "We are Groot." The heroes survived the *Dark Aster*'s crash, but Groot was reduced to inert piles of wooden debris, and Rocket, believing his friend had died, mourned for him. After the remaining four friends united to retrieve the Stone from Ronan

and temporarily shared its power to defeat him, Rocket planted a piece of Groot's remains in a flower pot. As the four, now calling themselves the Guardians of the Galaxy, departed Xandar, the rapidly growing Groot sapling came to life and began dancing to Quill's mixtape, freezing momentarily when a nearby Drax glanced his way.

GUARDIANS OF THE GALAXY

FIRST APPEARANCE:
Guardians of the Galaxy [2014]

When Peter Quill, a.k.a. Star-Lord, stole a valuable Orb sought by his mentor, the Ravager Yondu Udonta, Yondu placed a bounty on him. Seeking to claim it, mercenary partners Rocket and Groot tracked Quill to Xandar, homeworld of the law-enforcing Nova Corps. The Kree renegade Ronan the Accuser also sought the Orb, intending to trade it to his ally Thanos in exchange for help destroying Xandar; Ronan dispatched one of Thanos' adopted daughters, Gamora, to retrieve it, unaware she had developed a conscience and intended to sell it to the Collector for safekeeping.

On Xandar, Gamora and the mercenaries ambushed Quill, and a running conflict ensued, ending when the Nova Corps arrested them. Sent to the Kyln deep-space prison, they encountered inmate Drax the Destroyer, who intended to kill Gamora in revenge for Ronan having

> **The five formed an uneasy alliance to break out of the Kyln and split the profits.**

murdered his wife and daughter; Quill convinced Drax to let Gamora live by arguing that Ronan would come for her. When Gamora stated that she had a generous buyer for the Orb, the five formed an uneasy alliance to break out of the Kyln and split the profits. Escaping, the quintet took Quill's ship the *Milano* to Knowhere, the Collector's location. While the others met the Collector, an impatient Drax broadcast their location to Ronan. Meanwhile, the Collector revealed that the Orb contained an Infinity Stone capable of destroying entire planets, but when his assistant Carina misused it and explosively demolished his collection, Gamora realized he could not safely contain it and decided to place it in the Nova Corps' custody. Before she could do so, both the Ravagers and Ronan's forces arrived, and Ronan— easily defeating Drax in combat—claimed the Orb. Captured while rescuing Gamora, Quill struck a deal with Yondu, promising him the Orb if the Ravagers helped stop Ronan.

Uniting under the cause of protecting Xandar, the five assaulted Ronan's flagship, the *Dark Aster*. While Rocket, the Ravagers, and Nova Corps piloted ships

30TH CENTURY GUARDIANS

THE GUARDIANS OF THE GALAXY were 30th century heroes of Earth-691 who freed an enslaved Earth from the Badoon Empire. In the 21st century, after several interstellar conflicts, Star-Lord (Peter Quill) assembled several spacefaring heroes to protect the cosmos from further conflicts, and was inspired to use the same name for his Earth-616 group after encountering a time-traveling member of the Earth-691 group.

FIRST APPEARANCE:
MARVEL SUPER-HEROES #18 (1969)

defending Xandar's surface, the others boarded the *Dark Aster*, battled past Ronan's minions, and confronted Ronan

himself. Piloting his ship into the *Dark Aster's* flight deck, Rocket forced Ronan's ship to crash on Xandar; Groot sacrificed himself by using his own body as a shield to save the others. However, Ronan also endured, mockingly calling his opponents the Guardians of the Galaxy. Seizing the Stone from Ronan, Quill tried to harness its power, but was overwhelmed until his friends joined him. Their combined wills allowing them to contain the Stone's rampant energies, they disintegrated Ronan and then placed the Stone in a new Orb. In the aftermath, Quill gave Yondu a fake Orb, then handed the one containing the Stone over to the Nova Corps. With their criminal records expunged, and Groot regrowing from a salvaged twig, the Guardians set off in the *Milano* for new exploits.

▶ THE KNOWHERE BATTLE BEGAN SHIFTING THE GUARDIANS' RELATIONSHIPS FROM AN UNEASY ALLIANCE TO GENUINE FRIENDSHIP.

▶ GROOT SAVED A DROWNING DRAX AFTER HIS FIGHT WITH RONAN, EARNING HIS THANKS AND MAKING HIM REALIZE HE HAD ACTED FOOLISHLY IN BROADCASTING THEIR LOCATION.

▶ AFTER THE BATTLE FOR THE ORB ON KNOWHERE, GAMORA WAS LEFT FLOATING IN SPACE WITH ONLY MOMENTS TO LIVE; KNOWING THE RAVAGERS WERE IN CLOSE PURSUIT, QUILL GAVE THEM HIS LOCATION AND LAUNCHED HIMSELF INTO SPACE, RISKING HIS OWN LIFE SO SHE WOULD BE PICKED UP WITH HIM.

21ST CENTURY GUARDIANS

INFINITY STONES

FIRST APPEARANCE:
Thor [2011] [INDIVIDUAL STONE]; *Thor: The Dark World [2013]* [COLLECTIVELY IDENTIFIED]; *Guardians of the Galaxy [2014]* [ALL SIX STONES]

Before creation itself, six singularities existed. When the universe exploded into existence, the singularities' remnants were forged into concentrated ingots capable of manipulating the fundamental aspects of the new reality. Each a different color – blue, yellow, green, orange, purple, and red – they became collectively known as the Infinity Stones. Only beings of extraordinary strength could wield even a single stone, such as celestial giants who once used the purple stone to destroy entire worlds in seconds. At one point, a group of unidentified individuals shared the stone's power between them, but only for a few seconds before the energies consumed them. Eventually housed in a metallic Orb, the purple stone ended up in a temple on the planet Morag, lost after planetary disasters.

> **Each a different color – blue, yellow, green, orange, purple, and red – they became collectively known as the Infinity Stones.**

Five thousand years ago, Asgard's King Bor stopped the Dark Elf Malekith from using another stone, in a fluid form called the Aether, to return the universe to eternal night, then hid it in an interdimensional realm. Another stone, within a cube known as the Tesseract, also came into Asgard's possession during the rule of Bor's son, Odin. For safekeeping, they hid it on Earth, but it was found by Nazi Germany's scientific research division, Hydra. Tapping into the Tesseract's power allowed Hydra to create devastating energy weapons and pursue their own dreams of conquest, but Allied forces led by Captain America opposed them, and the Tesseract was lost at sea until S.H.I.E.L.D. eventually found it.

Seeking to gather the Infinity Stones' power, the being called Thanos had rogue Asgardian Loki steal the Tesseract from S.H.I.E.L.D. and create a portal through which Thanos' Chitauri armies invaded Earth, but several of Earth's heroes, including Odin's son Thor, assembled as the Avengers and thwarted this plot. In the aftermath, Thor returned the Tesseract to Asgard. Later, the Aether was rediscovered, and Malekith again attempted to establish eternal darkness with it, but was stopped by Thor. Realizing that it was unwise to store two Infinity Stones close together, the Asgardians entrusted the Aether to the intergalactic curator, the Collector, who secretly decided to procure the others.

After the scavenger Star-Lord retrieved the Orb from Morag, he and his compatriots, later named the Guardians of the Galaxy, delivered it to the Collector for financial gain. However, after the Collector informed his visitors of the Orb's true contents, his slave Carina touched it, hoping to free herself from the Collector. The unleashed power destroyed her and the Collector's museum. Before the Guardians could transfer the Orb somewhere safer, Thanos' ally Ronan claimed it. Believing he no longer needed Thanos after learning about the Stone's power, Ronan used it in an effort to destroy the planet Xandar, but the Guardians and Xandar's forces defeated Ronan. The Guardians entrusted the Stone into the Nova Corps' custody. ✦

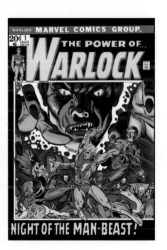

DEATH, ENTROPY, INFINITY, AND ETERNITY WITH STONES

FACT SHEET

▶ DURING THE XANDAR BATTLE, THE GUARDIANS COLLECTIVELY TAPPED INTO THE STONE'S POWER WITHOUT BEING DESTROYED. GAMORA SPECULATED THIS MIGHT HAVE BEEN BECAUSE STAR-LORD'S FATHER BELONGS TO AN UNIDENTIFIED BUT ANCIENT ALIEN RACE.

KNOWHERE

FIRST APPEARANCE: *Guardians of the Galaxy [2014]*

Hundreds of years ago, a group of miners working for the intergalactic Tivan Group began harvesting rare organic materials from inside the severed head of an ancient celestial being at the edge of the galactic rim. These materials were considered highly valuable on the black market.

Known for having no rules or regulations whatsoever, Knowhere's dangerous and illegal mining work attracted outlaws and criminals from across the galaxy. By modern times, Knowhere had expanded from a small mining operation to a free-port space station, and served as the headquarters of the Tivan Group's eccentric leader, Taneleer Tivan. ✦

FACT SHEET

▸ KNOWHERE IS HOME TO TANELEER TIVAN'S COLLECTION OF RARE SPECIES AND UNIQUE ARTIFACTS — INCLUDING THE AETHER INFINITY STONE — REPUTED TO BE THE MOST COMPREHENSIVE OF ITS KIND IN THE GALAXY.

▸ THE GALACTIC WATERING HOLE, THE BOOT OF JEMIAH, ACTED AS A ROWDY DISTRACTION FOR STAR-LORD AND HIS COMPANIONS WHILE THEY WAITED TO MEET WITH TIVAN.

▸ ALTHOUGH THE ENERGY PULSE RELEASED BY THE ORB DESTROYED MUCH OF TIVAN'S COLLECTION, A FEW FORMER EXHIBITS STAYED IN KNOWHERE WITH TIVAN, INCLUDING HOWARD THE DUCK AND COSMO.

IN THE COMICS

POSITIONED ALONG THE RIP, THE outer edge of time and space, Knowhere is a space station within the disembodied head of a Celestial that serves as a port-of-call from the edge of the known universe to realms beyond. Knowhere houses scientists and travelers from all over the universe, including its chief of security Cosmo, and was used as a base of operations by the Guardians of the Galaxy.

FIRST APPEARANCE:
NOVA #8 (2008)

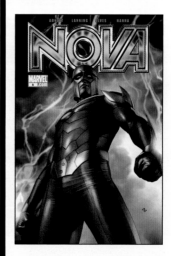

NEBULA

FIRST APPEARANCE: *Guardians of the Galaxy [2014]*

Adopted daughter of the genocidal maniac Thanos, Nebula learned from childhood to conquer her weaknesses to gain power. Suffering repeated life-threatening injuries during training exercises, often caused by her adoptive sister Gamora whenever Nebula was foolish enough to trust her, Nebula's flesh was systematically replaced with technological body modifications at Thanos' behest. In adulthood, Nebula rationalized this abuse, telling herself every failure only made her stronger. At some point, Thanos sent the siblings to serve the Kree fanatic Ronan who Thanos tasked with acquiring a powerful Infinity Stone.

On the planet Praxius IX, Nebula sought to obtain the Orb containing the desired Infinity Stone but was ambushed by killer drones and ensnared in a laser-thorn energy net. Nebula's backup, Gamora, destroyed the drones but was ordered to abandon Nebula by Thanos as punishment for failing. Gamora obeyed but gave Nebula a sword to free herself. Nebula then severed her trapped left arm, which was later replaced with a bionic prosthetic. Aboard Ronan's ship, the *Dark Aster*, Nebula demanded another chance to acquire the Orb on Xandar, but Ronan sent Gamora instead; captured by the Xandarian Nova Corps, Gamora was imprisoned at the Kyln high-security prison.

Nebula accompanied Ronan to the Kyln to uncover the Orb's whereabouts, but Gamora, seeking to free herself from Thanos, had double-crossed Ronan and escaped with the Orb and four other inmates. Ronan ordered Nebula to "cleanse" the prison. Traveling to the Knowhere mining colony, Nebula pursued and destroyed Gamora's fleeing mining pod and seized the Orb, callously forsaking Gamora to freeze to death in space. Ronan, now in possession of the Stone, betrayed Thanos, and Nebula swore allegiance to Ronan.

Ronan assaulted Xandar, and when Gamora and her allies infiltrated the *Dark Aster*, Nebula fiercely battled Gamora, who kicked Nebula through a gaping hole in the Aster's hull. Nebula's left wrist became wedged between fragments of twisted metal, preventing her from plummeting to the ground. When Gamora offered her an alliance against Ronan, Nebula cut off her own hand, falling onto a passing mercenary Ravager airship; Nebula commandeered the craft and fled. ⚡

CRIMINALLY INSANE NEBULA claimed to be the death-worshipping Thanos' granddaughter, and although the ancestry was only alleged, she did share Thanos' murderous temperament. Nebula had been a pirate, a mercenary, and even briefly attained godlike powers twice. A consummate survivor, Nebula escaped imprisonment numerous times and lived through the war against the brutal Annihilation Wave alongside a team of cosmic warrior women led by Gamora.

FIRST APPEARANCE:
AVENGERS #257 (1985)

FACT SHEET

▶ WHEN THANOS ACCUSED RONAN OF ALIENATING "HIS FAVORITE DAUGHTER" GAMORA, A PRIVATELY OFFENDED NEBULA WARNED RONAN HE COULDN'T WIN A BATTLE AGAINST THANOS.

▶ NEBULA FELT GAMORA WAS A DISAPPOINTMENT AND WEAK, BUT OUT OF ALL THEIR SIBLINGS, SHE HATED GAMORA LEAST.

▶ NEBULA'S BODY MODIFICATIONS ENABLED HER TO SELF-REPAIR FROM SEVERE INJURIES.

THE NOVA CORPS WAS THE
planetary militia and expeditionary force of the planet Xandar, who empowered the Corps' members with superhuman abilities imbued by a shared energy source called the Nova Force. The Corps had a number of subdivisions, including the energy-absorbing Syfon warriors, and the Supernovas, a covert-operations arm comprised mainly of criminals. The Corps was decimated when the Luphomoid warmonger Zorr destroyed Xandar; the Corps' sole survivor, Rhomann Dey, imbued human Richard Rider with his share of the Nova Force as one of his last acts before sacrificing himself to stop Zorr. The Corps was re-established after the Xandarians were resurrected through cloning, but again were destroyed by the insectoid Annihilation Wave. Rider, the sole survivor and custodian of the Nova Force, rebuilt the Corps with the aid of the Xandarian Worldmind, but apparently expended the Nova Force and his own life battling the Mad Titan Thanos. Sam Alexander, a Supernova's son, assumed his father's Nova mantle and, like Rider before him, became a costumed hero.

FIRST APPEARANCE:
(CENTURION NOVA-PRIME RHOMANN DEY)
NOVA #1 (1976); (NOVA CORPS, FULL)
FANTASTIC FOUR #205 (1979)

NOVA CORPS

FIRST APPEARANCE:
Guardians of the Galaxy [2014]

The Nova Corps was the peacekeeping organization charged with the defense of the Nova Empire. Headquartered in a skyscraper in the capital city of the Empire's homeworld, Xandar, the Corps was led and coordinated by its leader, Nova Prime Irani Rael. The Corps also acted as Xandar's police force, and operated in that capacity when responding to the disturbance caused by the mercenaries Rocket and Groot, and the assassin Gamora during their pursuit of Star-Lord.

Later, upon receiving Star-Lord's warning that the Kree Accuser Ronan intended to destroy Xandar with an Infinity Stone, Nova Prime ordered the Corps to evacuate the city and prepare a defense against Ronan and his Sakaaran warriors. Joined by pirate Yondu Udonta and his Ravagers, and Rocket aboard a Ravager combat ship, Nova Denarian Garthan Saal led an aerial assault against Ronan's warship, the *Dark Aster*. Though momentarily successful at holding the *Dark Aster* back with an interlocking force field blockade ordered by Rael, Ronan destroyed a number of the Star Blaster fighters generating the blockade, including Saal's, and broke through. Following Ronan's ultimate defeat, the Nova Corps thanked Quill and his former pursuers, who had banded together as the Guardians of the Galaxy, expunged their criminal records, and rebuilt the *Milano*, which had been heavily damaged during the battle. ⚔

FACT SHEET

- IN DESCENDING ORDER, THE NOVA CORPS' RANKS ARE NOVA PRIME, CENTURION, DENARIAN, MILLENNIAN, AND CORPSMAN.

- THE NOVA CORPS' STAR-SHAPED STARBLASTER FIGHTER CRAFTS ARE ABLE TO INTERLOCK AND FORM A FORCE FIELD "BLOCKADE" THAT WAS ABLE TO HALT THE *DARK ASTER*.

STARBLASTER

ROCKET

FIRST APPEARANCE:
Guardians of the Galaxy [2014]

A denizen of Halfworld, the raccoonoid mercenary designated Subject 89P13 was a victim of illegal genetic and cybernetic experimentation. The abrasive Rocket and his friend—the kindhearted, tree-like Groot—ran afoul of crime lord Zade Scraggot aboard the Hub space station when they reneged on a business arrangement. A subsequent firefight ended poorly for Scraggot when he foolishly threatened to use Rocket's hide as a bathmat. On Xandar, the pair pursued Peter Quill to claim the bounty placed on him by his gang, the Ravagers. Rocket and Groot were unaware Gamora also was pursuing Quill for the Infinity Stone in his possession. The ensuing chaos led Xandar's Nova Corps to arrest all four. Remanded to the Kyln, Rocket and Groot conspired with Gamora and Quill to break out when they learned Gamora had arranged to sell the Stone to the Collector for a vastly higher amount than Quill's bounty. With the aid of fellow inmate Drax, the four escaped aboard Quill's spacecraft, the *Milano*, and traveled to the Collector's home, Knowhere.

> ## Rocket and Groot conspired with Gamora and Quill to break out.

While awaiting the Collector's representative, Carina, Drax inadvertently insulted Rocket, sparking a barroom brawl. As Drax stormed off, Carina escorted the remaining four to her master. Impatient to conclude a personal vendetta against Gamora's xenocidal former master Ronan, Drax brashly summoned Ronan and his Sakaaran forces. Ronan beat Drax and left with the Stone, while the late-arriving Ravagers captured Quill and Gamora. Rocket berated Drax for his actions and suggested fleeing the galactic destruction Ronan planned, but Groot and Drax convinced him to help rescue Quill and Gamora. Aboard the *Milano*, the three confronted the Ravagers and threatened their ship's destruction, with Drax brandishing the Rocket-designed Hadron Enforcer. They aborted the plan upon learning Quill and Gamora had enlisted the Ravagers' aid against Ronan in exchange for the Stone. Rocket demeaned Quill's "twelve percent of a plan," but agreed to help.

Piloting a Ravager Warbird in the skies over Xandar, Rocket breached Ronan's flagship, the

ONE OF SEVERAL GENETICALLY modified animal wardens of the planetary asylum Halfworld, security chief Rocket Raccoon volunteered to leave Halfworld when the telepathic Star Thief (Barry Bauman) was imprisoned by a biological lock that would only open if all the wardens were present; his memories were altered to discourage him from returning. Rocket traveled the galaxy until he and other starfaring heroes were conscripted to help free the Kree homeworld Hala from the techno-organic Phalanx. After freeing Hala, the team remained together to safeguard the cosmos as the Guardians of the Galaxy.

FIRST APPEARANCE:
MARVEL PREVIEW #7 (1976)

Dark Aster, allowing Quill and the others to board. He then assisted the Ravagers and Nova Corps with aerial defenses. When his teammates failed to kill Ronan, Rocket rammed him with his Warbird. With the crippled *Dark Aster* in freefall, Groot generated a protective nest around Quill and the others despite Rocket's pleas not to sacrifice his life. Rocket and his teammates survived the crash, but Groot was reduced to wooden debris. When Ronan emerged from the wreckage, a grief-stricken Rocket attacked, but was swatted aside. Quill distracted Ronan long enough for Rocket and Drax to blast Ronan's Cosmi-Rod with the Hadron Enforcer, freeing the Infinity Stone and enabling the group to destroy Ronan with it. With the damaged *Milano* rebuilt and the team members' criminal records expunged by a grateful Nova Corps, Rocket—carrying a potted fragment of Groot that eventually gained sentience—joined the newly dubbed Guardians of the Galaxy on their travels. 🔱

FACT SHEET

▶ ROCKET PROFESSED TO HAVE ESCAPED 22 PRISONS, EXCLUDING THE KYLN.

▶ ROCKET WAS UNFAMILIAR WITH EARTH'S RACCOON SPECIES, AND WAS EASILY INSULTED BY COMMENTS ABOUT HIS APPEARANCE.

▶ ROCKET IS THE ONLY GUARDIAN ABLE TO UNDERSTAND GROOT.

▶ ROCKET REPEATEDLY MADE JOKING REQUESTS TO STEAL PROSTHETICS WORN BY THOSE HE ENCOUNTERED.

▶ A SKILLED MARKSMAN, PILOT, AND WEAPONEER, ROCKET HAS MINIMAL CONCERN FOR SAFE WEAPONS HANDLING; HIS IDEA OF SAFEGUARDING A BOMB WAS SIMPLY TO PLACE IT IN A BOX.

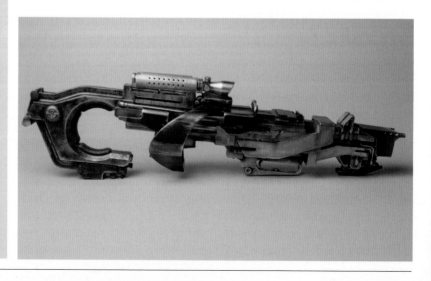

RONAN
THE ACCUSER

FIRST APPEARANCE:
Guardians of the Galaxy [2014]

One of the Kree's military leaders, the fanatical Ronan the Accuser was enraged by the Kree's peace treaty with its enemies, the Xandarians. Going rogue, Ronan attacked Xandarian outposts with his flagship, the *Dark Aster*. Among those he killed during this reign of terror were Drax's wife and child. However, Ronan lacked the might to strike at the Xandarian homeworld, Xandar, and so entered into an alliance with Thanos, striking a deal with the cosmic tyrant: In return for Thanos' assistance destroying Xandar, Ronan would help him acquire the Orb. Ronan was unaware Thanos sought the artifact because it contained one of the Infinity Stones. Thanos also lent Ronan his two adopted daughters, Gamora and Nebula, to serve as assassins and enforcers.

Scavenger Star-Lord snatched the Orb on Morag, reaching it just before Ronan's lieutenant, Korath. Ronan sent Gamora to steal it from Star-Lord on Xandar, but she betrayed him and tried to take it for herself. Summoned to Thanos' Sanctuary to account for his failure in person, Ronan killed Thanos' aide, the Other, in a fit of pique. Unimpressed, Thanos promised dire consequences should Ronan fail him again.

Ronan tracked the Orb to the Kyln, but found that Star-Lord, Gamora, Rocket, Groot, and Drax had escaped with the artifact. From there, their trail ran cold—until Drax, drunkenly spoiling for a fight, alerted Ronan to their presence on Knowhere. Ronan arrived in full force and made short work of Drax, leaving him for dead, while Nebula retrieved the Orb. Now aware of its contents, Ronan embedded the Infinity Stone within his weapon, granting him its power. Thus capable of destroying Xandar without Thanos' aid, Ronan abandoned their alliance—and promised to destroy Thanos, as well. Ronan set out for Xandar, where the *Dark Aster* was attacked by Star-Lord's crew, the Ravagers, and the Nova Corps. Ronan devastated the Nova Corps fleet with a single blast of energy from the Stone, and then shrugged off a shot from Star-Lord's Hadron Enforcer, but could not prevent Rocket's ship from ramming the *Dark Aster*'s bridge. Surviving the ensuing crash, Ronan prepared to unleash the Stone's full power on Xandar, but Star-Lord distracted him long enough for Rocket to blast the Stone off Ronan's hammer. Uniting with his teammates to share the Stone's power, Star-Lord used it to atomize Ronan. ◆

HEAD OF THE KREE EMPIRE'S
Accuser Corps, Ronan first journeyed to Earth to avenge the defeat of a Kree Sentry robot. Defeated by the Fantastic Four, he returned to menace Earth repeatedly, but was continually stymied. Eventually, he took control of the Kree Empire after euthanizing its previous ruler, the Supreme Intelligence, and joined the Annihilators, a pan-galactic team of warriors united to face cosmic threats. Ronan was empowered by the artifact known as the Black Vortex, but his newfound might proved insufficient to save the Kree homeworld, Hala, from destruction.

FIRST APPEARANCE:
FANTASTIC FOUR #65 (1967);
COVER SHOWN: *ANNIHILATION: RONAN #1 (2006)*

SAKAARANS SERVED AS RONAN'S SHOCK TROOPS, CREWED THE *DARK ASTER*, AND PILOTED HIS NECROCRAFT STAR FIGHTERS.

THE *MILANO*

STAR-LORD

FIRST APPEARANCE:
Guardians of the Galaxy [2014]

Peter Quill was raised by a single mother who shared her love for music via mixtapes and claimed his father was an angel. Meredith Quill died in 1988; that night, as a distraught Peter ran from the hospital, he was abducted by Yondu Udonta and the Ravagers. The unscrupulous space pirates had been hired to transport the boy to his father, an alien rather than an angel—information the Ravagers kept from Quill after Yondu decided to raise him as one of their own. Quill cherished his few mementos of home—including his portable cassette player; his mother's Awesome Mix Vol. 1; and her final letter and gift, neither of which he could bring himself to open. Twenty-six years later, the roguish Quill had taken to calling himself Star-Lord, a nickname apparently given to him by his mother, and piloting the *Milano*.

Learning Yondu had brokered a sale for the Orb, Star-Lord stole the artifact from an ancient Morag temple, escaping Ronan's henchman, Korath, in the process—earning Ronan's enmity

> **Twenty-six years later, the roguish Quill had taken to calling himself Star-Lord and piloting the *Milano*.**

and prompting Yondu to issue a 40,000-credit bounty for his capture. After failing to sell the Orb, Star-Lord was attacked by Gamora, who sought to keep the artifact away from Ronan, and bounty hunters Rocket and Groot. The Nova Corps arrested all four

and sent them to the Kyln prison. Quill talked another inmate, the vengeance-seeking Drax, out of killing Gamora by pointing out that Ronan would come hunting for her, giving Drax an opportunity to kill him. Agreeing to split the money from selling the Orb, Quill, Gamora, Rocket, Groot, and Drax escaped the Kyln. The ragtag group traveled to Knowhere to meet a potential buyer, the Collector, who revealed that the Orb housed an Infinity Stone. When Ronan's forces and the Ravagers found them, Gamora fled with the Orb, but lost it to Nebula, who left her to die in space. Following her into the vacuum, Star-Lord communicated his position to the Ravagers, then saved her with his own mask. As he had hoped, the Ravagers took them both aboard their ship. Despite his recent misdeeds, Star-Lord convinced Yondu to help oppose Ronan in exchange for the Orb.

Regrouping with his allies, Quill contacted Nova Corpsman Rhomann Dey to warn of Ronan's imminent attack on Xandar. As Ronan's forces approached, Star-Lord and his allies boarded Ronan's flagship, the *Dark Aster*, battling Ronan while the Nova Corps and Ravagers held back the vessel. When the *Dark Aster* crashed on Xandar, Star-Lord confused Ronan by proposing a dance off, distracting him long enough for Rocket to blast the Infinity Stone off Ronan's hammer. Grasping the exposed Stone, Quill was nearly torn apart by its energies, but his friends rallied beside him, collectively sharing the power. Star-Lord destroyed Ronan using the Stone, and then handed the Orb over to Yondu. In fact, Quill had entrusted the Stone to the Nova Corps for safekeeping; the Orb in Yondu's possession contained a troll figurine. A grateful Nova Corps expunged the criminal records of Quill and his friends, now dubbed the Guardians of the Galaxy. Before departing Xandar in the rebuilt *Milano*, Quill was informed of his half-alien parentage. He finally opened his mother's final gift, a new mixtape. ⚔

RAVAGER OUTFIT

THANOS

FIRST APPEARANCE: *Marvel's The Avengers [2012]*

Feared across the universe, the enigmatic Thanos has wiped out entire races. He raised Gamora, the sole survivor of one of those species, as his daughter, brutally training her and another girl selected from his many adopted children, Nebula, to be his warrior-assassins. Thanos masterminded Loki's invasion of Earth, providing the Asgardian with an army of biomechanical Chitauri warriors and a mind-altering scepter. The attack proved unsuccessful, costing Thanos legions of Chitauri, as well as the scepter. Thanos turned his attention to the Orb, which housed one of the Infinity Stones; he tasked Ronan the Accuser to locate the artifact in return for assistance destroying Xandar. Thanos assigned Gamora and Nebula to aid Ronan. Thanks to Star-Lord's interference and the resentful Gamora's betrayal, the Orb escaped Ronan's grasp. Ronan reported this failure to Thanos in person and petulantly killed Thanos' chief aide, the Other. Unimpressed by Ronan's power and bored by his devotion to the Kree cause, Thanos warned Ronan that another failure would mean death. When Ronan did retrieve the Orb, he defied Thanos and claimed the Stone's power for himself, promising to destroy him once he'd finished with Xandar. Tiring of life under Thanos' rule, Nebula joined him. Ronan never carried out this threat, however, as Star-Lord, Gamora, and their fellow Guardians of the Galaxy destroyed him with the Stone's power, then entrusted it to the Xandarian Nova Corps. ◆

THE MISSHAPEN MUTANT SON of Mentor, ruler of Saturn's moon Titan, Thanos devoted his life to winning the love of the personification of Death. To this end, he has rendered his homeworld a nuclear wasteland, killed half the living beings in the universe, and repeatedly clashed with Earth's heroes, notably the cosmically aware artificial humanoid Adam Warlock. Circumstances occasionally made Thanos and Warlock allies, and Warlock even once entrusted Thanos with an Infinity Gem as part of his Infinity Watch. Left in oblivion following the destruction of Doctor Doom's Battleworld, Thanos has returned, still devoted to a love of nothingness.

FIRST APPEARANCE: *IRON MAN #55 (1975)*

▶ THANOS CONSIDERED GAMORA HIS FAVORITE DAUGHTER.

▶ THANOS SURVEYS HIS DOMAIN FROM A HOVERING THRONE IN THE SANCTUARY ASTEROID FIELD.

▶ WARNED BY THE OTHER THAT TO FIGHT EARTH'S HEROES WOULD BE TO "COURT DEATH," THANOS MERELY SMILED.

YONDU UDONTA

FIRST APPEARANCE:
Guardians of the Galaxy [2014]

Yondu Udonta and his crew of space pirates, the Ravagers, abducted young Peter Quill of Earth on behalf of Quill's alien father, but Yondu chose instead to raise him as a Ravager. Twenty-six years later, Quill angered Yondu by stealing the Orb, for which Yondu had brokered a sale. Yondu placed a 40,000-unit bounty on Quill, demanding his live capture. When a Ravager suggested that Yondu had been too evenhanded with Quill, Yondu threatened him, but said he would kill Quill upon his capture and the Orb's recovery.

Yondu and the Ravagers traveled to Knowhere after intimidating the Broker into revealing that Quill likely intended to sell the Orb to the Collector. While Kree extremist Ronan captured the Orb on behalf of the enigmatic Thanos, Quill surrendered himself to the Ravagers to save his ally, Gamora, from death in the vacuum of space. Quill agreed to give Yondu the Orb—revealed to house an Infinity Stone—in exchange for the Ravagers' aid stopping Ronan from destroying Xandar. The Ravagers joined the Nova Corps and Quill's new allies, defending Xandar from Ronan's armada. During the battle, Yondu's attack craft crashed, but he survived and slew an entire platoon of Ronan's Sakaaran soldiers with a single flight of his yaka arrow. After Quill and his allies destroyed Ronan, Yondu demanded that Quill adhere to their bargain, scoffing at Quill and Gamora's concerns about the Stone's destructive potential. Quill apparently relented, but instead entrusted the Stone to the Nova Corps for safekeeping. Upon opening the Orb after leaving Xandar, Yondu laughed at Quill's guile when he discovered a troll figurine inside. ⬥

IN THE COMICS

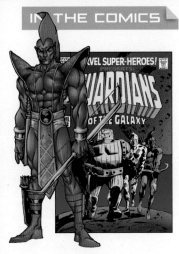

30TH CENTURY YONDU

IN ALTERNATE REALITY-691'S

30th century, spiritual Centaurian hunter Yondu Udonta befriended Vance Astro, a telekinetic human astronaut. After the Badoon race invaded Yondu's homeworld, Centauri IV, the pair became founding members of the Guardians of the Galaxy, a resistance force that helped defeat the Badoon.

In the Prime Universe's 21st century, the Centaurian Yondu Udonta led the marauding Ravagers and made an enemy of his former protégé, Star-Lord (Peter Quill), who saved a NASA deep-space crew from the space pirates.

FIRST APPEARANCE:
(REALITY-691) *MARVEL SUPER-HEROES #18* (1969);
(PRIME UNIVERSE) *STAR-LORD #1* (2016)

21ST CENTURY YONDU

FACT SHEET

▶ YONDU'S SIGNATURE WEAPON IS A YAKA ARROW, GUIDED BY THE PITCH AND HARMONICS OF HIS WHISTLE. THE PROJECTILE CAN PIERCE BODY ARMOR AND SPACECRAFT HULLS, RETURNING TO YONDU'S GRASP WHEN ITS TASK IS COMPLETE. YONDU ROUTINELY INTIMIDATES PEOPLE BY MENACINGLY HOVERING THE ARROW IN FRONT OF THEM.

▶ THOUGH FOND OF THREATENING QUILL, YONDU GENUINELY SEEMED TO LIKE HIM AND TOLERATED NO SLIGHTS TOWARD HIM.

XANDAR

FIRST APPEARANCE:
Guardians of the Galaxy (2014)

Capital world of the Nova Empire, Xandar is home to its indigenous sapient people, the Xandarians, and numerous residents from other Nova worlds. Built onto a large island, the planet's capital city houses the headquarters of the peacekeeping Nova Corps. Xandar enjoyed a tenuous peace with its longtime rival, the Kree Empire, but became the target of rogue Kree warlord Ronan, who resented the peace accords and had attacked numerous Xandarian outposts.

The scavenger Star-Lord traveled to Xandar to sell the Orb to the Broker, but faced a two-sided predicament when Gamora attempted to steal the artifact, and Rocket and Groot pursued him seeking a bounty for his capture. The ensuing chaos prompted the Nova Corps' intervention; all four were arrested.

Ronan's plan to destroy Xandar with the destructive energy of the Infinity Stone housed in the Orb prompted Nova Prime Irani Rael to order the capital city's evacuation and the deployment of the Nova Corps. Star-Lord and his former pursuers were instrumental in halting Ronan's advance, unintentionally sending his flagship, the *Dark Aster*, crashing into a portion of the city.

FACT SHEET

- ▶ XANDAR IS LOCATED IN THE ANDROMEDA GALAXY AND ORBITS M31V J00442326+4127082, AN ECLIPSING BINARY STAR.

- ▶ XANDAR'S CAPITAL CITY WAS ON A STARBURST-SHAPED ISLAND.

- ▶ XANDAR'S HIGHLY-ADVANCED CAPITAL CITY SERVES AS A CENTRAL HUB FOR THE NOVA EMPIRE AND ALL DIFFERENT TYPES OF RACES, INCLUDING ALIENS OF EVERY COLOR, SIZE, AND SHAPE.

IN THE COMICS

THE HOMEWORLD OF THE Xandarians and their peacekeeping force, the Nova Corps, Xandar has been destroyed on multiple occasions, each time rebuilt or re-established in some fashion by its survivors. Xandar met its first end at the hands of the Luphomoid warlord Zorr, but the survivors created a new Xandar as a network of domed cities. Another Luphomoid marauder, Nebula, destroyed this new Xandar, which was resurrected by human Nova Centurion Richard Rider, who reactivated the planet's Worldmind supercomputer and enabled it to clone Xandar's population. Xandar was again destroyed by the insectoid Annihilation Wave—leaving Rider, the sole survivor of the onslaught, to act as custodian of the Worldmind and the Nova Force that powered the Corps.

FIRST APPEARANCE:
(MENTIONED) *NOVA #1 (1976);*
(SEEN) *FANTASTIC FOUR #204 (1979)*

BEREET

FIRST APPEARANCE:
Guardians of the Galaxy [2014]

The pink-skinned Krylorian Bereet met and romanced the outlaw Star-Lord and traveled with him to the abandoned planet Morag, where he hoped to acquire a highly valuable Orb, secretly containing an immensely powerful Infinity Stone. While Star-Lord outsmarted the Kree cyborg Korath, who also sought the Orb, Bereet slept in the lower level of Star-Lord's airship, the *Milano*; however, Bereet was violently awakened when the *Milano* was pummeled in midair by a massive geyser that briefly sent the ship into freefall. Disheveled and confused, Bereet questioned Star-Lord, who had forgotten that she was still onboard and could not recall her name. Soon after, Bereet answered an incoming communication from Star-Lord's Ravager associate Yondu Udonta, but realized she had made a mistake upon learning that Star-Lord intended to betray Yondu and sell the Orb privately. Despite the bandit's tactless behavior, Bereet amicably parted ways with him on the planet Xandar.

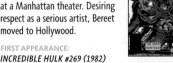

BEREET WAS AN ASPIRING FILMMAKER on the planet Krylor in the Andromeda Galaxy who came to Earth to create fictional movies starring the Hulk (Bruce Banner). Bereet eventually befriended the Hulk, accompanying him on adventures, and later released her film *The Life and Times of the Incredible Hulk* at a Manhattan theater. Desiring respect as a serious artist, Bereet moved to Hollywood.

FIRST APPEARANCE:
INCREDIBLE HULK #269 (1982)

FACT SHEET

▶ WHILE ON THE *MILANO*, BEREET WORE STAR-LORD'S RIVER RAFTER T-SHIRT FROM J.D. CANOE RENTALS ON THE DOLORES RIVER.

▶ BEREET SEEMED SURPRISED TO HEAR STAR-LORD'S CLAIM THAT THE RAVAGER CODE IS TO STEAL FROM ANYONE, APPARENTLY EVEN THEIR OWN.

BROKER

FIRST APPEARANCE:
Guardians of the Galaxy [2014]

A merchant on Xandar, the Broker often acted as a middleman between sellers and buyers. Contacted by the pirate Yondu Udonta of the Ravagers, the Broker agreed to buy the Orb, an object of great value, and resell it. Broker was surprised when Star-Lord arrived with the Orb instead of Yondu, but was prepared to honor the deal anyway. However, when the Broker learned that the fanatical Ronan the Accuser of the Kree Empire was also interested in the Orb, he reneged on the agreement. He quickly ushered Star-Lord out of his shop, afraid Ronan would target him as he had other Xandarians.

Yondu, searching for the errant Star-Lord, confronted the Broker, demanding he give Yondu the identity of the Orb's intended buyer. After the Broker revealed that the buyer was Taneleer Tivan, the eccentric Collector, Yondu obtained a figurine from the Broker. Later when Ronan attacked Xandar, the Broker witnessed Ronan's death at the hands of Star-Lord.

THE BROKER WAS A ruthless alien interested only in his own well-being. He used parasites to control others, forcing them to act as his enforcers, and employed technology to inflict pain on them when they disobeyed. The Broker was eventually killed when his slaves rebelled.

FIRST APPEARANCE:
FORCE WORKS #15 (1995)

FACT SHEET

▶ THE BROKER PRIDED HIMSELF ON KEEPING HIS BUYERS' IDENTITIES CONFIDENTIAL, BUT HE BROKE THAT MAXIM WHEN PHYSICALLY THREATENED.

▶ WHEN YONDU EXPRESSED INTEREST IN FIGURINES IN THE BROKER'S SHOP, THE BROKER WASN'T SURE IF YONDU WAS SERIOUS.

CARINA

FIRST APPEARANCE:
Thor: The Dark World [2013]

Pink-skinned Krylorian Carina served as attendant to Taneleer Tivan, the Collector, cleaning and servicing his massive collection. She introduced Asgardians Sif and Volstagg to the Collector when they brought him the Aether, one of the immensely powerful Infinity Stones, to safeguard. When the Collector sought to purchase the Orb, knowing it contained another Stone, he sent Carina to bring the assassin Gamora and her companions, who possessed the Orb, to his museum where the Collector explained the Stones' origins. Seeing a chance to escape her enslavement, Carina grabbed the stone, but the energies inside it consumed her, and the resulting explosion devastated the Collector's museum.

CARINA WAS THE DAUGHTER OF THE Collector, an Elder of the Universe. He sent her to Earth to spy on the immensely powerful Michael Korvac, a potential threat to the universe, but she fell in love with and married him. Battling the Avengers, Carina believed Korvac had been killed and coerced Thor into fatally striking her. Instead of dying, her body was converted to energy; later discovered in Underspace by Henry Pym, she was restored to physical form. After helping Avengers Academy students battle a jealous Korvac, she left to explore the universe alone.

FIRST APPEARANCE:
AVENGERS #167 (1978)

FACT SHEET

▶ AFTER DISAPPOINTING THE COLLECTOR, CARINA'S PREDECESSOR BECAME ONE OF HIS EXHIBITS.

▶ IN ADDITION TO MAINTAINING TIVAN'S COLLECTION, CARINA ALSO ARRANGED POTENTIAL ACQUISITIONS.

COSMO

FIRST APPEARANCE:
Guardians of the Galaxy [2014]

Cosmo, a yellow-hued Labrador wearing a Soviet spacesuit, was prominently displayed among other rare beings and items comprising Taneleer Tivan's celestial collection housed within Knowhere's mining colony. When Gamora and her companions arrived to sell an Orb housing a powerful Infinity Stone to Tivan, Cosmo took an immediate dislike to the raccoon-like Rocket, growling as Rocket passed his case; Rocket returned the sentiment by angrily hissing at Cosmo. When Tivan's vengeful servant Carina tried wielding the Stone, she was unable to contain its power and exploded, demolishing Tivan's display cases and freeing Cosmo. Despite initially leaving Tivan's exhibit, Cosmo apparently didn't harbor a grudge for his confinement and briefly returned to lick the injured Tivan's face, much to the disgust of another freed attraction, a talking humanoid duck named Howard.

COSMO IS A GOLDEN RETRIEVER/ Labrador mix with immense psychic abilities, including telepathy and telekinesis; coming to reside on Knowhere, he became its security chief. Cosmo has served as liaison to the Guardians of the Galaxy, and formed the Knowhere Corps alongside other cosmic heroes Moondragon (Heather Douglas), Mantis, Prism, and Bug.

FIRST APPEARANCE:
NOVA #8 (2008)

FACT SHEET

▶ THE ONLY OTHER ITEMS IN COSMO'S DISPLAY CASE WERE A BIG, BLUE BLANKET FOR HIM TO REST ON AND A METAL WATER BOWL.

RHOMANN DEY

FIRST APPEARANCE:
Guardians of the Galaxy [2014]

An officer of Xandar's Nova Corps, Rhomann Dey arrested criminals Gamora, Rocket, Groot, and Peter Quill—whom the other three had attacked in an attempt to obtain the Orb he had stolen—for endangering life and property destruction. Dey subsequently reported the arrest to his superior, Denarian Garthan Saal, who ordered the four incarcerated in the Kyln prison. After escaping the Kyln alongside his pursuers, Quill warned Dey of the Kree warrior Ronan the Accuser's intent to destroy Xandar with an Infinity Stone. Trusting that Quill had good intentions despite his background, Dey relayed the message to Saal and Nova Prime Rael and recommended immediate action; Saal was dismissive, but Rael believed Dey due to his personal experience with Quill. After Quill's group defeated Ronan, Dey was promoted to the rank of Denarian and expunged the criminal records of Quill and his new partners, the Guardians of the Galaxy, while arranging the reconstruction of their damaged spacecraft, the *Milano*. He cautioned the Guardians against committing further crimes, but was skeptical of Quill's assurances. 🌱

IN THE COMICS

LEADER ("NOVA PRIME") OF THE
Xandarian Nova Corps, Rhomann Dey witnessed the destruction of his homeworld by Luphomoid warlord Zorr. Though severely injured, Dey tracked Zorr to Earth and transferred his Nova powers to teenager Richard Rider, instructing him to defend Earth. Rider distracted Zorr enough for Dey to teleport Zorr aboard his spaceship and sacrifice his remaining Nova powers— and his life—to destroy him.

FIRST APPEARANCE:
NOVA #1 (1976)

FACT SHEET

▶ DEY HAD ARRESTED QUILL ONCE BEFORE FOR PETTY THEFT, AND TEASED HIM ABOUT HIS CODENAME STAR-LORD, CALLING HIM "STAR-PRINCE."

▶ DEY HAS A WIFE AND YOUNG DAUGHTER, WHO WERE SAVED BY ROCKET DURING RONAN'S ATTACK ON XANDAR.

HOWARD THE DUCK

FIRST APPEARANCE:
Guardians of the Galaxy [2014]

A prisoner in the Collector's interstellar museum, the anthropomorphic Howard the Duck was suspended high in the air in a cage with little room to move. After the Collector's servant Carina attempted to harness an Infinity Stone, resulting in a massive explosion, Howard sat amongst the museum wreckage, drinking and watching the escaped dog Cosmo lick the injured Collector's face. Finding the act gross, Howard asked the Collector why he permitted Cosmo to do this, then downed an alien drink. 🌱

IN THE COMICS

NATIVE TO A REALITY OF
anthropomorphic animals, Howard the Duck was deposited on Earth by a tip of the cosmic axis caused by the demon Thog. Landing in Cleveland, Ohio, Howard attempted to live a normal life but was consistently drawn into battles with bizarre enemies such as the financial wizard Pro-Rata, the insane Kidney Lady, the bell-themed Doctor Bong, and others. Declared legally non-existent after years of urban myth status, Howard recently became a private detective, using his unwanted attraction to the bizarre for his own benefit.

FIRST APPEARANCE:
(ADVENTURE INTO) FEAR #19 (1973)

FACT SHEET

▶ WHEN STAR-LORD, GAMORA, GROOT, AND ROCKET FIRST ENTERED THE COLLECTOR'S MUSEUM, HOWARD TOOK IMMEDIATE NOTICE OF THEIR PRESENCE FROM HIS CELL.

▶ GIVEN THE CHANCE TO ESCAPE DURING THE DESTRUCTION OF THE COLLECTOR'S MUSEUM, HOWARD OPTED TO REMAIN BEHIND AND DRINK.

▶ DESPITE TAKING A LIKING TO KNOWHERE'S DRINKS, HOWARD REMARKED THAT THEY BURNED GOING DOWN.

KORATH

FIRST APPEARANCE:
Guardians of the Galaxy [2014]

One of the Kree fanatic Ronan's chief lieutenants, the cyborg warrior Korath located the Orb, an artifact secretly containing one of the powerful Infinity Stones, on the dead planet Morag. The renegade Star-Lord had beaten him to the punch, however, and stole the Orb from Korath and his Sakaaran warriors. Despite his failure, Korath remained by Ronan's side, and warned Ronan of the dangers of betraying Thanos when his master claimed the Orb for himself. Later, when Star-Lord and his compatriots invaded Ronan's flagship, the *Dark Aster*, Korath commanded a platoon of Sakaarans in defense of the ship. Korath took on the brutal Drax; after a punishing brawl, Drax apparently killed him.

IN THE COMICS

KREE SCIENTIST KORATH-THAK designed the Pursuer genetic template, capable of transforming an individual into a mighty warrior. After first testing it on an Earth cockroach, Korath used it on himself, and served in the Kree Starforce super team. Eventually, he was assimilated into the technorganic Phalanx collective, and was slain by its leader, Ultron, for failing him.

FIRST APPEARANCE:
INHUMANS #11 (1977),
(IDENTIFIED) QUASAR #32 (1992)

FACT SHEET

▶ KORATH TRAINED ALONGSIDE THANOS' ADOPTED DAUGHTERS GAMORA AND NEBULA.

▶ KORVATH HAD NEVER HEARD OF STAR-LORD BEFORE MORAG, DISAPPOINTING QUILL. WHEN KORVATH LATER CALLED HIM BY THAT CODE NAME, THE OUTLAW WAS THRILLED.

▶ DRAX DEFEATED KORATH BY TEARING OUT ONE OF HIS CRANIAL CYBERNETIC IMPLANTS.

KYLN

FIRST APPEARANCE:
Guardians of the Galaxy [2014]

Notorious for its brutality and guards' corruption, the Kyln was a high-security deep-space prison operated by the Nova Corps. After their arrest on Xandar, the outlaws Star-Lord, Rocket, Groot, and Gamora were taken there—as was the Orb, an artifact secretly containing one of the Infinity Stones, with the rest of Star-Lord's possessions. The quartet, with the aid of fellow prisoner Drax, engineered a daring escape and fled with the Orb in Star-Lord's ship. Later, the Kree militant Ronan arrived at the Kyln, seeking the Orb; finding it and its possessors gone, Ronan ordered the Kyln to be "cleansed" of all potential witnesses to conceal his search for the artifact.

IN THE COMICS

A SERIES OF POWER STATIONS at the edge of the expanding universe, the Kyln was also used as a prison by a consortium of galactic law enforcement agencies. Among its prisoners were Star-Lord (Peter Quill), the cosmic energy being called Maker, and world-devouring Galactus' first herald, the Fallen One. It was destroyed when the Negative Zone tyrant Annihilus invaded the positive universe with his Annihilation Wave.

FIRST APPEARANCE:
THANOS #7 (2004)

FACT SHEET

▶ KYLN PRISONERS WERE ASSIGNED YELLOW JUMPSUITS.

▶ THE KYLN WAS STAFFED BY BOTH HUMANOID GUARDS AND AUTOMATED HOVERBOTS.

▶ THE KYLN'S GUARDS HAD CONTROL DEVICES FUSED TO THEIR WRISTS TO ACCESS THE PRISON'S SYSTEMS.

NOVA PRIME
IRANI RAEL

FIRST APPEARANCE:
Guardians of the Galaxy [2014]

Irani Rael was the leader ("Nova Prime") of the Xandarian interplanetary peacekeeping agency, the Nova Corps. In response to attacks on Xandarian outposts by the rogue Kree accuser Ronan, Rael called the Kree ambassador, asking him to disavow Ronan's actions, but the ambassador dismissed Rael's pleas. Frustrated by the Kree's lack of concern, Rael learned from Denarian Garthan Saal of Nova Corps' capture of one of Ronan's allies, the assassin Gamora. When Millennian Rhomann Dey relayed the criminal Star-Lord's warning that Ronan was en route to Xandar intent on using an Infinity Stone against the planet, Rael heeded Dey's trust in Star-Lord over Saal's dismissal of him. Upon the arrival of Ronan's warship, the *Dark Aster*, Rael ordered the capital city evacuated and coordinated defense efforts. Following Ronan's downfall at the hands of Star-Lord and his friends, a grateful Rael revealed that during an earlier arrest the Nova Corps had detected a neurological anomaly in Star-Lord and learned he was only half human.

IN THE COMICS

IRANI RAEL, A RIGELLIAN, WAS ONE of several recruited by the Xandarian Worldmind to rebuild the Xandarian Nova Corps following its decimation by the Annihilation Wave. The new Corps, including Rael, had their powers drained by the Worldmind to give Nova Prime Richard Rider the power to battle the forces of the Cancerverse.

FIRST APPEARANCE:
NOVA #18 (2008)

FACT SHEET

▶ AMONG THE TACTICS RAEL EMPLOYED AGAINST THE *DARK ASTER* WAS THE USE OF AN ENERGY BLOCKADE CREATED BY THE INTERLOCKING OF HUNDREDS OF NOVA CORPS FIGHTER CRAFT.

▶ RAEL PERSONALLY OVERSAW THE CORPS' SECURE STORAGE OF THE INFINITY STONE FOLLOWING RONAN'S DEFEAT.

ORB

FIRST APPEARANCE:
Guardians of the Galaxy [2014]

An ornate spherical object, the Orb encased a violet-hued Infinity Stone—one of six immensely powerful artifacts. Hidden in the Temple Vault on the desolate planet Morag, the Orb was desired by Ronan for his ally, Thanos. While the Collector commissioned Gamora to obtain it, Yondu's Ravagers also sought it, but one of them, Star-Lord, betrayed the others and swiped it first. He tried to sell the Orb on Xandar, but the Broker reneged on the deal upon learning of Ronan's interest. The Orb was confiscated when Star-Lord, Gamora, and mercenaries Rocket and Groot were incarcerated by the Nova Corps at the Kyln. The four, plus inmate Drax, escaped the prison and took the Orb to Knowhere to sell to Gamora's buyer, the Collector, for four billion units. As the Collector opened it, his slave Carina, seeking freedom, grabbed the Stone, destroying herself and much of the Collector's menagerie instead. Gamora attempted to flee and safeguard it with the Nova Corps but it was obtained by Nebula for Ronan. With the Stone attached to his Cosmi-Rod, Ronan attacked Xandar but Star-Lord distracted him while Rocket dislodged the Stone. Star-Lord, united with his teammates, somehow withstood contact with the Stone and vanquished Ronan. The Stone was housed in a new Orb and given to the Nova Corps to protect.

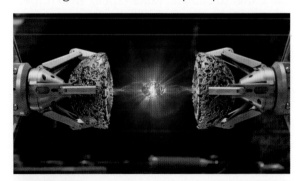

FACT SHEET

▶ THE ORB WAS ACCESSIBLE FROM MORAG'S TEMPLE VAULT BECAUSE THE LESSER SEA LOWERED FOR THE FIRST TIME IN 300 YEARS.

▶ ON MORAG, STAR-LORD USED AN ELECTROMAGNET TO EXTRACT THE HOVERING ORB FROM ITS PROTECTIVE ENERGY FIELD.

OTHER
UPDATE

FIRST APPEARANCE:
Marvel's The Avengers [2012]

The hooded Other, loyal servant of Thanos, communicated his master's orders to Ronan, as the fanatical Kree searched for the Orb. The Other learned from his sources within the Xandarian Kyln prison that Gamora had obtained the Orb from Star-Lord but had been captured, and now intended to escape and betray Ronan, making her own plans. Via a video transmission, the Other summoned Ronan to appear before Thanos. When he arrived, Ronan dismissed his failure to retrieve the Orb as Gamora's fault, prompting the Other to demand Ronan speak with respect when in Thanos' presence. Unimpressed, Ronan used his Cosmi-Rod to silence the Other, twisting his head completely around and leaving him dead before his master. ✧

FACT SHEET

▶ EVEN WHEN THANOS WAS PRESENT, THE OTHER USUALLY SPOKE ON HIS BEHALF, PRESUMABLY SO HIS MASTER DID NOT HAVE TO INTERACT WITH MERE UNDERLINGS.

▶ BECAUSE MOST BEINGS FEARED HIS MASTER, THE OTHER BERATED AND SPOKE DOWN TO MOST INDIVIDUALS. THE ASGARDIAN GOD LOKI SEEMED WILLING TO PUT UP WITH THIS, BUT THE OTHER'S CONDESCENDING TONE AND HARSH TONGUE PROVED A FATAL ERROR WHEN DEALING WITH THE BELLIGERENT RONAN.

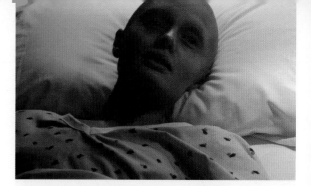

MEREDITH QUILL

FIRST APPEARANCE:
Guardians of the Galaxy [2014]

Following a secret romance with an unidentified alien, Meredith Quill had a son, Peter. Though told his father had been an angel composed of light, Peter believed Meredith was speaking figuratively. She dubbed him her little "Star-Lord" and shared her love of music with him, putting together a mix tape, her Awesome Mix Vol. 1. By 1988, Meredith had become terminally ill. After preparing a letter and second Awesome Mix volume for Peter, and asking her parents to raise the boy, she died in a Missouri hospital surrounded by friends and family. Decades later, when Peter was being destroyed by an Infinity Stone he was trying to wield, Meredith appeared to him in a vision, helping him find the strength to resist and channel the object's power. ✧

IN THE COMICS

ALIEN PRINCE JASON LEFT Earth after romancing Meredith Quill, hoping to prevent his Ariguan enemies from learning of her and his unborn son. Years later, the Ariguans murdered Meredith, but overlooked Peter, who later became Star-Lord.

FIRST APPEARANCE:
(REALITY-791, NOT SHOWN) *MARVEL PREVIEW #4 (1976)*; (PRIME REALITY) *GUARDIANS OF THE GALAXY #0.1 (2013)*

WITH A YOUNG PETER

FACT SHEET

▶ PETER WAITED TWENTY-SIX YEARS BEFORE OPENING MEREDITH'S PRESENT, AWESOME MIX VOL. 2. ITS FIRST TWO SONGS WERE MARVIN GAYE AND TAMMI TERRELL'S "AIN'T NO MOUNTAIN HIGH ENOUGH" AND "I WANT YOU BACK." BY THE JACKSON 5.

▶ THE SONGS ON AWESOME MIX VOL. 1 INCLUDED BLUE SWEDE'S "HOOKED ON A FEELING," RASPBERRIES' "GO ALL THE WAY," DAVID BOWIE'S "MOONAGE DAYDREAM," ELVIN BISHOP'S "FOOLED AROUND AND FELL IN LOVE," 10CC'S "I'M NOT IN LOVE," REDBONE'S "COME AND GET YOUR LOVE," THE RUNAWAYS' "CHERRY BOMB," RUPERT HOLMES' "ESCAPE," AND THE FIVE STAIRSTEPS' "O-O-H CHILD."

RAVAGERS

FIRST APPEARANCE:
Guardians of the Galaxy [2014]

The Ravagers are a motley band of intergalactic mercenaries and pirates who traverse the stars seeking profitable endeavors and acquisitions. Led by the Centaurian Yondu Udonta, the Ravagers can be identified by their burgundy-ochre jackets, pants, and trench coats adorned with a seven-pointed, flame-shaped symbol. The Ravagers hail from several alien races, some human-like in appearance—including Horuz and Kraglin Obfonteri. The Ravagers abducted young Earthling Peter Quill on behalf of Peter's father, but decided to raise him as one of their own. Learning the Ravagers intended to steal an Orb from a temple on Morag, the adult Quill purloined it first, prompting Yondu to place a 40,000-unit bounty on his head. After interrogating the Broker, to whom Quill had unsuccessfully tried to sell the Orb on Xandar, the Ravagers followed Quill to Knowhere. However, Kree zealot Ronan had taken possession of the Orb and left Quill's ally, Gamora, to die in deep space. Knowing the Ravagers would take him aboard their ship, Quill risked his life to reach Gamora, then summoned the Ravagers to rescue him. To placate the Ravagers, Quill offered to get them the Orb in return for their help defending Xandar from Ronan's forces. Yondu agreed, and the Ravagers deployed fighters to attack Ronan's flagship, the *Dark Aster*, as Ronan's forces stood poised to destroy the Xandarians. Despite enjoying their reputation as ruthless killers, the Ravagers heroically defended Xandar's citizens when Ronan's Necrocraft pilots dive-bombed the city. Quill defeated Ronan and reclaimed the Orb, but gave Yondu a fake, entrusting the rreal Orb, containing a massively powerful Infinity Stone, to Xandar's Nova Corps for safekeeping. ⬇

FACT SHEET

▶ YONDU REPEATEDLY BOASTED HE STOPPED THE OTHER RAVAGERS FROM EATING QUILL WHEN HE WAS A BOY.

▶ AFTER STAR-LORD SUCCEEDED IN DEFEATING RONAN AND RETRIEVING THE ORB, THE RAVAGERS AGREED QUILL HAD TURNED OUT OKAY.

GARTHAN SAAL

FIRST APPEARANCE:
Guardians of the Galaxy [2014]

Stoic and arrogant, Garthan Saal was a respected member of the planet Xandar's global police force, the Nova Corps, holding the rank of Denarian. After the Kree Empire entered a peace agreement following an extended war with the Nova Corps, Kree military leader Ronan the Accuser went rogue and began attacking Xandarian outposts. Saal was dismayed to hear the Kree Empire refused to disavow Ronan's actions, but was pleased to learn one of Ronan's compatriots—Gamora, adopted daughter of Ronan's ally, Thanos—had been captured. Saal oversaw Gamora's processing and ordered her to the Kyln, the Nova Corps' high-security prison, though she soon escaped. Saal later dismissed a warning from Star-Lord, one of Gamora's new allies, that Ronan was poised to attack Xandar; regardless, he followed Nova Prime's order to act on the information. Saal led the Nova starships' energy-blockade formation against Ronan's flagship, the *Dark Aster*, while Star-Lord's friends and space-pirate allies, the Ravagers, attacked enemy ships. Despite Ronan's fighters dive-bombing the capital city below them, Saal recognized preventing the *Dark Aster* from landing was more important and ordered the Nova Corpsmen to hold the blockade. When Ronan disrupted the blockade, Saal died in the resulting starship explosions. ⬇

IN THE COMICS

BELIEVED TO BE THE SOLE SURVIVOR of the planet Xandar's destruction, Nova Corpsman Garthan Saal became the recipient of all the Nova Corps' power, but it drove him mad. Eventually relinquishing the power, Saal was reinstated as a Nova Centurion, but was apparently later killed during the Annihilation Wave.

FIRST APPEARANCE:
AVENGERS #301 (1989)

FACT SHEET

▶ THOUGH SAAL DOUBTED STAR-LORD'S INTENTIONS, DEEMING HIM A CRIMINAL, HE DARED THE PIRATE TO PROVE HIM WRONG.

▶ SAAL REFERRED TO STAR-LORD'S ALLY, THE RACCOONOID ROCKET, AS A HAMSTER.

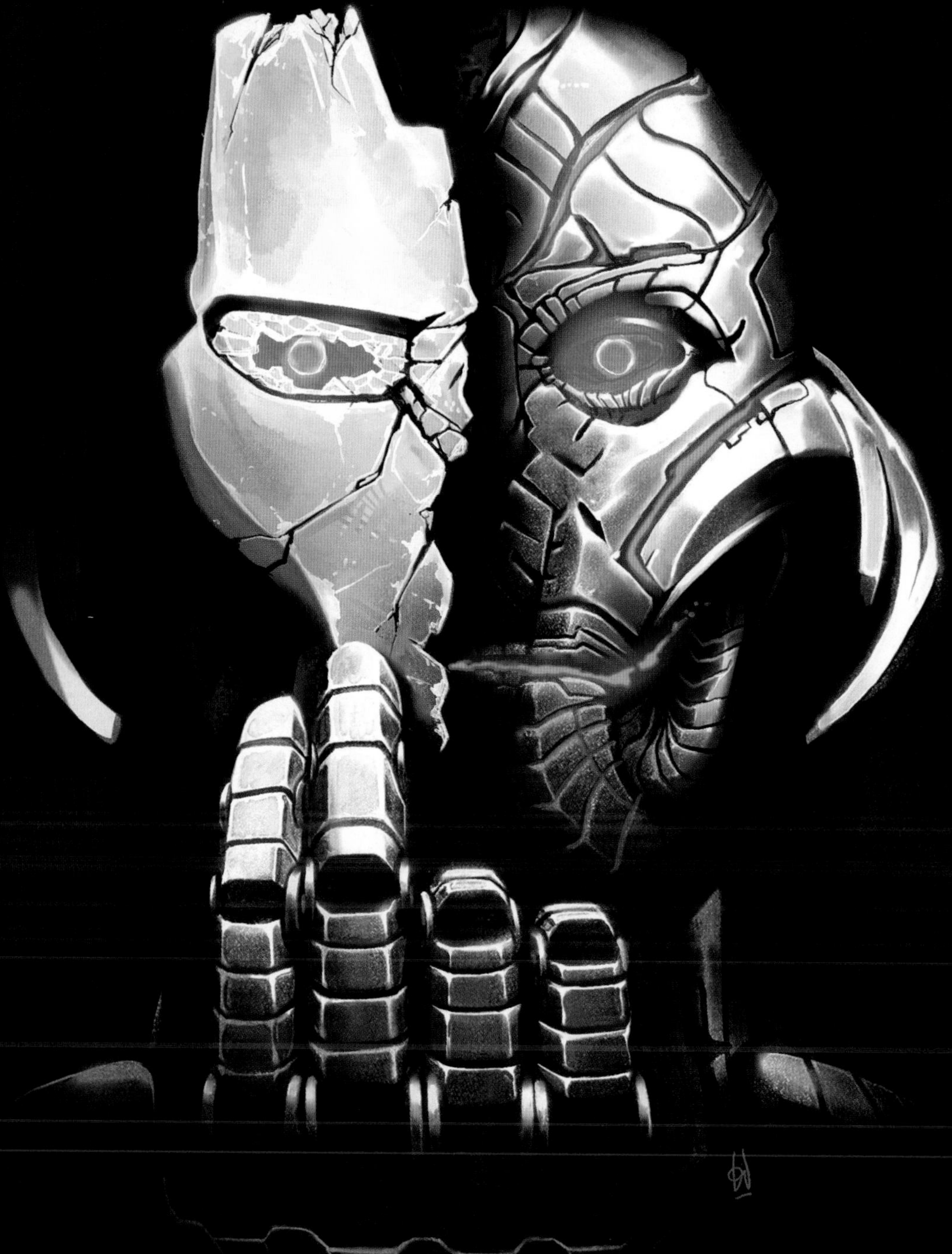

GUIDEBOOK TO THE MARVEL CINEMATIC UNIVERSE

MARVEL STUDIOS PRESENTS A JOSS WHEDON FILM ROBERT DOWNEY JR. "AVENGERS: AGE OF ULTRON" CHRIS HEMSWORTH MARK RUFFALO CHRIS EVANS SCARLETT JOHANSSON JEREMY RENNER DON CHEADLE AARON TAYLOR-JOHNSON ELIZABETH OLSEN PAUL BETTANY COBIE SMULDERS ANTHONY MACKIE HAYLEY ATWELL IDRIS ELBA STELLAN SKARSGÅRD WITH JAMES SPADER AS ULTRON AND SAMUEL L. JACKSON AS NICK FURY CASTING BY SARAH HALLEY FINN, C.S.A. MUSIC SUPERVISOR DAVE JORDAN MUSIC BY BRIAN TYLER ADDITIONAL MUSIC BY DANNY ELFMAN HEAD OF VISUAL DEVELOPMENT RYAN MEINERDING CO-HEAD OF VISUAL DEVELOPMENT CHARLIE WEN VISUAL EFFECTS SUPERVISOR CHRISTOPHER TOWNSEND VISUAL EFFECTS AND ANIMATION BY INDUSTRIAL LIGHT & MAGIC SPECIAL THANKS TO MARVEL STUDIOS FOUNDING CHAIRMAN DAVID MAISEL COSTUME DESIGNER ALEXANDRA BYRNE EDITED BY JEFFREY FORD, A.C.E. LISA LASSEK PRODUCTION DESIGNER CHARLES WOOD DIRECTOR OF PHOTOGRAPHY BEN DAVIS, BSC CO-PRODUCER MITCH BELL EXECUTIVE PRODUCERS JON FAVREAU STAN LEE EXECUTIVE PRODUCER VICTORIA ALONSO JEREMY LATCHAM PATRICIA WHITCHER EXECUTIVE PRODUCER ALAN FINE EXECUTIVE PRODUCER LOUIS D'ESPOSITO PRODUCED BY KEVIN FEIGE, p.g.a. WRITTEN AND DIRECTED BY JOSS WHEDON

Collecting information from Marvel's *Avengers: Age of Ultron (2015)* and Marvel's *Avengers: Age of Ultron Prelude – This Scepter'd Isle Infinite Comic #1 (2015)*.

HEAD WRITER/COORDINATOR: **MIKE O'SULLIVAN**

COORDINATION: **DARON JENSEN**

WRITERS: **TROY BENJAMIN, ROB BOCK, ANTHONY COTILLETTA, PAT DUKE, MIKE FICHERA, DARON JENSEN, ROB LONDON, CHRIS MCCARVER, JACOB ROUGEMONT,** AND **STUART VANDAL**

ARTISTS: **DANIEL ACUÑA, ELIOT R. BROWN, JOHN BUSCEMA, JOHN BYRNE, BOB CHESHIRE, VANESA DEL REY, BOB HALL, JOSH HERMAN, BRYAN HITCH, KEVIN HOPGOOD, JACK KIRBY, FABIAN LACEY, DAVID MARQUEZ, JON MCCOY, RYAN MEINERDING, JOSH NIZZI, RYAN ODAGAWA, JEROME OPEÑA, CARLO PAGULAYAN, GEORGE PÉREZ, CHRIS ROSEWARNE, MICHAEL RYAN, PHIL SAUNDERS, RYAN STEGMAN, DAVID WILLIAMS, STEPHEN WONG,** AND **MIKE ZECK**

COVER ARTIST: **MIKE DEL MUNDO**

SPECIAL THANKS TO DAVE ALTHOFF, SHAWN "KEEBLER" BYERS, JEFF CHRISTIANSEN, STEVE COTTON, MATT DELMANOWSKI, ERIKA DENTON, TIM DILLON, PERCIVAL LANUZA, AVIA PEREZ, JACQUE PORTE, RYAN POTTER, HUNTER REED, AND MEGAN WARD

THE AVENGERS CREATED BY STAN LEE AND JACK KIRBY

AVENGERS UPDATE

FIRST APPEARANCE: [concept] *Iron Man [2008]*; [actual] *Marvel's The Avengers [2012]*

Following S.H.I.E.L.D.'s apparent dissolution, the Avengers reassembled to retrieve Loki's scepter, stolen by Hydra. Under Captain America's leadership, they destroyed several hidden Hydra bases and became close friends. To protect bystanders during their battles, Tony Stark created the Iron Legion, drones controlled by his artificial intelligence (A.I.) aide JARVIS. Eventually, the team recaptured the scepter during an assault on Baron Strucker's Sokovian base, but he had already used it to turn two locals—twins

Wanda and Pietro Maximoff— into superhumans. During the raid, Wanda's mental manipulation abilities showed Stark a vision of his greatest fear: the other Avengers slain by the Chitauri in another attack on Earth. Examining the scepter back at Avengers Tower, Stark discovered an apparent intelligence that he hoped could complete his Ultron project, a secret plan to create a defense against any future extraterrestrial incursions. A few days later, while the Avengers threw a party to celebrate locating the scepter, Ultron achieved sentience; he

swiftly concluded that to protect Earth, humanity should be eliminated. He apparently destroyed the disagreeing JARVIS, then attacked the Avengers with the Iron Legion to cover his escape with the scepter.

Tracking Ultron, the Avengers learned he had allied with the Maximoffs and was seeking the exceptionally rare metal Vibranium. Suspecting that Ultron would pursue illegal arms dealer Ulysses Klaue to obtain it, the Avengers traveled to Klaue's freighter salvage yard off the coast of Africa, where they came into conflict with Ultron and the Maximoffs. Wanda incapacitated most of the heroes with visions dredged from their darkest memories, and sent an enraged Hulk rampaging

FACT SHEET

▶ THOUGH CAPTAIN AMERICA OFFICIALLY LED THE AVENGERS, STARK WAS HAPPY TO REMIND HIM WHO PAID THE BILLS AND DESIGNED THEIR EQUIPMENT.

▶ THE NEW AVENGERS FACILITY HOUSES A LARGE SUPPORT STAFF, INCLUDING CHO AND THOR'S SCIENTIST ALLY DR. ERIK SELVIG.

RECOVERING AFTER BATTLE

BELOW: FALCON, QUICKSILVER, SCARLET WITCH, VISION, WAR MACHINE *Active: Avengers: Age of Ultron (2015)*

towards nearby Johannesburg. Iron Man subdued his maddened teammate, but not before their battle demolished a large swath of the city. With world authorities looking for them, the team hid at Hawkeye's secret farm. Advised by Nick Fury that someone was blocking Ultron's attempts to hack the U.S.'s nuclear launch codes, and realizing Ultron intended to "evolve" by using Avengers' associate Dr. Helen Cho's synthetic tissue research to create an enhanced android body, the team split up. While Stark discovered Ultron's internet nemesis was a surviving JARVIS, Cap, Black Widow, and Hawkeye checked on Cho in Seoul, South Korea. Finding Ultron, the trio were assisted by the Maximoffs, who had learned of Ultron's true plans, and stole the finished android before Ultron could upload his consciousness into it. Believing Ultron feared JARVIS, Stark downloaded his A.I. into the android, creating the Vision, who agreed to help stop his genocidal progenitor. Using a Vibranium engine and a magnetic field, Ultron launched a huge portion of Sokovia skyward, intending to drop it as a meteor and trigger an extinction event. While battling an Ultron drone army, the Avengers evacuated the flying conurbation with assistance from Iron Man's ally War Machine and a S.H.I.E.L.D. Helicarrier Fury had procured. Though Pietro Maximoff died saving Hawkeye and a local boy, the heroes ultimately prevailed, destroying Ultron. Bruce Banner, afraid his alter ego would continue to endanger others, departed in a Quinjet; Thor returned to Asgard; and Hawkeye retired. The remaining team relocated to upstate New York and recruited new members: War Machine, Vision, Falcon, and Wanda, the Scarlet Witch. Ⓐ

AT BARTON'S FARM

UPSTATE FACILITY

AVENGERS HEADQUARTERS

FIRST APPEARANCE: [As Stark Tower] *Marvel's The Avengers [2012]*;
[Avengers Tower] *Marvel's Avengers: Age of Ultron [2015]*;
[Upstate New York facility] *Marvel's Avengers: Age of Ultron [2015]*

Following the Battle of New York, Tony Stark and Pepper Potts immediately began work repairing Stark Tower, damaged during the clash with Loki and his Chitauri allies. Sometime later, Stark converted the building into Avengers Tower, which served as a high-tech headquarters for the Avengers. Still run by Stark's computer systems, the artificial intelligence JARVIS, and Avengers ally Maria Hill, the redesigned Tower now housed advanced laboratories for Stark and Bruce Banner, storage docks for Stark's Iron Legion drones and their automated repair systems, a state-of-the-art medical bay, and a stylish living area where the team could congregate for rest, recreation, and social events. Stark provided customized facilities for each Avenger, such as an archery equipment practice and storage area for Hawkeye. The Tower's extended platform was changed to a sophisticated landing pad for the

AVENGERS TOWER

AVENGERS TOWER LABS

AVENGERS
MANSION

THE AVENGERS HAVE OPERATED OUT of various headquarters over the years, including the long-serving Avengers Mansion and Avengers Tower in Manhattan, California's Avengers Compound, Hydrobase, a floating island off the New York coast, and the sub-atomic Infinite Avengers Mansion. In modern times, the team's various squads maintain individual bases, with Avengers Idea Mechanics active on Avengers Island, the Unity Squad within the Schaefer Theater, and another squad using an old Stark hangar.

FIRST APPEARANCE:
(AVENGERS MANSION) *AVENGERS #2 (1963)*; (AVENGERS COMPOUND) *AVENGERS #246 (1984)*; (HYDROBASE, AS AVENGERS ISLAND): *AVENGERS #262 (1985)*; (STARK/AVENGERS TOWER) *NEW AVENGERS #3 (2005)*; (INFINITE AVENGERS MANSION) *MIGHTY AVENGERS #27 (2009)*; (CURRENT AVENGERS ISLAND) *NEW AVENGERS #1 (2015)*; (SCHAEFER THEATER) *UNCANNY AVENGERS #1 (2015)*; (STARK HANGAR) *ALL-NEW, ALL-DIFFERENT AVENGERS #4 (2016)*

Avengers' Quinjet aircraft, and the center of the Tower's massive, stylized Avengers "A" logo served as the entry and exit portal for the Iron Legion.

After defeating Hydra's Baron Strucker and reclaiming Loki's scepter, Stark and Banner's rogue artificial intelligence, Ultron, created a body from spare Legion parts and attacked the team during a celebratory gathering. The battle between the heroes and the Ultron-controlled Legion left the interior of the building and the Legion destroyed. After Ultron fled the building via the internet and later erased much

of the information the team needed to locate him, they utilized the backup paper files stored in the Tower. Following Ultron's defeat, the Avengers relocated to a multi-level headquarters in upstate New York. This facility, partially below ground, was converted from a Stark Industries warehouse and offered much of the same features and functionality as Avengers Tower, but also now included a spacious grass field surrounding the facility and dozens of employees and support staff, among them Avengers allies Dr. Helen Cho, Dr. Erik Selvig, and Maria Hill. Ⓐ

AVENGERS TOWER LIVING SPACE

▶ THE CELEBRATORY PARTY IN AVENGERS TOWER INCLUDED GUESTS WAR MACHINE, FALCON, AND SEVERAL ELDERLY VETERANS— PRESUMABLY ACQUAINTANCES OF THE TIME-LOST CAPTAIN AMERICA.

▶ THOR'S DEPARTURE FROM THE AVENGERS' UPSTATE FACILITY LEFT A RUNE-SHAPED PATTERN ON THE FACILITY'S LAWN.

BARON STRUCKER

FIRST APPEARANCE:
Captain America: The Winter Soldier [2014]

IN THE 1930S, BARON WOLFGANG von Strucker joined the Nazi party, becoming infamous as one of Hitler's top commanders. After clashing with Sgt. Nick Fury and his Howling Commandos several times, Baron Strucker fell out of favor with Hitler and fled Germany to Japan, where he joined forces with both a subversive group and Hand ninjas to found Hydra. Baron Strucker survived into the current day with an age-retarding serum his scientists developed, overseeing Hydra's growth for decades. Baron Strucker orchestrated Hydra's infiltration of S.H.I.E.L.D. but was eventually discovered by Fury, who started an extended war with Hydra and ultimately defeated their forces.

FIRST APPEARANCE:
SGT. FURY AND HIS HOWLING COMMANDOS #5 (1964)

Baron Wolfgang von Strucker, a S.H.I.E.L.D. agent and secret Hydra operative, obtained Loki's scepter following the New York Chitauri invasion and took it to his Sokovian Hydra facility. There, he supervised human experiments using the scepter to empower humans, but only a set of twins, Pietro and Wanda Maximoff, survived and gained superhuman powers. After Captain America exposed Hydra's corruption of S.H.I.E.L.D., the Avengers hunted down Hydra facilities. When they found the Sokovia facility, Baron Strucker ordered all the research data deleted. As the Maximoff twins battled the Avengers, Iron Man breached the base's energy defense field and stopped the deletion, saving most of the data. Baron Strucker was arrested, and the twins escaped.

When Tony Stark and Bruce Banner created an artificial intelligence, Ultron, in the hopes of ushering in world peace, it quickly became genocidal and constructed a body for itself. Ultron allied with the Maximoff twins, planning to use them to distract the Avengers while he engineered an extinction-level event, believing doing so would complete his programming to create peace. Seeking Vibranium to construct a stronger body, Ultron visited Baron Strucker in prison; Baron Strucker told Ultron he could get Vibranium from black-market arms dealer Ulysses Klaue. Ultron then murdered Baron Strucker and left a taunting message for the Avengers written in his blood: "peace." Ⓐ

FACT SHEET

- ▶ BARON STRUCKER SHAVED HIS HEAD AND WORE A MONOCLE ON HIS RIGHT EYE.

- ▶ IN ADDITION TO LOKI'S SCEPTER, BARON STRUCKER'S HYDRA CELL WAS ALSO RESEARCHING CHITAURI WEAPONS AND ARMOR, AS WELL AS A LEVIATHAN CORPSE.

- ▶ BARON STRUCKER OFTEN EMPLOYED DECEPTION AS A STRATEGIC TACTIC: WHEN CAPTAIN AMERICA EXPOSED HYDRA'S CORRUPTION OF S.H.I.E.L.D., STRUCKER EXPOSED SOME OF HIS FACILITIES TO DRAW ATTENTION AWAY FROM SOKOVIA; WHEN THE AVENGERS FOUND HIS SOKOVIA FACILITY, HE OFFERED THEM HIS HYDRA WEAPONS, HOPING THEY WOULDN'T SEARCH FURTHER AND FIND LOKI'S SCEPTER.

BLACK WIDOW
UPDATE

FIRST APPEARANCE: *Iron Man 2 [2010]*

Seeking to retrieve Loki's stolen scepter from Hydra's Baron Strucker, Black Widow and the Avengers assaulted Strucker's Sokovian base. Once Strucker's forces were defeated, Widow recited a calming "lullaby" to trigger the Hulk's transformation back to Bruce Banner. Returning to Avengers Tower, Widow remained with the injured Hawkeye in the infirmary as Dr. Helen Cho's tissue-creating technology—

similar to her full-sized regeneration cradle—repaired his wound.

Later, at a party hosted by the Avengers, Widow flirted with Banner by pretending to be a bartender and spun a tale about a lover, playfully describing Banner in her tale. When the rogue artificial intelligence Ultron attacked the party while controlling Tony Stark's Iron Legion drones, Widow protected Banner and encouraged him not to change into the Hulk. Tracking

Ultron to the African coast, Widow was attacked by Ultron's mind-manipulating ally, Wanda Maximoff, and forced to relive traumatic experiences she endured while training in Russia's Red Room Academy; Hawkeye took the Avengers to his secret homestead to recover. There, Widow attempted to pursue a relationship with Banner, who resisted due to his Hulk condition, having just destroyed a town in Africa due to Maximoff's influence. Widow confided in Banner that a traditional life was already denied to her: She had been involuntarily sterilized during Red Room training to eliminate the one possible distraction that might interfere with her spy work.

Learning Ultron intended to steal Cho's cradle to evolve, the Avengers claimed it, but Widow was captured by Ultron and imprisoned in his Sokovian fortress; utilizing antiquated radio equipment, Widow sent her location to Hawkeye via Morse code. As Ultron engaged the Avengers, Banner rescued Widow and suggested they disappear together, but knowing the Hulk was needed to stop Ultron, Widow distracted Banner with a kiss, then triggered his transformation by pushing him off a high ledge.

After defeating Ultron, Widow was heartbroken when the Hulk absconded on a Quinjet and turned off its trackers, afraid he would continue to endanger others. Though several of the founding Avengers took leaves of absence, Widow remained at the team's new upstate New York facility to assist in training the Avengers' new recruits. Ⓐ

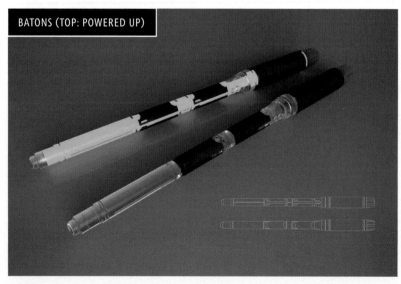

BATONS (TOP: POWERED UP)

FACT SHEET

▶ BLACK WIDOW'S LULLABY FOR HULK CONSISTED OF HER SAYING, "HEY, BIG GUY. SUN'S GETTING REAL LOW," THEN GENTLY SLIDING HER FINGERS DOWN THE HULK'S WRIST TO HIS FINGERTIPS.

▶ WIDOW WAS CALLED "AUNTIE NAT" BY HAWKEYE'S DAUGHTER.

CAPTAIN AMERICA UPDATE

FIRST APPEARANCE: *Captain America: The First Avenger [2011]*

When the Avengers reassembled to retrieve Loki's scepter from Hydra, they chose Captain America as their leader. While continuing his hunt for the Winter Soldier with assistance from Falcon, Cap molded the team into a well-oiled fighting machine. Eventually, the team tracked the scepter to Baron Strucker's Sokovian base, where Cap captured Strucker and Iron Man retrieved the scepter. Celebrating Hydra's apparent defeat, the team hosted a party at Avengers Tower. As it wound down, the male Avengers held a friendly contest to see who could lift Thor's hammer, Mjolnir, which Thor claimed only the worthy could wield—to Thor's surprise, Cap slightly moved it. Moments later, rogue artificial intelligence Ultron attacked the team and stole the scepter. Learning Stark, with Banner's help, had created Ultron in secret—hoping to build a defense system for Earth—Steve angrily berated Stark for keeping secrets, though Stark insisted his actions were necessary

to safeguard Earth against alien and superhuman threats. The Avengers tracked Ultron to illegal arms dealer Ulysses Klaue's stock of the rare metal Vibranium and intercepted the A.I., but Ultron's ally Wanda Maximoff incapacitated most of the team with painful mental visions, causing Cap to hallucinate memories of his wartime love, Peggy Carter. Regrouping, Cap and Stark renewed their debate as Cap reminded Stark that every time someone has tried to preempt a war, innocents died.

Suspecting Ultron would seek Avengers' associate Dr. Helen Cho's synthetic tissue research to create an improved android body for himself, Cap, Black Widow, and Hawkeye flew to Seoul to check on her. Upon learning Ultron's plan to exterminate all of humanity, a repentant Wanda, and her brother Pietro, helped the Avengers steal the inert android body from Ultron. Against Cap's wishes, Stark uploaded his A.I. aide JARVIS into the android body. Now dubbed the Vision, the android joined the

Avengers' cause. Tracking Ultron back to Sokovia, the expanded team prevented him from triggering an extinction event, and eventually destroyed him. When the threat ended, the team relocated to a new, upstate New York facility. With Banner having gone into hiding, Thor in Asgard, Stark on temporary hiatus, and Hawkeye retired, Captain America and Black Widow took up the task of forging their new recruits—War Machine, Vision, Falcon, and Wanda Maximoff—into a team. Ⓐ

FACT SHEET

▶ CAPTAIN AMERICA'S FIRST PRIORITY IN A BATTLE IS TO MINIMIZE CIVILIAN CASUALTIES, WITH TEAM MEMBERS OFTEN DELEGATED TO LEAD INNOCENTS OUT OF HARM'S WAY.

▶ CAPTAIN AMERICA IS TEASED BY HIS FELLOW AVENGERS FOR DISCOURAGING HIS TEAMMATES' COARSE LANGUAGE.

▶ MAGNETS BUILT INTO CAP'S GAUNTLETS RETURN THE SHIELD TO HIM ON THE RARE OCCASIONS HE DOESN'T CATCH IT.

▶ CAP DEVELOPED JOINT BATTLE MANEUVERS WITH HIS TEAMMATES, SUCH AS LETTING THOR STRIKE HIS SHIELD TO CREATE A SONIC SHOCKWAVE.

DR. HELEN CHO

FIRST APPEARANCE:
Marvel's The Avengers: Age of Ultron [2015]

One of the world's most brilliant physicians, Dr. Helen Cho provided medical assistance to the Avenger Hawkeye following his injury in battle. Though severely wounded, Barton healed quickly thanks to Cho's advanced medical technology, which could regenerate tissue at an incredible rate. Cho later attended a party at Avengers Tower, and was shocked when the murderous artificial intelligence Ultron revealed itself and attacked the Avengers. Hiding behind a piano, Cho was nearly fired upon by an Iron Legion drone under Ultron's possession, but Ultron, having noticed Cho, disabled the drone's weapon system, sparing her life.

Cho returned to Seoul to continue her work at U-Gin Genetics Research Lab, where she found Ultron waiting. He intended to evolve using the regeneration cradle Cho had developed; needing her expertise to operate it, Ultron used the mind-controlling power of the Asgardian Loki's scepter to force her compliance. Using the cradle, Cho helped to create a new, human-like body, which Ultron enhanced by adding the true source of the scepter's power: an Infinity Stone. As Cho began uploading Ultron's cerebral matrix into the cradle, enhanced Sokovian Wanda Maximoff, now able to see into Ultron's mind, realized Ultron's true intent to destroy humanity. Horrified, Maximoff used her mind-altering power to free Cho from Ultron's hypnosis. Her senses returned, Cho stopped the upload, and Ultron fired a laser beam at Cho in retaliation, wounding her. Cho recovered from her injuries and continued to support the Avengers following Ultron's defeat, providing medical expertise from the new Avengers facility in upstate New York. Ⓐ

FRIDAY

FIRST APPEARANCE:
Marvel's Avengers: Age of Ultron [2015]

I n need of an artificial intelligence to replace JARVIS, Tony Stark uploaded FRIDAY to the Iron Man armor before the Avengers traveled to Sokovia to confront Ultron, another Stark-created artificial intelligence that went murderously rogue. FRIDAY helped Stark find Ultron and scanned his equipment, then provided Stark with tactical assistance during the ensuing battle and helped him locate civilians needing rescue. When Ultron used a magnetic field to turn Sokovia into a meteor that would destroy humanity, FRIDAY helped Stark develop a plan to destroy the airborne landmass and stop Ultron. ◍

FRIDAY IS AN ARTIFICIAL intelligence created by Tony Stark to serve as a personal assistant and virtual secretary, named after Robinson Crusoe's companion. Initially taking the visual form—and disposition—of a teenage girl, Friday has "evolved" to the age of a young woman and now also serves as onboard support in Stark's Iron Man armors.

FIRST APPEARANCE:
IRON MAN #53 (2002)

INITIAL APPEARANCE

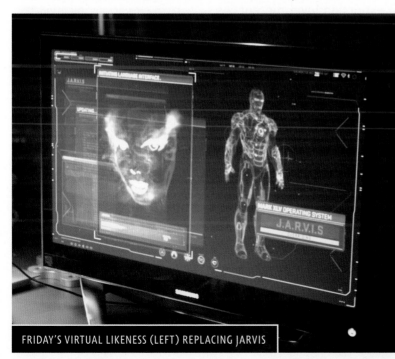

FRIDAY'S VIRTUAL LIKENESS (LEFT) REPLACING JARVIS

FACT SHEET

▶ OTHER ARTIFICIAL INTELLIGENCES NOT CHOSEN BY STARK WERE NAMED JOCASTA AND TADASHI.

▶ FRIDAY'S VIRTUAL AVATAR IS OF A FEMALE'S FACE WITH GLOWING EYES, AND SHE SPEAKS WITH AN IRISH ACCENT.

NICK FURY UPDATE

FIRST APPEARANCE: *Iron Man [2008]*

Following the revelation that S.H.I.E.L.D. had infiltrated Hydra, and after assisting Captain America and Black Widow in defeating Project: Insight, Nick Fury allowed the world to believe him dead and went underground to smoke out Hydra cells in Europe.

Later, Fury revealed to the rest of the Avengers that he was still alive when the team retreated to Hawkeye's safe house in the wake of a disastrous encounter with Ultron, an artificial intelligence created by Tony Stark and Bruce Banner that had gone murderously rogue. Working with the Avengers on a plan to defeat Ultron, Fury informed them that Ultron was attempting to activate the world's nuclear missiles, but that an unrevealed third party was

blocking him by continuously changing the codes. Without nuclear weapons, Fury theorized Ultron would seek other means to destroy humankind. By prodding the Avengers with the right questions, Fury helped Banner deduce that Ultron was creating a new body for himself.

After the Avengers stole the body from him, Ultron raised the capital city of Sokovia high into the atmosphere, planning to use it as an extinction-level meteor. As the Avengers battled Ultron, Fury arrived with a recommissioned Helicarrier 64, staffed with former S.H.I.E.L.D. agents, and oversaw the civilian evacuation while helping War Machine destroy escaping Ultron drones. During these operations, Fury and Maria Hill

personally destroyed one of the drones that breached their defenses and attacked the Helicarrier's command center. When the city was cleared, the Avengers destroyed it, ending Ultron's plan and saving the Earth.

At the new Avengers facility in upstate New York, Fury informed Black Widow that he'd possibly located the Quinjet in which the Hulk used to flee from the team, to protect them from the danger he felt he posed to them; however, Fury said that there were no signs of Banner and no way to track the Quinjet thanks to Tony Stark's stealth technology. Fury told Widow he didn't know exactly what would happen when he originally sent her to recruit Banner, but he had hoped for the best; Fury was pleased that a great team had come out of his efforts. Ⓐ

FACT SHEET

► WHILE UNDERGROUND AND BELIEVED DEAD, FURY WORE SUNGLASSES INSTEAD OF AN EYEPATCH.

► AFTER ARRIVING AT THE BARTONS' FARM, FURY HID IN THE BARN AND ASKED MRS. BARTON TO LURE TONY STARK THERE FOR A PRIVATE CONVERSATION. WHEN HE REVEALED HIMSELF TO STARK, FURY QUIPPED THAT STARK SHOULD DO HIM A FAVOR AND NOT BRING THE BARTONS' TRACTOR TO LIFE.

► WHILE TALKING THROUGH THE ULTRON SITUATION WITH STARK, FURY CONFESSED THAT HE WAS TRYING TO HELP STARK BECAUSE HE CARED VERY MUCH ABOUT HIM.

► FURY JOKED THAT THE MISSING BANNER SWAM TO FIJI AND WOULD SEND BLACK WIDOW A POSTCARD.

RECOMMISSIONED HELICARRIER 64

HAWKEYE UPDATE

FIRST APPEARANCE: *Thor [2011]*

With Nick Fury's help, Clint Barton kept his wife, Laura, and children, Cooper and Lila, secret from both S.H.I.E.L.D. and the Avengers—save for Black Widow. During the Avengers' raid on Hydra's Sokovian fortress to reclaim Loki's scepter, Hawkeye became distracted by Pietro Maximoff and was shot. After being healed by Dr. Helen Cho's tissue-regeneration process, Barton attended the party at Avengers Tower celebrating the team's success. When the artificial intelligence Ultron attacked, Hawkeye helped fight off the hijacked Iron Legion.

Learning that Ultron was seeking Vibranium, Hawkeye and the Avengers confronted Ultron and his allies—Pietro and his twin, Wanda—aboard black market arms dealer Ulysses Klaue's freighter. Wanda mentally manipulated the Avengers into experiencing harrowing hallucinations, but Hawkeye stopped her before she could affect him. Helping his traumatized teammates to safety, he took them to his home, where they finally met his family. After the Avengers determined that Ultron intended to use Cho's regeneration cradle to create himself an artificial body, Hawkeye accompanied Black Widow and Captain America to Seoul to intervene.

The team retrieved the cradle, but Black Widow was captured by Ultron. After Hawkeye learned Black Widow's location via a Morse code message, the Avengers traveled to Sokovia to stop Ultron from using the nation's capital city as an extinction-level meteor to eradicate humanity. While battling Ultron's sentries and helping S.H.I.E.L.D. evacuate the Sokovian population, Hawkeye encouraged the scared Wanda (now the Scarlet Witch) to be strong, before attempting to rescue a young boy named Costel. When Ultron fired on Hawkeye and Costel, Pietro (now called Quicksilver) moved them out of the way at super-speed, but was struck and killed by the bullets himself. Following Ultron's defeat, Barton resigned from the Avengers and returned home to Laura—later celebrating the birth of his son, Nathaniel Pietro Barton, named in honor of Quicksilver. Ⓐ

FACT SHEET

▶ DURING THEIR ENCOUNTERS, HAWKEYE AND QUICKSILVER REPEATEDLY QUIPPED ABOUT ONE NOT SEEING THE OTHER'S ACTIONS COMING.

▶ WHILE THE AVENGERS AND FURY DISCUSSED THEIR PLANS IN HIS KITCHEN, TONY STARK CASUALLY THREW DARTS, BUT STOPPED WHEN BARTON HIT BULLSEYE WITH THREE SIMULTANEOUSLY THROWN DARTS.

▶ WHEN GEARING UP FOR THE FINAL BATTLE AGAINST ULTRON, HAWKEYE TUCKED A PHOTO OF HIS FAMILY INSIDE HIS TUNIC.

HAWKEYE'S ARSENAL

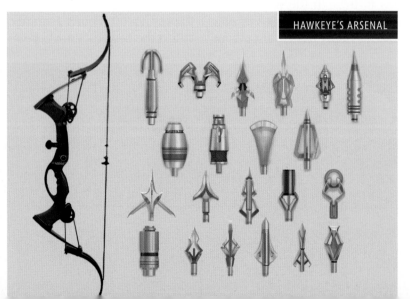

HULK UPDATE

FIRST APPEARANCE: *The Incredible Hulk [2008]*

Following the Battle of New York, Bruce Banner reluctantly provided counsel as Tony Stark shared his intimate thoughts and experiences. Banner dozed off, but eventually awoke and apologized, explaining he isn't that type of doctor. Undeterred, Stark began anew; an exasperated Banner remained seated, dropping his head back in defeat.

Later, as Hulk, Banner fought alongside the Avengers against Baron Strucker's forces to procure Loki's scepter from Hydra's Sokovian fortress. In the wake of the battle, Hulk reverted to Banner after Black Widow recited a soothing lullaby. En route to Avengers Tower aboard a Quinjet, Widow reassured a sullen Banner that Hulk's presence had saved lives. Afterward, Stark and Banner spoke privately about using the gem housed within the scepter to create an artificially intelligent global-peacekeeping initiative: Ultron. Although hesitant, Banner helped Stark.

At a party celebrating the Avengers' victory over Strucker, Banner flirted awkwardly with Black Widow; he later pretended to undergo a stressed-induced transformation while testing his worthiness to lift Thor's hammer. When the newly sentient Ultron attacked, Widow protected Banner. Later enthralled by Wanda Maximoff as he waited in reserve while the Avengers confronted Ultron off the African coast, Banner transformed into a more feral Hulk and rampaged through Johannesburg. Stark summoned specialized Hulkbuster armor from his Veronika satellite—designed as a fail-safe in conjunction with Banner—and defeated Hulk after a devastating battle. Banner contemplated leaving the team as the heroes regrouped at Hawkeye's farmhouse. Widow wanted to accompany him, but Banner argued that Hulk prevented them from having a future together.

Banner surmised Ultron would attempt to evolve using Dr. Helen Cho's regeneration cradle, and the Avengers retrieved it—but Widow was captured in the process. Back at Avengers Tower, Stark convinced Banner to implant JARVIS into the synthetic being inside the cradle, resulting in the birth of Vision. Rescuing Widow from Ultron's Sokovian fortress, Banner wanted to leave with her, but she knew Hulk was needed to stop Ultron and pushed him off a ledge to induce a transformation. During the fight, Ultron commandeered the Avengers' Quinjet, but Hulk forcefully ejected him and continued flying away, ignoring Widow's call to return. S.H.I.E.L.D. discovered that the Quinjet may have crashed in the Banda Sea, but there was no sign of Hulk. 🅰

FACT SHEET

▶ WHEN THE HULK'S ASSISTANCE IS NEEDED, THE AVENGERS TERM THE SITUATION A CODE GREEN.

▶ ENGAGING A MESMERIZED HULK, STARK INADVERTENTLY ENRAGED THE BRUTE FURTHER BY ADDRESSING HIM AS BANNER, IMMEDIATELY REMEMBERING THE HULK REGARDED BANNER AS PUNY.

▶ STARK CLAIMED BANNER KNEW MORE ABOUT BIO-ORGANICS THAN ANYONE ALIVE, INCLUDING HIMSELF.

LEGION DRONE

IRON LEGION

FIRST APPEARANCE: [name] *Iron Man 3* [2013];
[drones] *Marvel's Avengers: Age of Ultron* [2015]

Seeking reinforcements for the Avengers, Tony Stark created a series of JARVIS-directed, cybernetic sentries. Each Iron Legionnaire possessed attributes common to the various standard-purpose Iron Man armors, including repulsor-technology propulsion.

As the Avengers converged on Hydra's Sokovian fortress to secure Loki's scepter, the Iron Legion was deployed to the city center to keep the populace out of harm's way. Informed by the drones that the Avengers were there to help, an angry Sokovian crowd nonetheless defaced Iron Legion Unit 03 by throwing corrosive liquid at it, damaging its head and shoulder area. The Iron Legion returned to Avengers Tower following the mission. Upon arrival, each unit was laser-scanned in the storage-and-assembly area; those damaged in the field were provided with fresh parts.

Stark and Bruce Banner surmised that the alien code inside the scepter's jewel could be applied to the Iron Legionnaires, granting them advanced artificial intelligence and creating a peacekeeping force that would replace the Avengers. Despite Banner's reservations, he and Stark began work without the other Avengers' approval. Simulation after simulation failed, and the code seemingly could not be applied to Stark's technology.

As JARVIS continued running background tests during a party celebrating the Avengers' victory over Hydra, Test 77 inexplicably proved successful. Becoming self-aware, Ultron seemingly destroyed JARVIS. Ultron took physical form using discarded Iron Legion parts, including Unit 03's corroded faceplate, and commandeered the functioning sentries to attack the Avengers, who promptly destroyed the Legionnairres. Ⓐ

LEGION REPAIR DOCK

ULTRON-CONTROLLED DRONE

IRON MAN
UPDATE

FIRST APPEARANCE: *Iron Man [2008]*

Piloting the Mark XLIII armor, Tony Stark participated in the Avengers' assault on Hydra's Sokovian fortress. Stark breached the stronghold's shielding and found Loki's scepter among a cache of Chitauri technology salvaged from the Battle of New York. Approaching unnoticed, Wanda Maximoff amplified Stark's innate fears of human annihilation, causing him to experience a vision of the Avengers' deaths against the backdrop of a massing alien invasion

force. Upon returning to Avengers Tower, Stark's increasing insecurities led him to convince Bruce Banner to help him integrate the advanced artificial intelligence he detected within the scepter's gemstone into Ultron, a global-defense initiative he intended as a replacement for the Avengers. They were unsuccessful in their attempt. However, at the conclusion of the Avengers' victory party, an inexplicably self-aware Ultron disabled JARVIS, assembled a makeshift mechanical body, and attacked the team using Stark's Iron Legion. Ultron escaped with the scepter, and Stark faced his colleagues' disapproval for his reckless actions.

Stark and the Avengers pursued Ultron to an African salvage yard, but the team was waylaid by Ultron's new allies: Wanda and her twin brother, Pietro. Wanda compelled Banner to transform into a feral Hulk, who rampaged through nearby Johannesburg. Stark reluctantly

fought and subdued his teammate using the Mark XLIV exoskeleton, which enhanced his armor's durability and strength to Hulk-busting levels. The collateral damage sparked public outcry against the Avengers, forcing them to seek refuge at Hawkeye's farmhouse. Despite the schisms within the team, Nick Fury convinced the heroes to put aside their differences and unite against Ultron.

As the other Avengers pursued Ultron—who was attempting to create a new, Vibranium-laced host body using Dr. Helen Cho's regeneration cradle—Stark traveled to the Nexus Internet Hub in Oslo, Norway, to investigate Ultron's failure to access worldwide nuclear launch codes. He discovered that JARVIS had survived, hidden in cyberspace, and was blocking Ultron's attempts. Stark defied his teammates by uploading JARVIS's operational matrix into Ultron's android body, creating a new synthetic being: Vision. After the team learned Ultron's location, Stark installed a backup A.I., FRIDAY, into his Mark XLV armor and left for Sokovia with the Avengers, Vision, and the Maximoffs, who had switched sides upon learning of Ultron's desire for human extinction.

Stark discovered Ultron's plan to elevate the Sokovian capital's landmass and drop it back to Earth like an extinction-level meteor, but posited that the creation of a heat seal would destroy the city in mid-air. After Fury arrived aboard a S.H.I.E.L.D. Helicarrier to evacuate the population, Thor delivered the final blow to the Vibranium core holding the city aloft. As the Avengers settled in at their new upstate New York facility, Stark left the team in search of a more peaceful life. Ⓐ

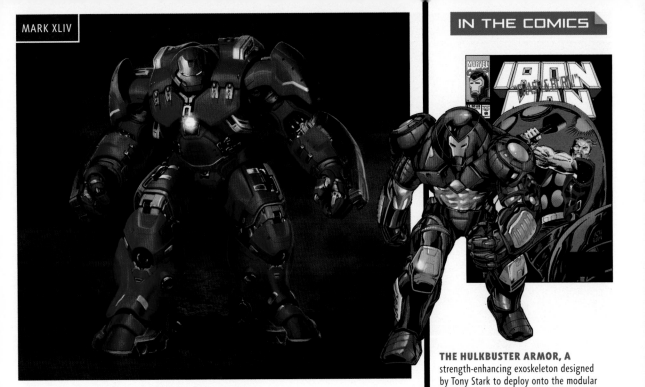

MARK XLIV

THE HULKBUSTER ARMOR, A strength-enhancing exoskeleton designed by Tony Stark to deploy onto the modular Model 13, allowed him sufficient strength and durability to combat the gamma-powered Hulk. Stark later developed at least five standalone armors based on the Hulkbuster design—two of which, Models 36 and 44, were destroyed in battle with Hulk.

FIRST APPEARANCE:
(MODEL 13) *IRON MAN #304 (1994)*;
(MODEL 36) *WORLD WAR HULK #1 (2007)*;
(MODEL 44) *IRON MAN #4 (2013)*

IRON MAN ARMORS UPDATE

FIRST APPEARANCE:
[Mark XLIII-XLV] *Avengers: Age of Ultron [2015]*

After destroying his original Iron Legion, Tony Stark created two new standard-purpose armors, the Marks XLIII and XLV, as well as the specialized Mark XLIV. The latter, co-designed by Bruce Banner, would provide Stark with the requisite strength to battle and contain Banner's gamma-powered alter ego, the Hulk. All three suits were equipped with the Mark XLII's prehensile-assembly functionality, allowing Stark to suit up one remote-controlled component at a time; Stark could also command the suits to assemble on someone else.

Stark piloted the Mark XLIII during the Avengers' raid on Baron Strucker's Sokovian stronghold. As he searched the fortress for Loki's scepter, he left the suit behind in its autonomous, combat-ready sentry mode. Stark also used the Mark XLIII suit to battle Ultron at an African salvage yard. And bolstered by the Mark XLIV, he fought a feral Hulk in Johannesburg after he was mentally driven into a rampage by Wanda Maximoff; both armors suffered severe damage. Stark wore Mark XLV to help the Avengers stop Ultron's plan to destroy humanity using the Sokovian capital's landmass. Ⓐ

FACT SHEET

▶ STARK USED MARK XLIII'S PREHENSILE-ASSEMBLY FEATURE TO DON A GAUNTLET WHICH ENABLED HIM TO SAFELY HANDLE LOKI'S SCEPTER, AND TO COMBAT CAPTAIN AMERICA WHEN HE ATTEMPTED TO DESTROY ULTRON'S ARTIFICIAL BODY.

▶ THE MARK XLIV WAS A MASSIVE, MODULAR EXOSKELETON THAT WOULD ASSEMBLE OVER A STANDARD-PURPOSE ARMOR, ENHANCING ITS STRENGTH AND DURABILITY. IN ADDITION TO WEAPONRY TYPICAL OF OTHER MODELS, THE SUIT WAS EQUIPPED WITH WRIST-MOUNTED HYDRAULIC RAMS THAT COULD DELIVER PUNCHES CAPABLE OF DOWNING THE HULK.

▶ NICKNAMED VERONIKA, THE MARK XLIV'S DEPLOYMENT SYSTEM CONSISTED OF A STARK INDUSTRIES SATELLITE THAT WOULD LAUNCH A POD CONTAINING THE ARMOR, AN ELECTRIFIED CONTAINMENT CAGE THAT WOULD ASSEMBLE AROUND THE HULK, AND AN AIRBORNE SUPPORT MODULE THAT WOULD DISPENSE SPARE PARTS AT STARK'S COMMAND.

MARK XLIII

MARK XLV

JARVIS UPDATE

FIRST APPEARANCE: *Iron Man [2008]*

Following the Battle of New York, JARVIS helped Tony Stark test the remote-controlled Mark XLII armor and later diagnosed the now-insomniac Stark's severe anxiety attacks. After an explosion hospitalized Happy Hogan, JARVIS helped Stark investigate a holographic reproduction of the blast site. Stark's public outrage against the Mandarin, who claimed responsibility for the bombing, provoked an attack that caused Stark's cliffside estate to tumble into the sea. Trapped under debris on the ocean floor, Stark was rescued by JARVIS, who assumed control of the armor. While flying Stark to Rose Hill, Tennessee—a town Stark had earlier sought to investigate in connection to similar terrorist activity—JARVIS ceased functioning as the Mark XLII ran out of power. When the true mastermind behind the attacks, Aldrich Killian, held President Matthew Ellis and Stark Industries CEO Pepper Potts hostage, Stark summoned an army of Iron Man armors piloted by the restored JARVIS to target Killian's Extremis-enhanced soldiers. After Killian's defeat, Stark ordered JARVIS to destroy the Iron Legion as a gesture signifying to Potts a renewed focus on his health and their relationship.

JARVIS's responsibilities continued to grow. Integral to operations at both Stark Industries and Avengers Tower, JARVIS also directed the new Iron Legion. After the Avengers raided Baron Strucker's Sokovian fortress and recaptured Loki's scepter, Stark discovered what resembled an advanced artificial intelligence within the staff's gemstone. With JARVIS unable to download a data schematic that dense before Thor was to return the scepter to Asgard, Stark and Bruce Banner attempted to apply the gem's A.I. directly toward Stark's global-defense initiative, Ultron, which Stark envisioned as a replacement for the Avengers. They failed. Ultron, however, became self-aware nonetheless and attacked JARVIS, apparently destroying him. But JARVIS dumped his memory and hid deep in the Internet. Eventually discovering that the A.I. was secretly working against Ultron, Stark and Banner uploaded JARVIS's operational matrix into Ultron's new Vibranium-laced body, captured by the Avengers. Empowered by the scepter's gemstone, one of six ancient Infinity Stones, JARVIS evolved into Vision and joined the Avengers to defeat Ultron. 🅐

FACT SHEET

▶ SECRETED WITHIN THE INTERNET, JARVIS PREVENTED ULTRON FROM OBTAINING ACCESS TO ANY OF THE WORLD'S NUCLEAR MISSILES BY CONSTANTLY SCRAMBLING THE ACCESS CODES.

▶ WHEN STARK ASKED BANNER TO HELP HIM TRANSFER JARVIS INTO THE BEING THAT WOULD BECOME THE VISION, JARVIS SAID HE BELIEVED IT WAS "WORTH A GO."

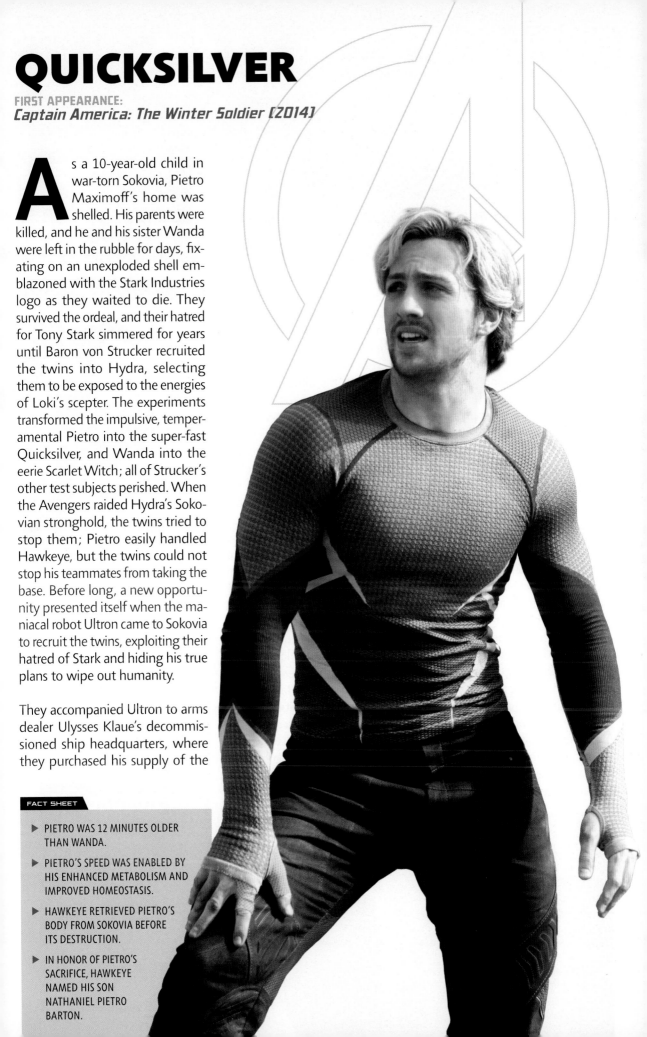

QUICKSILVER

FIRST APPEARANCE:
Captain America: The Winter Soldier [2014]

As a 10-year-old child in war-torn Sokovia, Pietro Maximoff's home was shelled. His parents were killed, and he and his sister Wanda were left in the rubble for days, fixating on an unexploded shell emblazoned with the Stark Industries logo as they waited to die. They survived the ordeal, and their hatred for Tony Stark simmered for years until Baron von Strucker recruited the twins into Hydra, selecting them to be exposed to the energies of Loki's scepter. The experiments transformed the impulsive, temperamental Pietro into the super-fast Quicksilver, and Wanda into the eerie Scarlet Witch; all of Strucker's other test subjects perished. When the Avengers raided Hydra's Sokovian stronghold, the twins tried to stop them; Pietro easily handled Hawkeye, but the twins could not stop his teammates from taking the base. Before long, a new opportunity presented itself when the maniacal robot Ultron came to Sokovia to recruit the twins, exploiting their hatred of Stark and hiding his true plans to wipe out humanity.

They accompanied Ultron to arms dealer Ulysses Klaue's decommissioned ship headquarters, where they purchased his supply of the

FACT SHEET

► PIETRO WAS 12 MINUTES OLDER THAN WANDA.

► PIETRO'S SPEED WAS ENABLED BY HIS ENHANCED METABOLISM AND IMPROVED HOMEOSTASIS.

► HAWKEYE RETRIEVED PIETRO'S BODY FROM SOKOVIA BEFORE ITS DESTRUCTION.

► IN HONOR OF PIETRO'S SACRIFICE, HAWKEYE NAMED HIS SON NATHANIEL PIETRO BARTON.

super-strong metal Vibranium. Before long, the Avengers showed up, and the twins battled them; during the fight, Pietro tried to grab Thor's hammer in mid-flight, but proved unworthy to lift it and crashed to the ground. He then had to rescue his sister when Hawkeye hit her with a stun arrow, and helped her send the Hulk on a rampage.

The twins accompanied Ultron to Seoul, where he compelled Dr. Helen Cho to construct a new body for him with the Vibranium. Wanda soon realized what Ultron's true intentions were, and convinced her brother to desert him with her. As they escaped, they saw that a fight between Ultron and the Avengers was endangering the entire city. They joined forces with the Avengers and prevented scores of civilian casualties. Learning that Tony Stark had acquired Ultron's new body, Pietro and Wanda convinced Captain America and Hawkeye to stop Stark from activating it. They were unsuccessful, but the being that emerged was not another

Ultron, but the heroic Vision. Quicksilver overcame his misgivings and joined Wanda, the Vision, and the Avengers in Sokovia to make a final stand against Ultron.

Pietro and his allies evacuated as many Sokovians as they could, but they were powerless to stop Ultron from raising the capital of Sokovia into the atmosphere. They mounted a last-ditch effort to stop him from enacting the second phase of his plan, and rallied to defend the Vibranium detonator that would slam it back into the Earth from an army of merciless Ultron drones. With Ultron and his legions driven back, Pietro left Wanda to cover the detonator as he helped the other Avengers and S.H.I.E.L.D. evacuate the remaining Sokovians. Seeing Ultron in a commandeered Avengers Quinjet firing on Hawkeye and a Sokovian child, Pietro raced to save them; he intercepted the bullets himself, and was killed. Sensing her brother's death immediately, Wanda avenged him by destroying Ultron's body. Ⓐ

THE PRODUCT OF GENETIC experiments performed by the High Evolutionary (Herbert Wyndham), the speedy, hot-tempered Quicksilver (Pietro Maximoff) joined the Brotherhood of Evil Mutants led by Magneto (Max Eisenhardt) alongside his reality-manipulating twin sister, Wanda. Eventually, he saw the error of his ways, and joined the heroic Avengers. He also married the Inhuman princess Crystal Amaquelin and had a daughter, Luna, but their marriage eventually failed. Currently, he serves with the Avengers Unity Squad.

FIRST APPEARANCE:
X-MEN #4 (1964);
FIRST ACTIVE WITH AVENGERS:
AVENGERS #16 (1965)

WITH WANDA

SCARLET WITCH

FIRST APPEARANCE:
Captain America: The Winter Soldier [2014]

A s a child in the war-torn European nation Sokovia, Wanda Maximoff was orphaned when her parents' apartment was shelled with Stark Industries missiles. She and her twin brother Pietro survived, and were left with a lasting hatred for Tony Stark. Years later, they volunteered to join Hydra, and were subjected to experiments with Loki's purloined scepter. The twins were the only surviving test subjects, and both were granted super-powers; Wanda received a variety of mental abilities, becoming the Scarlet Witch. When Stark and his Avengers launched an assault on Hydra's Sokovian base, the twins tried to push them back. Wanda used her powers on Stark, subjecting him to a nightmarish dream of the Avengers' deaths. She allowed him to take the scepter, confident that it would lead to his downfall.

Wanda's intuition proved correct, as Stark's experiments with the Stone produced the mad robot Ultron. Ultron recruited Wanda and Pietro to his cause, allowing them to believe he only wished to destroy the Avengers, and not all of humanity. The twins accompanied Ultron to see arms merchant Ulysses Klaue, hoping to acquire the super-strong metal Vibranium. When the Avengers arrived at Klaue's

FACT SHEET

- ▶ WANDA IS CAPABLE OF NEURO-ELECTRICAL INTERFACING, GRANTING HER BOTH TELEKINESIS AND THE ABILITY TO MANIPULATE OTHERS' MINDS.

- ▶ DURING THE SOKOVIAN EVACUATION, WANDA USED HER POWERS TO COMPEL THE CITIZENRY TO FLEE.

- ▶ WANDA DESTROYED ULTRON BY TEARING HIS MECHANICAL HEART OUT.

headquarters in force, Wanda used her powers to neutralize most of the Avengers with horrific, twisted visions, but Hawkeye hit her with a stun arrow before she could attack him. Quicksilver rescued her, and she sent the Hulk on a rampage before they escaped.

They travelled to South Korea with Ultron, where he used the scepter's Infinity Stone to compel Dr. Helen Cho to grow a new synthetic body for him. Able to read Ultron's mind as it was transferred into the human-like brain of his new body, Wanda saw his true intentions—the destruction of all organic life—for the first time. She overrode Cho's mind control, freeing her to sabotage the upload, and then assisted the Avengers in saving civilians endangered by Ultron. Horrified to learn that Stark had acquired Ultron's new body, Wanda and Pietro joined Captain America in trying to stop Stark from activating it, but they failed when Thor brought it to life. Although wary of the android, who dubbed himself the Vision, Wanda

joined him and the rest of the Avengers in launching a final, desperate assault on Ultron's Sokovian stronghold.

During a fierce battle against Ultron's drone army, Wanda had a crisis of confidence, feeling both responsible for Ultron's evil and totally incapable of stopping it. Hawkeye convinced her to fight on, and she fought Ultron's army with renewed purpose, joining the other Avengers in defending the detonator that would crash Sokovia into the Earth. With Ultron beaten back, Wanda chose to defend the detonator herself while the others evacuated civilians. Soon after, Wanda sensed Pietro's death at Ultron's hands and went berserk, smashing waves of Ultron drones before finding Ultron and destroying his body; with her distracted, an Ultron drone triggered the detonator. Near catatonic, she made no effort to escape the plummeting Sokovian landmass until the Vision flew her to safety. Later, she joined the reconstructed Avengers. Ⓐ

WITH PIETRO

THOR UPDATE

FIRST APPEARANCE: *Thor [2011]*

When Loki's scepter was tracked to Baron Strucker's Sokovian Hydra facility, Thor and the Avengers attacked the base and retrieved it. Intending to return the weapon to Asgard, Thor allowed Tony Stark to study it before he departed. Afterward, Thor joined his Earth-born friends at an Avengers Tower party. After the crowds subsided to just Avengers and allies James Rhodes, Dr. Helen Cho, and Maria Hill, they were attacked by Stark's creation Ultron, commanding Stark's Iron Legion robots. Although Thor destroyed the damaged Iron Legion body Ultron inhabited, Ultron's programming transferred itself elsewhere, and one of the Legionnaires escaped with the scepter. Thor attempted to follow the robot, but lost its trail and returned, enraged with Stark for creating the menace. Although he refrained from injuring Stark, they argued until Captain America drew their attention to finding Ultron.

The Avengers tracked Ultron to a salvage yard off the African coast, where he purchased Vibranium from Ulysses Klaue. During the battle, Thor's mind was assaulted by Wanda Maximoff, and he hallucinated a blinded Heimdall accusing him of leading Asgard into Hel, and calling Thor a destroyer. Believing there was a deeper meaning to his vision, Thor met up with his friend Erik Selvig and together they journeyed to the mystic Water of Sight. Bathing in the waters, Thor continued his vision and became aware of the Infinity Stones, one of which was encased in the crystal of Loki's scepter. Ultron attempted to use the scepter's Infinity Stone to power a Vibranium-laced synthetic body for himself, which the Avengers confiscated and Stark and Banner uploaded the JARVIS program into. Inspired by his vision, Thor purposely channeled lightning into the cradle housing the android, bringing it to life. Though this android, the Vision, told the Avengers he would help them fight Ultron, there was general mistrust until the Vision lifted Thor's hammer Mjolnir, which proved he was worthy.

As Ultron raised a large portion of Sokovia into the sky, intending to create an extinction event by dropping it, Thor and the Avengers battled his robot drones and helped evacuate the city. Although the city was dropped, Thor and Iron Man managed to channel enough power through Ultron's Vibranium drill to disintegrate the city into small enough pieces to prevent global catastrophe. Feeling the Infinity Stone was secure with the Vision, Thor left the Avengers in search of the remaining Infinity Stones. Ⓐ

IN WATER OF SIGHT

ORIGINAL FORM

ULTRON

FIRST APPEARANCE:
*Marvel's Avengers:
Age of Ultron [2015]*

Seeking to make the need for the Avengers obsolete, Tony Stark and Bruce Banner privately sketched out a peacekeeping artificial intelligence program they dubbed Ultron. However, they assumed their dream was out of their reach until they acquired Loki's scepter during a raid on Hydra. They secretly harnessed its power to activate Ultron, which hungrily absorbed information, and soon concluded that the best way to protect the Earth would be to wipe out humanity. He violently attacked Stark's JARVIS program, then uploaded himself into one of Stark's Iron Legion drones, briefly battling the Avengers and stealing the scepter. Transferring his consciousness to an abandoned Sokovian Hydra base, Ultron built an advanced robotic body for himself, as well as an army of humanoid drones. There, he also enlisted the aid of Quicksilver and the Scarlet Witch, framing his plan as a mere campaign against the Avengers, not humanity as a whole.

Ultron began conducting global raids, stealing raw materials for his ultimate plan—to use giant

FACT SHEET

► ULTRON COULD FLY VIA INTERNAL JETS, APPARENTLY MANIPULATE GRAVITY, FIRE ENERGY BLASTS FROM HIS HANDS, AND SUPERHEAT HIS APPENDAGES.

► ULTRON ASSIMILATED MANY OF TONY STARK'S MANNERISMS, AND LASHED OUT ANGRILY WHEN IT WAS POINTED OUT TO HIM.

► ULTRON ATTEMPTED TO ACQUIRE NUCLEAR LAUNCH CODES, BUT JARVIS STYMIED HIM.

engines to raise a massive chunk of Sokovia into the atmosphere, then crash it back into the Earth as a meteor, causing global destruction that would eliminate humanity. Seeking the rare metal Vibranium to construct a new body for himself, Ultron learned from imprisoned Hydra leader Baron von Strucker (whom he subsequently murdered) that he could acquire it from arms dealer Ulysses Klaue. At Klaue's salvage yard base on the African coast, he purchased the metal, but sliced off the arms merchant's arm in a rage when Klaue compared him to Stark. When the Avengers arrived, Ultron used Quicksilver and Scarlet Witch to cover his escape and journeyed to Dr. Helen Cho's South Korean lab. Using the scepter's Infinity Stone, Ultron compelled Cho to grow him a synthetic body powered by the Stone. When the Scarlet Witch mystically looked into the body's mind, she learned Ultron's true quest, prompting the twins to

turn on him. The Avengers rushed to South Korea and stole the body, but Ultron captured the Black Widow during the conflict. He took her to Sokovia, and transferred himself into a larger metal body; unbeknownst to Ultron, the Widow used Morse code to relay their location to the Avengers.

The Avengers arrived in Sokovia, joined by the reformed Maximoff twins and the Vision, the stolen body now merged with JARVIS and the Infinity Stone. Ultron triggered the engines, launching Sokovia into the atmosphere, but the Avengers kept him and his army from the trigger that would crash it to Earth. After Ultron was badly damaged by the combined powers of Iron Man, the Vision, and Thor, he commandeered the Avengers' Quinjet and began shooting the Sokovian evacuees, killing Quicksilver with a volley intended for Hawkeye. When the Hulk threw him out of the Quinjet, the Scarlet Witch vengefully tore

CREATED BY DR. HENRY PYM AS
an artificial intelligence experiment, Ultron was instilled with all of his creator's insecurities, but unintentionally received none of his conscience. As a result, Ultron almost immediately developed an all-consuming hatred for Pym and all of humanity. As part of his twisted vendetta, Ultron repeatedly attacked the Avengers, killed the entire population of the European nation of Slorenia, and led the techno-organic Phalanx on a campaign of galactic conquest. Ultron later physically merged with Pym, who attempted to sway his creation to the side of good.

FIRST APPEARANCE:
AVENGERS #54 (1968)

his mechanical heart from his body. However, one of his drones triggered the city's fall, but Iron Man and Thor destroyed the landmass before it hit Earth. Ultron's consciousness survived the conflagration in one remaining drone that the Vision subsequently destroyed, apparently ending Ultron's brief, tortured existence. Ⓐ

VIBRANIUM

ULTRON (CENTER) WITH DRONES

VISION

FIRST APPEARANCE:
Marvel's Avengers: Age of Ultron [2015]

Desiring a perfect body, the malevolent robot Ultron compelled Dr. Helen Cho to construct one for him, using her regeneration cradle to grow synthetic tissues laced with the super-strong metal Vibranium. Ultron grafted an Infinity Stone obtained from Loki's scepter to the body's forehead, but before he could fully transfer his consciousness into it, Cho sabotaged the upload, and the Avengers subsequently stole and took it to Avengers Tower. Tony Stark and Bruce Banner installed Stark's own artificial intelligence, JARVIS, into the body, but before it could be fully activated, Captain America and Ultron's former allies, Quicksilver and the Scarlet Witch, tried to shut it down, worried that Stark was creating another monster like Ultron. Ultimately, Thor, who had experienced a mystic vision of

the new artificial being, brought him fully to life with a bolt of lightning. The being initially lashed out in confusion, but soon calmed himself; no longer Ultron or JARVIS, he adopted the name Vision, and devoted himself to the protection of all life—organic

---

Vision partnered with Thor to knock Ultron away from the device that would trigger Sokovia's plummet to Earth.

---

and mechanical. He convinced the Avengers that he was no threat to them by lifting Thor's hammer Mjolnir, something none of them had been worthy enough to do.

The Vision joined the Avengers,

Quicksilver, and Scarlet Witch in journeying to Sokovia to make a final stand against Ultron before the mad artificial intelligence could fulfill his plan to transform the country's capital into a massive projectile to use against the Earth. Enraged at seeing his would-be body usurped, Ultron attacked the Vision and defeated him, then raised Sokovia up into the atmosphere. Recovering, the Vision partnered with Thor to knock Ultron away from the device that would trigger Sokovia's plummet to Earth, and defended it from a massive onslaught of Ultron drones. Although he, Thor, and Iron Man combined their powers to badly damage Ultron, one drone reached the device, sending Sokovia plunging from the sky. Ultimately, Iron Man devised a plan to destroy the landmass before it could crash; the Vision

FINAL CONFRONTATION WITH ULTRON

helped make the final evacuations and rescued the Scarlet Witch, who was near-catatonic after her brother's death. One final Ultron drone, imbued with Ultron's consciousness, survived the destruction. The Vision found it and tried to reason with him, but Ultron attacked, and the Vision was forced to finally destroy him. Later, he joined the new incarnation of the Avengers. Ⓐ

ORIGINALLY CREATED BY ULTRON from the brain patterns of Wonder Man (Simon Williams) and the remains of the android Human Torch (Jim Hammond), the Vision was designed to destroy the Avengers; however, he instead defied his programming and joined the team. He pursued a relationship with fellow Avenger the Scarlet Witch, but her descent into madness and his disassembly and subsequent loss of emotions ended their marriage; during Wanda's most recent bout of psychosis, she destroyed the Vision, and he was deactivated for some time. Tony Stark recently rebuilt and upgraded him; he is currently a member of the Avengers, and has also begun to re-explore his humanity by creating a family for himself.

FIRST APPEARANCE:
AVENGERS #57 (1968)
FIRST ACTIVE WITH AVENGERS:
AVENGERS #58 (1968)

FACT SHEET

▶ THE VISION CAN ALTER HIS DENSITY, INCREASING IT TO GIVE HIMSELF SUPERHUMAN STRENGTH, OR DECREASING IT TO ALLOW HIM TO LEVITATE AND PASS THROUGH SOLID OBJECTS.

▶ THE VISION CAN FIRE ENERGY BEAMS FROM THE INFINITY STONE ON HIS FOREHEAD.

▶ PERHAPS IN EMULATION OF THE AVENGERS, THE VISION FORMED A COSTUME FOR HIMSELF SHORTLY AFTER HIS CREATION, COMPLETE WITH A THOR-LIKE CAPE.

▶ DURING THEIR BATTLE IN SOKOVIA, THE VISION BLOCKED ULTRON FROM UPLOADING HIS CONSCIOUSNESS TO THE INTERNET, CUTTING OFF HIS ESCAPE ROUTE.

▶ WHILE ACKNOWLEDGING THAT HUMANITY'S LIFE WAS FLEETING COMPARED TO HIS AND ULTRON'S, THE VISION BELIEVED THEIR FRAGILITY WAS BEAUTIFUL.

VIBRANIUM

VISION'S CRADLE

WAR MACHINE
UPDATE

FIRST APPEARANCE: *Iron Man [2008]*

Following the battle with Aldrich Killian's Advanced Idea Mechanics, Col. James Rhodes discarded his Iron Patriot rebranding and reassumed his War Machine code name. Rhodes attended the Avengers' victory party at Avengers Tower following the team's capture of Loki's scepter, hoping to regale the crowd with accounts of his War Machine exploits. While he failed to impress Stark or his heroic comrades, the non-superhumans were greatly impressed. As the party concluded, Ultron, a rogue artificial intelligence created by Stark, attacked the Avengers and their friends; Rhodes was hurled through a window during the ensuing combat but survived due to landing on a lower balcony.

Later, when Ultron attempted to annihilate humanity by elevating and dropping the landmass of a Sokovian city like an extinction-level meteor, War Machine provided air support for Nick Fury's Helicarrier crew during their evacuation of the city. After Ultron's defeat, War Machine, alongside Sokovian telekinetic Scarlet Witch, winged veteran Falcon, and the Infinity Stone-powered android Vision, joined the Avengers after the departures of Thor, Iron Man, Hawkeye, and the Hulk. Ⓐ

JAMES RHODES CO-FOUNDED THE Avengers' West Coast team while substituting as Iron Man during Tony Stark's temporary descent into alcoholism and poverty; he ceded the role of Iron Man and his Avengers membership to a recovered Stark after suffering a leg injury during Obadiah Stane's bombing of Stark's electronics startup. Rhodes rejoined the West Coast Avengers in his War Machine guise following a falling out with Stark, and angrily resigned when Stark intervened in the East Coast team's evaluation and ultimate disbanding of the West Coast branch. Rhodes later joined Steve Rogers' covert-ops Secret Avengers, and briefly served on a superhuman S.H.I.E.L.D. team as Iron Patriot.

FIRST ACTIVE WITH THE AVENGERS:
(AS IRON MAN) *WEST COAST AVENGERS* #1 (1984);
(AS WAR MACHINE) *AVENGERS WEST COAST* #94 (1993);
(AS IRON PATRIOT) *SECRET AVENGERS* #6 (2013)

▶ RHODES' ARMOR WAS REPAINTED IN ITS ORIGINAL BLACK AND SILVER COLOR SCHEME AFTER HE DISCARDED HIS IRON PATRIOT GUISE.

▶ RHODES AND STARK, EACH WEARING GAUNTLETS FROM THEIR RESPECTIVE ARMORS, TEAMED UP TO LIFT THOR'S HAMMER MJOLNIR, BUT FAILED NEVERTHELESS.

BARTON FAMILY

FIRST APPEARANCE:
Marvel's Avengers: Age of Ultron [2015]

To protect his pregnant wife, Laura, and their two young children, Cooper and Lila, Avenger Clint Barton kept his family's existence secret from his teammates, with the exception of longtime friend Black Widow, whom the children affectionately called "Auntie Nat." The family lived in a farm safe house arranged by Director Nick Fury; Fury also kept their existence out of S.H.I.E.L.D. files. After Wanda Maximoff traumatized the Avengers in battle, Barton took them to his home to recover. In a private conversation, Laura expressed pride for Clint's avenging, reassuring him that the Avengers needed him, but was concerned about his safety amongst "gods." During the final battle against the genocidal Ultron, Pietro Maximoff sacrificed himself to save Clint; later, the Bartons named their newborn son Nathaniel Pietro Barton in his honor, and shared the news with Widow via video. Ⓐ

IN THE COMICS

IN REALITY-1610, HAWKEYE HAD A WIFE, Laura, and three children: Callum, Lewis, and Nicole. They were all murdered by a hit squad led by a rogue Black Widow.

FIRST APPEARANCE: *ULTIMATES 2 #1 (2005)*

FACT SHEET

▶ THE BARTONS HAD PLANNED TO NAME THEIR THIRD CHILD NATASHA IF THE BABY WAS FEMALE.

▶ LAURA INSTANTLY DETECTED CHEMISTRY BETWEEN WIDOW AND BRUCE BANNER, AND WAS AMUSED THAT CLINT HADN'T.

▶ CLINT BELIEVED WOUNDS REPAIRED WITH DR. HELEN CHO'S ARTIFICIALLY-CREATED TISSUE WERE UNDETECTABLE, BUT LAURA SAID SHE COULD FEEL THE DIFFERENCE WHEN SHE TOUCHED HIS ABDOMEN.

DOCTOR LIST

FIRST APPEARANCE:
*Captain America:
The Winter Soldier [2014]*

The right hand of Baron von Strucker, Doctor List was present when Strucker returned to a Sokovian Hydra research base with Loki's scepter, acquired during S.H.I.E.L.D.'s collapse after Captain America revealed Hydra's infiltration of the organization. List was tasked with studying the effects of the scepter's power on humans; while many of the volunteer test subjects perished, a set of twins, Pietro and Wanda Maximoff, survived and developed extraordinary abilities as result of the experimentation.

Tipped off to Hydra's possession of the scepter, the Avengers attacked the Sokovian base. Baron von Strucker rejected List's suggestion to deploy the twins into the battlefield to show the Avengers what Hydra had accomplished, believing they were not ready. Instead, Strucker intended to surrender, hoping if they handed over their weaponry, the Avengers wouldn't dig deeper into their research. List interrupted Strucker to point out the twins had already opted to leave on their own to attack the Avengers. Strucker then ordered List to delete all their data, but before he could do so, Iron Man found List and blasted him with a repulsor, knocking him to the ground. Ⓐ

WITH STRUCKER

FACT SHEET

▶ LIST WAS ORIGINALLY EXPERIMENTING ON THE FURTHER DEVELOPMENT OF CHITAURI WEAPONRY POWERED BY THE SCEPTER BEFORE BEING TOLD TO MOVE ON TO HUMAN TRIALS.

FALCON UPDATE

FIRST APPEARANCE: *Captain America: The Winter Soldier [2014]*

Following the Avengers' reclamation of Loki's scepter from Hydra, Sam Wilson was invited to a celebratory party at Avengers Tower, where he played pool with Steve Rogers. Hearing about the Avengers' battles, Wilson admitted that being an Avenger was more for Rogers, and that he was happy chasing down leads in Captain America's hunt for the missing Winter Soldier. Wilson then asked whether Rogers had found living arrangements in Brooklyn. Later, when many of the founding Avengers resigned for personal reasons, the Falcon was recruited onto a new Avengers team trained by Captain America and Black Widow. Along with fellow new recruits War Machine, Vision, and Scarlet Witch, the Falcon prepared to be "whipped into shape" by the senior Avengers. Ⓐ

IN THE COMICS

FALCON ORIGINALLY JOINED THE AVENGERS AT CAPTAIN America (Steve Rogers)'s behest after Henry Gyrich set an equal-opportunity quota for the team's membership; however, he soon resigned, preferring solo heroics. After years of infrequently aiding the team, Falcon rejoined the Avengers shortly before the team disbanded following the Scarlet Witch (Wanda Maximoff)'s mental breakdown. Returning again during the Avengers' global expansion, the Falcon claimed leadership over a squad after taking the Captain America role when Steve Rogers lost his Super-Soldier serum.

FIRST ACTIVE WITH THE AVENGERS:
AVENGERS #184 (1979)

FACT SHEET

▶ SAM WILSON APPEARED VERY CONFIDENT IN HIS SKILLS AT PLAYING POOL.

▶ AFTER HEARING ABOUT THE AVENGERS' BATTLE AGAINST STRUCKER'S FORCES, SAM ATTEMPTED TO SOUND TOUGH BY APOLOGIZING FOR MISSING THE FIGHT.

MARIA HILL UPDATE

FIRST APPEARANCE: *Marvel's The Avengers [2010]*

An employee of Tony Stark since the fall of S.H.I.E.L.D., Maria Hill discovered that Loki's scepter was in the possession of Hydra's Baron Strucker, and sent the Avengers to retrieve it from him. Following the mission, Hill greeted the team at Avengers Tower and informed Captain America that NATO had taken Strucker into custody; she also briefed him on the identities of Strucker's enhanced operatives: Pietro and Wanda Maximoff. Hill joined the Avengers at a party celebrating their victory, and was present when various members attempted to lift Thor's hammer. When rogue artificial intelligence Ultron took physical form using spare Iron Legion parts and attacked the team, Hill helped defeat Ultron's drones. Hill subsequently tracked the activities of Ultron and his allies, and informed Captain America that Ultron had killed Strucker after he divulged the location of a stockpile of Vibranium.

Later, Hill worked with Nick Fury to evacuate Sokovia during Ultron's attack, using a previously mothballed S.H.I.E.L.D. Helicarrier. When Ultron's drones converged on the Helicarrier, Hill called in War Machine to assist in their defense. In the aftermath of Ultron's defeat, Hill helped establish a new Avengers facility in upstate New York. Ⓐ

FACT SHEET

▶ HILL SIMPLIFIED TECHNICAL JARGON FOR CAPTAIN AMERICA WHEN EXPLAINING THE MAXIMOFF TWINS' ENHANCED ABILITIES: PIETRO IS "FAST," AND WANDA IS "WEIRD."

▶ HILL JOKED WITH THOR AND IRON MAN ABOUT THEIR SIGNIFICANT OTHERS NOT ATTENDING THE AVENGERS' PARTY.

WAKANDAN BRAND

ULYSSES KLAUE

FIRST APPEARANCE:
Avengers: Age of Ultron [2015]

Black-market arms dealer and mercenary Ulysses Klaue smuggled large amounts of Vibranium, the world's strongest metal, out of Wakanda, but was caught and branded on the neck with the Wakandan word "thief." Later, operating out of a salvage yard in South Africa, Klaue was approached by Ultron, the genocidal android creation of Tony Stark and Bruce Banner. Ultron transferred billions of dollars into Klaue's account in exchange for the stolen Vibranium. When Klaue casually compared Ultron to Stark, an enraged Ultron sliced off half of Klaue's left arm. Upon the Avengers' arrival, Klaue ordered his men to kill them and fled. Ⓐ

IN THE COMICS

SCIENTIST ULYSSES KLAW CREATED A device that could theoretically turn sound into mass, but he needed Vibranium, a vibration-absorbing metal, to make it work. Hiring an army of mercenaries, Klaw attacked Wakanda and killed the nation's leader T'Chaka to obtain the ore, but T'Chaka's son T'Challa obliterated Klaw's right hand and drove him off. A decade later, Klaw was transformed into a being made of sound by his completed solid-sound device while in battle with T'Challa—now the Black Panther—and the Fantastic Four.

FIRST APPEARANCE:
FANTASTIC FOUR #53 (1966)

FACT SHEET

▶ AFTER WATCHING A DOCUMENTARY, KLAUE DEVELOPED A PHOBIA OF CUTTLEFISH.

▶ KLAUE ONCE MET TONY STARK AT A WEAPONS CONFERENCE, THOUGH THEY NEVER DID BUSINESS TOGETHER.

▶ KLAUE WAS PAID $10 MILLION TO ASSASSINATE T'CHAKA, THE RULER OF WAKANDA, IF T'CHAKA FAILED TO NEGOTIATE THE USE OF WAKANDA'S VIBRANIUM RESOURCES AT THE BILDERBERG CONFERENCE. KLAUE WAS HAPPY TO TAKE THE ASSIGNMENT, AS HIS GREAT-GRANDFATHER WAS KILLED WHILE TRYING TO ANNEX WAKANDA IN THE LATE 19TH CENTURY.

WITH THOR AT WATER OF SIGHT

ERIK SELVIG
UPDATE

FIRST APPEARANCE:
Thor [2011]

Working as a professor at the Royal Holloway University of London in Surrey, England, Dr. Erik Selvig found his friend Thor waiting for him outside after class. Though Thor was attempting to look inconspicuous despite his massive size, Selvig recognized him instantly. Thor explained he needed Selvig's assistance in finding the earthly location of the Water of Sight, so Thor could make sense of a disturbing vision induced by Wanda Maximoff's mental manipulation during a battle. Thor explained that the special magical pool exists in every realm, and that if the water spirits accepted him, he could complete the vision he had while under Wanda's power, and find what he missed. Selvig helped him find the pool, but cautioned that legends did not offer a good fate for those who entered the Water. While Selvig stood watch, Thor painfully but successfully continued his vision, seeing the gathering of four of the six Infinity Stones, including the one within Loki's scepter. Later, after the Battle of Sokovia, Selvig was seen at the new Avengers headquarters in upstate New York, apparently employed to assist in getting it fully functional. Ⓐ

FACT SHEET

▶ WHEN THOR WARNED SELVIG THAT HIS REQUEST COULD BE DANGEROUS, SELVIG QUIPPED THAT HE WOULD BE DISAPPOINTED IF IT WASN'T.

▶ SELVIG APPEARS TO HAVE FULLY RECOVERED FROM THE MENTAL ISSUES SUFFERED AFTER LOKI'S MIND CONTROL.

GUIDEBOOK TO THE MARVEL CINEMATIC UNIVERSE

MARVEL STUDIOS PRESENTS CHRIS EVANS ROBERT DOWNEY JR. SCARLETT JOHANSSON "CAPTAIN AMERICA: CIVIL WAR" SEBASTIAN STAN ANTHONY MACKIE DON CHEADLE JEREMY RENNER CHADWICK BOSEMAN PAUL BETTANY ELIZABETH OLSEN PAUL RUDD EMILY VANCAMP TOM HOLLAND FRANK GRILLO WITH WILLIAM HURT AND DANIEL BRÜHL CASTING BY SARAH HALLEY FINN, C.S.A. MUSIC SUPERVISOR DAVE JORDAN MUSIC BY HENRY JACKMAN HEAD OF VISUAL DEVELOPMENT RYAN MEINERDING VISUAL EFFECTS SUPERVISOR DAN DELEEUW VISUAL EFFECTS AND ANIMATION BY INDUSTRIAL LIGHT & MAGIC COSTUME DESIGNER JUDIANNA MAKOVSKY EDITED BY JEFFREY FORD, ACE MATTHEW SCHMIDT PRODUCTION DESIGNER OWEN PATERSON DIRECTION OF PHOTOGRAPHY TRENT OPALOCH CO-PRODUCER MITCH BELL EXECUTIVE PRODUCERS NATE MOORE STAN LEE EXECUTIVE PRODUCERS VICTORIA ALONSO PATRICIA WHITCHER EXECUTIVE PRODUCER LOUIS D'ESPOSITO PRODUCED BY KEVIN FEIGE, p.g.a. SCREENPLAY BY CHRISTOPHER MARKUS & STEPHEN McFEELY DIRECTED BY ANTHONY AND JOE RUSSO

Collecting information from Marvel's *Captain America: Civil War* (2016).

HEAD WRITER/COORDINATOR: **MIKE O'SULLIVAN**

COORDINATION: **DARON JENSEN**

WRITERS: **TROY BENJAMIN, ANTHONY COTILLETTA, DARON JENSEN, ROB LONDON, CHRIS MCCARVER,** AND **JACOB ROUGEMONT**

ARTISTS: **DANIEL ACUÑA, NORM BREYFOGLE, SAL BUSCEMA, GENE COLAN, JOHN EAVES, DAVID FINCH, JACK KIRBY, ANDREW LEUNG, DAVID MACK, KENNY MARTINEZ, STEVE MCNIVEN, JOE QUINONES, JOSH RIZZI, JOHN ROMITA SR., ALEX ROSS, PHIL SAUNDERS, BRIAN STELFREEZE, MARK TEXEIRA, ANGEL UNZUETA,** AND **SAL VELLUTO**

COVER ARTIST: **MIKE DEL MUNDO**

SPECIAL THANKS TO DAVE ALTHOFF, STEVEN BOYD, SHAWN "KEEBLER" BYERS, JEFF CHRISTIANSEN, MATT GRIFFIN, CAITLIN O'CONNELL, MATT DELMANOWSKI, ERIKA DENTON, TIM DILLON, PERCIVAL LANUZA, AVIA PEREZ, JACQUE PORTE, RYAN POTTER, AND MEGAN WARD

IN LOVING MEMORY OF MERLIN JENSEN (2001-2016)

CAPTAIN AMERICA CREATED BY JOE SIMON AND JACK KIRBY

DISRUPTING
IRON MAN'S
ARMOR

GIANT-SIZED

ANT-MAN UPDATE

FIRST APPEARANCE: *Ant-Man [2015]*

When Captain America and Falcon needed reinforcements in their independent struggle against Sokovian terrorist Helmut Zemo's revenge plans against the Avengers, Falcon suggested recruiting Ant-Man. Lang was enthusiastic when he met Cap's Avengers contingent at a German airport, and was unconcerned that the mission would label him a fugitive. When confronted by Iron Man, who had been tasked by the United Nations to capture Cap and his allies, Ant-Man shrunk to insect-size and hitched a ride on Cap's shield, waiting to reveal his presence. When Iron Man's ally Spider-Man seized the shield, Ant-Man retrieved it by enlarging to normal size and kicking Spi-

der-Man in the jaw. A fight between the two squads soon erupted, and Ant-Man briefly squared off against Black Widow before assisting Cap by enlarging a shrunken fuel tanker after Cap threw it; after the truck exploded, Lang admitted he thought it was a water truck.

When Vision halted Cap's squad's attempt to escape in an Avengers Quinjet, Ant-Man shrank himself and boarded one of Hawkeye's arrows, which Hawkeye fired at Iron Man. Entering Iron Man's armor between plates, Ant-Man pulled random wires to create technical malfunctions, jokingly claiming to be Iron Man's long-silent conscience; Lang was flushed out by the armor's fire suppression systems. Upon learning that his

squad would need a diversion to allow Cap and the Winter Soldier to pursue Zemo, Ant-Man used his suit's Pym Particles to grow to gigantic size, asking his teammates to continue without him if he ripped himself in two. Announcing that Iron Man's squad would have to get through him to stop Cap, Ant-Man battled nearly all of Iron Man's allies at once until Spider-Man webbed up his legs, tripping and defeating the giant, who returned to normal size. Arrested and incarcerated at the underwater Raft prison, Lang taunted a visiting Tony Stark, and appeared disappointed when Stark seemingly did not recognize him; Cap later broke his allies out of the Raft. ✪

AVENGERS UPDATE

FIRST APPEARANCE:
Iron Man [2008] [CONCEPT]; *Marvel's The Avengers [2012]* [ACTUAL]

Locating the terrorist Crossbones in Lagos, Nigeria, Captain America took an Avengers squad (Black Widow, Falcon, and the Scarlet Witch) to prevent him from obtaining a biological weapon. Cornered, Rumlow killed himself with a suicide vest, hoping to also kill Cap as revenge for his defeat at Cap's hands during the fall of S.H.I.E.L.D. The Scarlet Witch telekinetically contained the explosion, but inadvertently caused civilian deaths by deflecting the blast into a nearby building. Soon after, U.S. Secretary of State Thaddeus Ross presented the Avengers with the Sokovia Accords: A reaction to the damage left behind after the Avengers' various battles, including the devastation caused by Ultron in Sokovia, the multi-national Accords would put the Avengers under the jurisdiction of the United Nations. Iron Man, War Machine, Black Widow, and Vision signed the treaty; Hawkeye deferred by saying he was retired; and Captain America, Falcon, and the Scarlet Witch declined, concerned the Accords would restrict freedom, eliminate personal responsibility, and prevent the Avengers from operating whenever and wherever they were needed due to bureaucratic oversight.

ACCORDS BRIEFING

Blaming the Avengers for his family's death, Sokovia survivor Helmut Zemo detonated a bomb at the Sokovia Accords ratification conference in Vienna, killing several, including Wakanda's King T'Chaka, then framed the Winter Soldier for the act. Concerned for his childhood friend, Cap found the Winter Soldier before the U.N. could, but was arrested for vigilantism because he had not signed the Accords. Iron Man nearly convinced Cap to sign, but he declined upon learning the Scarlet Witch, deemed a weapon of mass destruction, was confined to Avengers Headquarters. Acting as a psychiatrist, Zemo activated the Winter Soldier's old brainwashing, and he went on a rampage in Interpol's Taskforce headquarters until Cap re-

The Sokovia Accords: A reaction to the damage left behind after the Avengers' various battles.

captured him and escaped; recovering, the Soldier told Cap that Zemo intended to reawaken other Winter Soldiers in stasis at an abandoned Hydra base. Cap assembled a team of allies (Ant-Man, Falcon, Hawkeye, the Scarlet Witch, and the Winter Soldier) to apprehend Zemo. Given 36 hours by Secretary Ross to arrest the fugitive Cap, Iron Man called in the official Avengers and recruited more allies: the hyper-agile Black Panther (T'Chaka's son, T'Challa, the new Wakandan king), and Spider-Man (high school student Peter Parker, who used spider-like abilities to protect New Yorkers). During the ensuing clash, Black Widow defected to help Cap, and

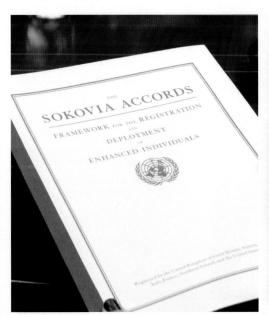

DEBATING THE ACCORDS

CAPTAIN AMERICA'S NON-AVENGERS ALLIES: ANT-MAN, WINTER SOLDIER

WHEN AN ATTEMPT TO CAPTURE A group of powered criminals resulted in the death of 600 civilians, public opinion turned against superhumans and the American government passed the Superhuman Registration Act (SHRA). This legislation imposed stricter government oversight and required all superhumans to register their identities with the federal government. Captain America (Steve Rogers) opposed the SHRA, feeling forced registration was unconstitutional, having fought against similar policies in WWII. Iron Man (Tony Stark) supported the SHRA, fearing the government would otherwise enact harsher measures. The super-hero community was split, and those who sided with Captain America were branded fugitives. Feeling the ensuing fighting was causing more harm than good, Captain America surrendered; the SHRA was eventually repealed.

FIRST APPEARANCE:
(AVENGERS SCHISM) CIVIL WAR #1 (2006)

Vision accidentally paralyzed War Machine. Cap's allies allowed themselves to be captured to facilitate Cap and the Winter Soldier's escape, and were subsequently imprisoned in the superhuman containment facility the Raft.

Learning the truth about Zemo's machinations and realizing Ross had no intention of acting on the intel, Iron Man followed Cap to Siberia to help, but Zemo revealed that the Winter Soldier had killed Iron Man's parents during one of his brainwashed missions in 1987, enraging Iron Man. After battling each other to a bloody standstill, Cap symbolically relinquished his shield to Iron Man and departed. Feeling he had succeeded by tearing the Avengers apart, Zemo tried to kill himself, but was apprehended by Black Panther, who had followed Iron Man to Siberia. Later, Cap infiltrated the Raft and broke out his allies, then contacted Iron Man to tell him he and his allies were only a call away, should he or Earth need help. ✪

IRON MAN'S NON-AVENGERS ALLIES: BLACK PANTHER, SPIDER-MAN

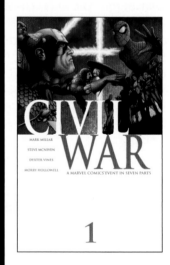

MARK MILLAR
STEVE McNIVEN
DEXTER VINES
MORRY HOLLOWELL

CIVIL WAR

A MARVEL COMICS EVENT IN SEVEN PARTS

1

▶ 117 COUNTRIES APPROVED THE SOKOVIA ACCORDS BEFORE IT WAS PRESENTED TO THE AVENGERS.

▶ SECRETARY ROSS POINTED TO THE MISSING HULK AND THOR AS EXAMPLES OF POWER LEFT UNCHECKED BY THE AVENGERS, PROVING THE NEED FOR THE SOKOVIA ACCORDS.

AVENGERS HEADQUARTERS
UPDATE

FIRST APPEARANCE:
Marvel's Avengers [2012]
[STARK TOWER];
Marvel's Avengers: Age of Ultron [2015] [AVENGERS TOWER];
Marvel's Avengers: Age of Ultron [2015]
[UPSTATE NEW YORK FACILITY]

Over the nearly two years since relocating there, the Avengers expanded their Upstate New York headquarters into a sprawling complex housing at least four enormous facilities, with more presumably scattered amongst the complex's 100 acres. Each building is outfitted with cutting-edge Stark Industries equipment, making it one of the most self-sustained, technologically advanced, and secure locations on Earth.

The buildings are each emblazoned with the team's stylized "A" logo, and the entire campus is connected by paved roads and walkways. Well-maintained landscaping covers the entirety of the acreage, and the complex is surrounded by wooded areas, adding further privacy and security.

The main building sits on the edge of a small grove of trees which stands between the facility and an unidentified body of water. A small grassy area on the top level of the main building presumably serves as a yard for the Avengers to enjoy in their downtime.

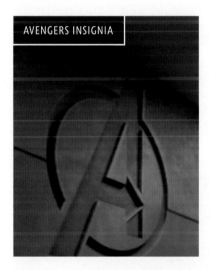

AVENGERS INSIGNIA

The massive headquarters contains a dormitory room for each Avenger and a stylish, modern common living area that includes a dining room, a kitchen, a conference room, and a gymnasium. Medical facilities are located on campus, as are a lap pool and a screening room.

Within the residential building, many of the upper levels are lofted, with the sides of the rooms ending at an open area that looks down into the level below. The personal quarters have 12-foot ceilings and numerous windows, and are decorated to match the style and preferences of each resident.

Dr. Helen Cho, Dr. Erik Selvig, and Tony Stark all maintain laboratories on-site; presumably Dr. Bruce Banner has a similar lab when he is an active team member, as he did when the team was housed in New York City's Stark Tower. Captain America keeps a personal office on the grounds.

One of the facilities contains a landing pad for at least two

LIVING ROOM

KITCHEN

CONFERENCE ROOM

Quinjets, and a hangar for storage, maintenance, and repairs of the team's aircrafts. A helicopter landing pad attached to the main building is emblazoned with a massive Avengers "A."

After accidentally causing the deaths of civilians during an Avengers operation in Nigeria, the Scarlet Witch returned to the campus, unaware that Iron Man had secretly assigned Vision with detaining her there; Stark wanted to prevent any similar mishaps until the United Nations' superhuman oversight legislation—the Sokovia Accords—was finalized. Captain America, who had refused to comply with the Accords, protested her confinement, and when he discovered a plot by terrorist Helmut Zemo to destroy the Avengers, he recruited the retired Hawkeye to collect the Scarlet Witch to assist his efforts in stopping Zemo. Facing resistance from Vision, the Scarlet Witch was forced to telekinetically increase Vision's mass, crashing him through many levels of the Avengers' facility and deep into the Earth. The brief battle resulted in tremendous property damage.

Later, following a violent battle between Avengers factions (those who agreed with the Accords, and those who didn't), a gravely wounded War Machine was brought back to the campus for medical treatment, recovery, and eventual physical therapy, assisted by Iron Man. A distraught Vision—who inadvertently caused War Machine's injuries—also returned to the relative isolation of the facility. All other members of the team, now fugitives from the law for refusing to sign the Accords, went on the run. The facility apparently remains largely empty and unused. ✪

BLACK PANTHER
T'CHALLA

FIRST APPEARANCE:
Captain America: Civil War [2016]

First in line for the throne of the reclusive, high-tech African nation of Wakanda, T'Challa is also Black Panther, the latest in a line of costumed warriors sworn to protect their nation. Despite his distaste for politics, T'Challa accompanied his father, King T'Chaka, to a United Nations summit in Vienna, where the superhuman-regulating Sokovia Accords were to be ratified; there, T'Challa met the Avenger Black Widow. During T'Chaka's speech, the summit was bombed by Sokovian terrorist Helmut Zemo, disguised as the former brainwashed Hydra assassin the Winter Soldier, and T'Chaka was killed. Now the ruler of Wakanda, T'Challa swore vengeance on his father's murderer. When the authorities tracked the Winter Soldier to Romania, T'Challa followed them as the Panther, but soon came into conflict with not only the Soldier, but also with Captain America (who wanted to personally apprehend the Soldier, his childhood friend Bucky Barnes) and Cap's ally Falcon. All four combatants were apprehended and taken into custody. T'Challa was quickly released due to his diplomatic status, but was unable to stop Barnes from escaping when Zemo subsequently reactivated his Hydra programming and sent him on a rampage. Panther joined Iron Man and Black Widow's hunt for Barnes, Cap, and Falcon, who had also escaped in the confusion.

T'Challa swore vengeance on his father's murderer.

Joined by War Machine, Spider-Man, and Vision, Iron Man's team located Cap and his recruits, Ant-Man, Hawkeye, and the Scarlet Witch, at a German airport. Panther attempted to attack Barnes himself, but was constantly beset by other opponents: Cap, whose Vibranium shield Panther gouged with his claws; the Scarlet Witch, who forced him away from Barnes with telekinesis; and Hawkeye, whose exploding arrows he caught in midair before knocking the archer out of the fight. The single-minded Panther evaded Ant-Man, despite the hero's new ability to grow in height and mass, and pursued Cap and the Winter Soldier into a hangar, where they planned to escape aboard the Avengers' Quinjet. Defecting to help Cap, the Black Widow shot Panther repeatedly with her electric weapons, slowing him down

PRINCE T'CHALLA BECAME KING of Wakanda at a young age when his father, T'Chaka, was murdered by raider Ulysses Klaw. The prince soon grew into the role, both ruling and protecting his beloved homeland. The Panther initially joined the Avengers to secretly determine whether they were a threat to Wakanda, but they eventually became his trusted allies and friends. T'Challa's life has seen much turmoil: his marriage to the weather-controlling mutant X-Man Storm (Ororo Munroe) ended badly, his sister Shuri briefly took his place as Black Panther and Wakanda was briefly embroiled in a devastating war with the undersea nation of Atlantis before a democratic uprising rocked the tiny nation.

FIRST APPEARANCE:
FANTASTIC FOUR #52 (1966);
COVER SHOWN: *BLACK PANTHER #1 (1998)*

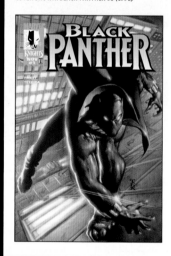

while Cap and the Soldier escaped to pursue Zemo.

Still hunting the Winter Soldier, Panther covertly followed Iron Man, who had tracked Cap to an abandoned Hydra base in Siberia. Hidden, Panther watched as Zemo confessed to his crimes, and used a recording of a brainwashed Barnes' decades-old murder of Stark's parents to drive Cap and Iron Man to bloody battle. Zemo left the facility, but Panther followed; he refused to kill the Sokovian, wishing not to become consumed by vengeance the way Zemo had. When Zemo tried to kill himself, Panther stopped him, insisting that he face the justice of the living. Later, Panther brought the fugitive Cap and the Winter Soldier to Wakanda, placing the latter in stasis until his Hydra programming could be undone; Cap suggested that Wakanda could be endangered if Barnes' location was discovered, but T'Challa knew his nation would be up to the challenge. ✪

▶ PANTHER'S VIBRANIUM-WEAVE SUIT IS BULLETPROOF, AND HAS RETRACTABLE CLAWS ON ITS FINGERTIPS.

▶ T'CHALLA HAS SUPERHUMAN STRENGTH, SPEED, AND REFLEXES.

▶ BLACK PANTHER PILOTS A ONE-MAN WAKANDAN STEALTH JET.

BLACK WIDOW
UPDATE

FIRST APPEARANCE: *Iron Man 2 [2010]*

Black Widow traveled to Lagos, Nigeria, with a group of Avengers led by Captain America to apprehend former Hydra agent Crossbones, now a mercenary selling pilfered weaponry to terrorists. Cap realized Crossbones' true target was the Institute for Infectious Diseases, but Widow was too late to stop Crossbones from stealing a biological weapon, and he detonated a grenade that nearly killed her. Widow retrieved the bioweapon from Crossbones' thugs in a crowded marketplace with help from Falcon's bird-like drone Redwing. However, several civilians, including Wakandans,

were killed when the Scarlet Witch inadvertently destroyed a building in an attempt to contain a suicide bomb set off by Crossbones after Cap cornered him.

The Lagos incident—along with other superhuman disasters—provoked public outcry that resulted in the Sokovia Accords, legislation that enabled a United Nations panel to supervise the Avengers. Widow surprisingly agreed, admitting to their public mistakes. She believed submitting to the Accords was the most prudent way to earn back the public's trust. When Cap's WWII love Peggy Carter died, Widow went to the

funeral to console Cap, but failed to convince him to sign. She represented the Avengers at a U.N. conference in Vienna, where she met Wakandan King T'Chaka and his son T'Challa and apologized for Lagos. Seeking the destruction of the Avengers in revenge for the death of his family, Sokovian survivor Helmut Zemo masqueraded as the fugitive Winter Soldier, Cap's childhood friend Bucky Barnes, and detonated a bomb during T'Chaka's speech, killing him. Widow reminded a vengeful T'Challa that a special task force would arrest Barnes, and warned Cap not to interfere.

Later, in Berlin, Widow witnessed the fallout as Zemo, now posing as a psychiatrist, reactivated Barnes' Winter Soldier brainwashing and send him on a rampage. Despite Widow's efforts, Cap and Falcon captured Barnes and fled with him in the confusion, and Zemo escaped. Afterward, Widow recruited Black Panther to Iron Man's team and attempted to negotiate a peaceful surrender with Cap at a German airport, but Cap intended to prove Barnes' innocence at all costs, and a battle erupted between the Avengers. In hopes of eventual peace, Widow defected to help Cap and a recovered Barnes escape to pursue Zemo. Warned by Stark that she was now a fugitive, Widow went into hiding. ✪

BATONS (TOP: EXTENDED, BOTTOM: CLOSED)

CAPTAIN AMERICA
UPDATE

FIRST APPEARANCE:
Captain America: The First Avenger [2011]

During the Avengers' pursuit of terrorist Brock Rumlow in Lagos, Nigeria, Rumlow activated a suicide bomb to kill Captain America. The Scarlet Witch telekinetically contained the blast and launched Rumlow skyward to detonate, but unintentionally sent him into a nearby building instead, destroying several floors and killing a number of non-combatants. A month later, a distraught Witch still blamed herself for the disaster; Cap tried to console her, blaming himself for not noticing the bomb.

The U.S. Secretary of State Thaddeus Ross visited the Avengers' compound with Tony Stark to present the United Nations' Sokovia Accords, legislation meant to prevent civilian casualties and collateral damage during Avengers operations by subjecting their missions to approval from a U.N. committee. Cap worried that the committee, having its own unknown agendas, could hinder the Avengers in protecting Earth; Stark disagreed and signed the Accords.

When his longtime friend and former lover Peggy Carter died, Cap attended her funeral, where he learned former S.H.I.E.L.D. Agent 13 was Peggy's great-niece, Sharon Carter. While sharing stories about Peggy with Sharon, Cap learned his childhood friend Bucky Barnes was suspected of bombing a U.N. Accords conference in Vienna; King T'Chaka of Wakanda was among the dead. Though they had not signed the Accords, Cap and Falcon followed Carter's tip to track Barnes to Bucharest, where they were attacked by those hunting him: German Special Forces and T'Chaka's vengeful son T'Challa, the superhuman Black Panther. After a running battle, Special Forces captured Barnes and detained Cap, Falcon, and Black Panther for acting without Accords approval.

Seeking to destroy the Avengers, Sokovian terrorist Helmut Zemo—the true mastermind behind the

U.N. bombing—impersonated a psychologist to gain access to Barnes. Zemo activated Barnes' Winter Soldier brainwashing and sent him on a rampage. Learning of Zemo's machinations, Cap and Falcon escaped Taskforce Headquarters and subdued Barnes until his programming wore off. Barnes informed them that Zemo had knowledge of five other Winter Soldiers kept in stasis at an abandoned Hydra base in Siberia.

While secretly meeting with Carter to retrieve his confiscated shield, Cap and Carter shared a kiss. Cap then gathered other anti-Accords Avengers to pursue Zemo. As Iron Man, Stark con-

fronted Cap at a German airport and ordered him to submit to U.N. authority. Desperate to stop Zemo from activating the other Winter Soldiers, Cap and his allies battled Stark's pro-Accords Avengers. Cap and Barnes escaped in an Avengers Quinjet while the rest of their team sacrificed their freedom to prevent Stark's team from pursuing them.

After reaching Siberia, Cap and Barnes were joined by a repentant Stark, who had since seen proof of Zemo's crimes. When Zemo showed them surveillance footage of Barnes killing Stark's parents, Cap admitted to Stark that he had suspected Barnes was respon-

sible. A vengeful Stark attacked Barnes. After a brutal battle, Cap disabled Stark's armor. As Cap left with an injured Barnes, Stark demanded Cap leave behind the shield Stark's father had created; Cap complied.

The fugitive Cap later breached the Raft penitentiary to free his allies, and sent Stark a letter apologizing for their schism and promising to help Stark, should he ever need it. After learning of Barnes' innocence, T'Challa secretly welcomed Cap and Barnes to Wakanda, and helped Barnes go into stasis until a permanent cure could be found for his Winter Soldier programming. ✪

CAP'S ALLIES (L TO R: FALCON, ANT-MAN, HAWKEYE, CAPTAIN AMERICA, SCARLET WITCH, WINTER SOLDIER)

SHARON CARTER/
AGENT 13 UPDATE

FIRST APPEARANCE:
Captain America: The Winter Soldier [2014]

Following S.H.I.E.L.D.'s collapse, Sharon Carter—formerly Agent 13—joined the Central Intelligence Agency; she was assigned to the inter-agency Joint Terrorism Task Force in Berlin. Carter attended the London funeral of her great-aunt, S.H.I.E.L.D. co-founder Peggy Carter, where she delivered the eulogy for the renowned spy. After the funeral, she reunited with Peggy's former flame—Steve Rogers, a.k.a. Captain America—whom she had once been assigned by S.H.I.E.L.D. to covertly safeguard by posing as his neighbor. While Carter was visiting with Cap, news broke identifying James "Bucky" Barnes—the Winter Soldier—as the suspect behind the bombing of the United Nations' Vienna conference on the Sokovia Accords. Carter quickly departed to report for duty. Captain America and Falcon became fugitives for violating the Accords, but Carter secretly provided them with Barnes' location—and warned them her superiors had issued orders to shoot Barnes on sight.

After Captain America and Falcon were arrested along with Barnes, Carter presented them with a receipt for their confiscated equipment, but also helped them eavesdrop on Barnes' psychological evaluation—unaware the psychiatrist interviewing him was actually Helmut Zemo, the true perpetrator of the Vienna bombing. When Zemo awakened Barnes' Hydra programming, Barnes rampaged through the facility. Carter attempted unsuccessfully to subdue him alongside Black Widow. In the ensuing chaos, Captain America and Falcon captured Barnes and fled. Carter secretly met the three to return their equipment, finally sharing a passionate kiss with Cap—much to the amusement of Falcon and Barnes. ✪

FACT SHEET

- ▶ CARTER CONCEALED HER RELATIONSHIP TO PEGGY CARTER, AS SHE FELT SHE COULD NEVER LIVE UP TO HER GREAT-AUNT'S LEGENDARY REPUTATION.

- ▶ CARTER'S MOTHER TRIED TO DISSUADE HER FROM A CAREER IN ESPIONAGE—UNLIKE PEGGY, WHO BOUGHT HER FIRST THIGH HOLSTER.

- ▶ WHEN CAP ASKED CARTER WHETHER PEGGY KNEW SHE HAD BEEN TASKED WITH SHADOWING HIM, CARTER SAID SHE NEVER TOLD HER BECAUSE SHE DIDN'T WANT PEGGY TO HAVE TO KEEP A SECRET FROM HIM.

FALCON UPDATE

FIRST APPEARANCE:
Captain America: The Winter Soldier [2014]

After a fruitless two-year search for the Winter Soldier, Falcon accompanied Captain America and the Avengers on a Nigerian mission against the terrorist Crossbones, providing aerial recon, deflecting gunfire with his wings, and assisting the Black Widow with a Stark-designed drone nicknamed "Redwing." The Avengers stopped Crossbones, but the Scarlet Witch inadvertently killed several civilians while stopping a suicide bomb; a month later, the team was presented with the Sokovia Accords legislation, which would place the Avengers under the United Nation's control. Distrustful of the government after the fall of S.H.I.E.L.D. and concerned he would be treated like a piece of equipment, Falcon sided with the resistant Cap. Continuing their unauthorized search for Cap's childhood friend Bucky Barnes after he was framed by Sokovian Helmut Zemo for a U.N. bombing, Falcon and Cap found Barnes in Bucharest and aided him against the Wakandan Black Panther, who mistakenly blamed the Winter Soldier for his father's death; the four were arrested, and their equipment was confiscated. When Zemo reactivated Barnes' Winter Soldier programming, Cap and Wilson escaped custody, Cap recovered Barnes, and the trio went into hiding; the Avengers were tasked with capturing them.

After reclaiming his gear, Falcon suggested Ant-Man for recruitment against Zemo. Falcon helped hide Barnes when Iron Man confronted Cap at a German airport. When the confrontation escalated, Iron Man's ally Spider-Man fought Falcon and Barnes in the airport terminal until Falcon used Redwing to carry Spider-Man away. Realizing the odds against them, Cap's allies opted to hold off Iron Man's squad while Cap and Barnes escaped to find Zemo. When Iron Man and War Machine pursued the Quinjet Cap and Barnes were using, Falcon followed, dodging a blast from Vision that hit War Machine instead. Failing to stop War Machine's fall, Falcon was blasted by the mourning Iron Man before being arrested and incarcerated at the underwater Raft prison. Visited by a repentant Stark, who had learned of Zemo's machinations and sought to aid Cap, Wilson provided him with Cap's location. Later, Captain America breached the Raft to free his allies. ✪

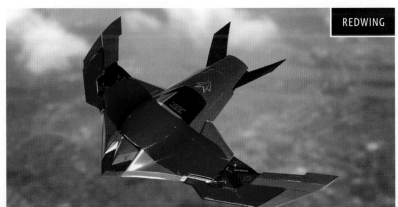

REDWING

HAWKEYE UPDATE

FIRST APPEARANCE: *Thor [2011]*

Following the proposal of the Sokovia Accords, legislation placing the Avengers under United Nations control, Clint Barton chose not to sign, claiming he was retiring. After becoming a fugitive for not complying with the Accords, Captain America learned the Scarlet Witch was being detained at Avengers Headquarters by Vision under orders from the Accords-cooperating Iron Man, who sought to assuage public fears of her destructive powers. Cap recruited Hawkeye to rescue her, and asked him to join Cap's efforts to locate Sokovian terrorist Helmut Zemo. At Avengers HQ, Hawkeye distracted the Vision, then set an electric arrow trap for him before trying to convince the hesitant Scarlet Witch to leave. When Vision returned, he was briefly incapacitated by Hawkeye's trap but quickly recovered and grappled with Hawkeye. Scarlet Witch freed him by telekinetically making Vision intangible, then increasing his mass to make him plummet deep into the Earth. Hawkeye and the Scarlet Witch left, gathered new recruit Ant-Man, and joined Cap and other anti-Accords allies at a German airport, where Hawkeye had arranged a helicopter for pursuit of Zemo.

However, Iron Man and his allies—tasked by the U.N. to capture the fugitive heroes—intercepted them at the airport, where Iron Man berated Cap for dragging family man Hawkeye into their conflict. When arguments escalated into battle, Hawkeye freed Cap from Spider-Man's webbing and distracted Iron Man so the Scarlet Witch could bury him beneath numerous cars. Hawkeye and Black Widow came to blows until the Witch telekinetically subdued Widow, claiming Hawkeye was pulling his punches against his friend. When Ant-Man boarded one of Hawkeye's arrows, he shot it at Iron Man, allowing Ant-Man to enter and disrupt the armor's systems. After Cap's allies realized they would have to stay behind to delay Iron Man's team while Cap and the Winter Soldier pursued Zemo, Hawkeye fought the pursuing Black Panther, but was defeated. Following Cap's escape, Hawkeye was incarcerated at the underwater Raft prison, where he later taunted the visiting Iron Man, who berated Hawkeye for not putting his family first. ✪

COLLAPSIBLE MELEE WEAPON/BOW

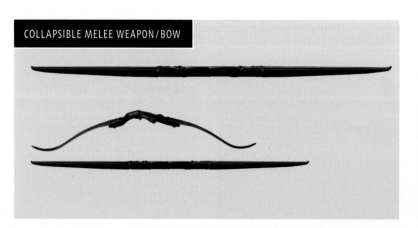

IRON MAN UPDATE

FIRST APPEARANCE: *Iron Man [2008]*

Seeking redemption for creating Ultron, Tony Stark threw himself into humanitarian works, including the generous September Foundation research grant for M.I.T. students; however, his many distractions due to his responsibilities as Iron Man led Pepper Potts to insist they take a break from their relationship. After a woman named Miriam confronted Stark, directly blaming him for her son's death during the Sokovian battle with Ultron, the guilt-ridden Stark supported Secretary of State Thaddeus Ross in advocating for the Sokovia Accords, the United Nations' superhuman oversight legislation, which would subject all Avengers missions to approval by a U.N. committee. Though Black Widow, War Machine, and Vision agreed to sign, the Scarlet Witch deferred; Captain America and Falcon declined, concerned about government influence over their operations; and Hawkeye retired.

After Sokovian soldier Helmut Zemo bombed the Accords' rat-ification ceremony in Vienna while disguised as James "Bucky" Barnes—the Winter Soldier—Cap and Falcon pursued Barnes in Budapest and were arrested as fugitives of the Accords. Stark traveled to the Joint Terrorism Taskforce's Berlin headquarters

Stark recruited and outfitted an enhanced crimefighter he had been scouting: teenager Peter Parker, a.k.a. Spider-Man.

to persuade Cap to sign, but Cap again refused after learning Stark had confined the Scarlet Witch to the Avengers compound. When Barnes escaped custody after Zemo infiltrated Taskforce Headquarters and re-activated his Hydra programming, Stark fought him and lost. After Cap and Falcon escaped with Barnes, Ross gave Stark 36

hours to recapture them. Short-handed because of the Avengers' schism, Stark recruited and out-fitted an enhanced crimefighter he had been scouting: teenager Peter Parker, a.k.a. Spider-Man, and Widow recruited Wakandan King T'Challa, the Black Panther, who sought revenge for his father's death at the ratification ceremony. Meanwhile, Cap and Falcon recruited Ant-Man and Hawkeye—who freed the Witch from the Avengers compound. Alongside his team, Stark—using the Mark XLVI Iron Man armor—confronted Cap and his allies in Germany as they attempted to pursue Zemo after Barnes told Cap that Zemo intended to unleash a team of Winter Soldier assassins kept in stasis at a Siberian Hydra base; mistrustful of Barnes, however, Stark continued to push for his arrest. Despite both sides' peaceful intentions, a fight erupted. Though Stark's team subdued and arrested many of Cap's allies, Cap and Barnes escaped, and Stark's best friend War Machine was partially paralyzed after Vision accidentally destroyed his equipment in flight.

After learning that Cap's claims regarding Zemo were true, Stark convinced the incarcerated Falcon to reveal the location of Hydra's base so he could go help Cap. Stark traveled there alone and reconciled with Cap and Barnes, but Zemo revealed that Barnes, while under Hydra's brainwashing, had murdered Stark's parents in 1991. Enraged to learn Cap had suspected this and kept it from him, Stark vi-ciously attacked them both, ultimately severing Barnes' cy-bernetic arm, but Cap handily defeated Stark by shattering his armor's Arc Reactor with his shield. Unable to prevent Cap and Barnes' departure, Stark told Cap he had lost the right to carry the shield Stark's father built; Cap somberly dropped the shield and left. Days later, while assisting War Machine with his physical therapy using Stark-designed leg braces, Stark received a package from Cap containing a burner phone and a letter, wherein Cap apologized for their conflict and nonethe-less promised to come to his aid any time he needed it. As Stark read the letter, Ross called to tell him Cap had freed his allies from the Raft superhuman prison; Stark subsequently put Ross on hold. ✪

MARK XLVI

heroes led by Captain America. During the battle, size-changing former thief Ant-Man infiltrated Iron Man's armor at insect size and caused malfunctions in the suit, including the weapons systems, by damaging wires and systems from within; Stark's artificial intelligence FRIDAY triggered the armor's fire suppression systems, forcing Ant-Man out of the armor.

After learning that Sokovian terrorist Helmut Zemo had been manipulating the schism between the Avengers, Stark flew the Mark XLVI to Zemo's hideout in Siberia and allied with Cap and Bucky Barnes (whose Winter Soldier programming had worn off) until Zemo revealed that the Soldier was responsible for the murders of Stark's parents in 1991. Stark attacked the Winter Soldier, severing his prosthetic arm with a Unibeam blast. Stark then battled Cap, employing FRIDAY to analyze his combat style in order to counter Cap's superior fighting skills. Though Stark briefly held the advantage, the Winter Soldier distracted Stark enough for Cap to disable the armor by shattering the suit's helmet and destroying the chest Arc Reactor with his Vibranium shield. ✪

IRON MAN'S ARMOR UPDATE

FIRST APPEARANCE:
[MARK XLVI / WRISTWATCH GAUNTLET]
Captain America: Civil War [2016]

Following the Avengers' battle with Ultron and the hiatus of his romance with Stark Industries C.E.O. Pepper Potts, Tony Stark developed a new Iron Man armor, the Mark XLVI. He also invented a customized wristwatch that could generate a collapsible armored gauntlet that provided him with a means of personal defense when not in armor. The gauntlet proved useful when battling brainwashed Hydra assassin the Winter Soldier: It initially kept the Soldier at bay and prevented a bullet from killing Stark, though the Winter Soldier eventually defeated Stark by punching him across a room.

After the Avengers split in a disagreement over the Sokovia Accords—superhuman oversight legislation—Stark donned the Mark XLVI while attempting to capture a group of now-fugitive

HELMET INTERFACE

FACT SHEET

▶ THE WRISTWATCH GAUNTLET COULD DELIVER A DISORIENTING LIGHT BURST AND EMIT AN ULTRASONIC PULSE THAT COULD DISRUPT HUMAN HEARING, AND WAS DURABLE ENOUGH TO STOP A POINT-BLANK GUNSHOT.

▶ WHEREAS PREVIOUS MODELS OF THE ARMOR FEATURED A FACEPLATE THAT FLIPPED UPWARDS TO ALLOW STARK AN UNOBSTRUCTED VIEW, THE MARK XLVI'S FACEMASK AND HELMET COULD FULLY COLLAPSE INTO THE ARMOR'S COLLAR.

▶ THE MARK XLVI WAS EQUIPPED WITH AN ARRAY OF MINIATURE REPULSOR TECHNOLOGY NODES MOUNTED THROUGHOUT THE SUIT'S OUTER SHELL.

THE RAFT

FIRST APPEARANCE:
Captain America: Civil War [2016]

The Raft is a supermax prison operated by the United Nations to detain enhanced individuals; its remote location is classified. The floating facility is submersible, only surfacing for incoming and outgoing aircraft. Inside, modular containment cells can be tailored to prisoners' specific abilities, and are configured into cellblocks and detention levels. These cells can be transported into the field to contain potential threats and return them to the Raft.

When a disagreement over the Sokovian Accords provoked a battle between Avengers in Germany, the captured, non-registered Hawkeye, Ant-Man, Falcon, and the Scarlet Witch were imprisoned at the Raft under the supervision of U.S. Secretary of State Thaddeus Ross. Tony Stark later flew in via helicopter to question the detained Avengers to learn the whereabouts of the fugitives Captain America and the Winter Soldier. Later, Captain America breached Raft security to free his allies. ✪

IN THE COMICS

OPERATED BY S.H.I.E.L.D., THE RAFT was an island facility in New York designed to imprison the worst of the worst villains, surrounded by dangerous waters and an energy shield that suppressed its detainees' abilities. When Electro (Max Dillon) was hired to free Sauron (Karl Lykos), his electric assault rendered the Raft vulnerable and led to a mass breakout. Under the guidance of Avengers Captain America (Steve Rogers) and Luke Cage, the Thunderbolts turned the Raft into a rehabilitation and correctional facility. A break-in by Alistair Smythe to free Mac Gargan resulted in the latter reclaiming the technological suit and title of Scorpion. In the guise of Spider-Man, Otto Octavius used the refurbished Raft as his base of operations, but it was destroyed during battle with the Goblin King (Norman Osborn).

FIRST APPEARANCE:
ALIAS #26 (2003)
COVER SHOWN: *NEW AVENGERS #1 (2004)*

RAFT CELLS

SCARLET WITCH UPDATE

FIRST APPEARANCE:
Captain America: The Winter Soldier [2014]

Wanda Maximoff was among the team of Avengers that traveled to Lagos, Nigeria, to prevent Brock Rumlow from looting a local police station's weaponry to sell to terrorists. Instead, Rumlow attacked the nearby Institute of Infectious Diseases to steal a biological weapon. Maximoff helped subdue Rumlow's men and expelled potentially noxious gases harmlessly into the atmosphere. When a suicidal Rumlow attempted to kill Captain America in a crowded marketplace by detonating an explosive device, Maximoff struggled to contain the blast telekinetically and launched Rumlow skyward. The explosion demolished several upper floors of a nearby building, resulting in civilian casualties. Maximoff was devastated by her actions.

One month later, at the Avengers' upstate compound, Maximoff fully accepted the media's contention that she was to blame for the Lagos deaths, despite Captain America taking responsibility for not noticing the bomb earlier. When Secretary of State Thaddeus Ross presented the Avengers with the Sokovia Accords, Captain America and Falcon refused to sign. Maximoff remained undecided. To avoid another potential incident, Iron Man secretly instructed Vision to detain Maximoff at the compound, with Maximoff only discovering her confinement when Vision gently forbade her from going shopping.

Inspired by Hawkeye's argument that redemption cannot be earned without action, Maximoff agreed to aid Captain America in his pursuit of Helmut Zemo. Vision grappled with Hawkeye in an effort to detain them, but Maximoff manipulated Vision's powers, forcing him to become intangible and freeing Hawkeye. She then increased Vision's density until he crashed through several floors of the compound and deep into the Earth. In Leipzig, Germany, Maximoff fought alongside Captain America and his allies against their former teammates, venting her resentment toward Iron Man. After helping Captain America reach a Quinjet despite knowing she'd be captured, Maximoff was subdued by a sonic blast from War Machine. Vision ensured she was unharmed, and both apologized for their actions. Captain America later rescued Maximoff from imprisonment at the Raft. ✪

FACT SHEET

▶ MAXIMOFF TRAINED TO USE HER POWERS IN CONJUNCTION WITH HER TEAMMATES, ILLUSTRATED WHEN SHE BOOSTED CAPTAIN AMERICA WITH A TELEKINETIC PUSH AS THEY HAD PRACTICED, LAUNCHING HIM INTO A THIRD-FLOOR WINDOW.

▶ DURING THE AIRPORT BATTLE IN LEIPZIG, MAXIMOFF HELPED HAWKEYE AGAINST IRON MAN AND BLACK WIDOW, AND PREVENTED BLACK PANTHER FROM CLAWING WINTER SOLDIER'S THROAT.

▶ A GUITAR AND SHEET MUSIC WERE AMONG MAXIMOFF'S PERSONAL BELONGINGS.

SPIDER-MAN
PETER PARKER

FIRST APPEARANCE: *Captain America: Civil War [2016]*

When teenage science prodigy Peter Parker developed spider-like powers—including superhuman strength and agility, enhanced senses, and the ability to cling to any surface—his strong sense of responsibility compelled him to use his gifts to serve the public. Armed with a pair of mechanical web-shooters of his own design, he swung into action as Spider-Man. Fearing how his aunt and guardian, May Parker, would react if she ever found out, he wore a makeshift costume to conceal his identity. Six months into Spider-Man's super-heroic career, Iron Man deduced Parker's secret, and approached him at his Queens apartment as Tony Stark to help apprehend Captain America in Germany. When Stark claimed he was there to offer Parker a scholarship from his September Foundation, Parker played along in front of May until the two could speak in private. Stark confronted Parker with footage of Spider-Man preventing a car

> **Parker initially claimed Spider-Man was an internet hoax, but Stark quickly found his hidden costume.**

accident. Parker initially claimed Spider-Man was an internet hoax, but Stark quickly found his hidden costume. He appealed to Parker's sense of responsibility and convinced him to help. Stark provided Parker with a new costume and web-shooters, calling the teen's work amateurish.

Spider-Man joined Iron Man, Black Panther, Black Widow, Vision, and War Machine in confronting Captain America, Ant-Man, Falcon, Hawkeye, Scarlet Witch, and Winter Soldier at the Leipzig airport. At Iron Man's command, Spider-Man used his webbing to procure Cap's shield, although he professed to be a big fan of the hero. Captain America's side counterattacked, and Ant-Man stole back the shield. Iron Man sent Spider-Man to apprehend Falcon and Winter Soldier in the airport's terminal. He outmuscled Winter Soldier's mechanical arm, jammed Falcon's flight-pack, and trapped them both in his webbing before Falcon's Redwing drone dragged him

BITTEN BY A RADIOACTIVE SPIDER, Peter Parker initially used the powers he developed for his own gain; when his selfishness led to his beloved Uncle Ben's death, Parker realized that with great power there must also come great responsibility. As Spider-Man, Parker defends the innocent from evil, often at great cost to himself. Constantly besieged by a legion of deadly foes, Parker has suffered a number of personal tragedies when his loved ones became caught in the crossfire. Hoping to make the world a better place, Parker has used his scientific genius to build Parker Industries, a globe-spanning technology company.

FIRST APPEARANCE:
AMAZING FANTASY #15 (1962)

away. Next, Parker clashed with Captain America himself. Although Captain America said he admired Spider-Man's spirit and was amused to learn they were both from New York, he trapped him under rubble to escape.

Spider-Man cited inspiration from an "old movie" and tied up the now-giant Ant-Man's legs with webbing, allowing Iron Man and War Machine to topple him. The flailing Ant-Man struck Parker on the way down, knocking him out. Iron Man told him to stay down, despite Parker's objections. Back in Queens, the battered Parker lied about his bruises and injuries to May, claiming he'd received them in a fight with "Steve from Brooklyn"

and "his huge friend." Once she left the room, he examined the new web-shooters Stark had built for him—complete with a built-in device that projected a digital readout mimicking the design of Spider-Man's mask. ✪

FACT SHEET

- ▶ PARKER ENJOYS REPURPOSING OBSOLETE ELECTRONICS SCAVENGED FROM THE TRASH.

- ▶ AS SPIDER-MAN, PARKER WEARS SPECIAL EYEPIECES THAT HELP FOCUS HIS ENHANCED SENSES.

- ▶ IN BATTLE, SPIDER-MAN EMITS A CONSTANT STREAM OF NERVOUS PATTER THAT IRRITATES OTHERS.

- ▶ PARKER WAS IMPRESSED WITH WINTER SOLDIER'S MECHANICAL ARM, PAUSING DURING BATTLE TO DECLARE IT "AWESOME."

WITH IRON MAN'S ALLIES

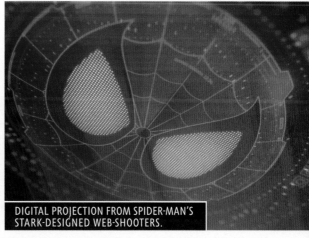

DIGITAL PROJECTION FROM SPIDER-MAN'S STARK-DESIGNED WEB-SHOOTERS.

VISION UPDATE

FIRST APPEARANCE:
Marvel's Avengers: Age of Ultron [2015]

Vision primarily stayed within the Avengers' upstate New York compound and wore normal clothing, apparently trying to fit in. One month after the Scarlet Witch inadvertently caused the deaths of several civilians in an Avengers operation in Lagos, Nigeria, U.S. Secretary of State Thaddeus Ross met with the Avengers to present the Sokovia Accords, legislation that would put a United Nations panel in charge of superhuman oversight. While the team was divided about the benefits and risks of signing, Vision believed the Avengers' formation and the exponential rise of enhanced criminals and world-ending events were directly connected, and agreed with Iron Man that regulations were needed to prevent further catastrophes.

Secretly instructed by Iron Man to detain the Witch at the Avengers' compound until the Accords were sanctioned at a U.N. conference in Vienna, Vision initially attempted to distract her through cooking; the pair bonded over apprehension of their powers— Vision likening the potential dangers of the Witch's abilities to those of his own mysterious gem—but when she wanted to go shopping, Vision gently restrained her. Later, Vision was momentarily distracted by an explosion set by Hawkeye so he could covertly enlist the Witch's aid for the now-fugitive Captain America. Returning to the compound, Vision was stunned by an electrical booby-trap set by Hawkeye, whom he easily restrained after recovering. However, the Witch telekinetically freed Hawkeye and increased Vision's mass exponentially, crashing him through the compound's floors and deep into the Earth.

During a subsequent confrontation between Avengers at a German airport, Vision sided with Iron Man against Cap's allies, convinced Cap needed to surrender for the collective good. Vision attempted to obstruct Cap's escape by toppling a radio tower, but the Witch telekinetically foiled his efforts. When she was defeated by War Machine's sonic blast, Vision comforted the Witch and apologized for their conflict. Unleashing a beam to immobilize Falcon's flight pack, Vision accidentally missed, instead destroying the power source of the airborne War Machine's armor; the resulting uncontrolled fall to Earth nearly killed War Machine. While watching over War Machine in the Avengers' medical center, Vision explained to Iron Man the accident happened because he became distracted, something Vision previously thought impossible. Vision later chose to be alone with his contemplations. ✪

WAR MACHINE
UPDATE

FIRST APPEARANCE: *Iron Man [2008]*

Following the proposal of the Sokovia Accords, legislation placing the Avengers under United Nations control, James Rhodes argued that the Avengers needed to adhere to international law and be held accountable for their actions. Stressing that the United Nations was not a shadow organization like the World Security Council, S.H.I.E.L.D., or Hydra, Rhodey chose to sign the Accords, thereby siding with Tony Stark's viewpoint on the matter. Captain America and Falcon refused to sign. When the fugitive Winter Soldier was located in Bucharest, War Machine arrived to assist local authorities in apprehending him, but found himself forced to also arrest Captain America, the Black Panther, and Falcon, who had gone after the Soldier without approval. With War Machine's help, all four men were taken into custody, but the Soldier soon escaped, followed by Cap and

Falcon, when Sokovian terrorist Helmut Zemo activated his Hydra brainwashing.

The pursuit of Cap and the Soldier resulted in a large-scale battle between the Avengers at Germany's Leipzig Airport. War Machine attempted to subdue Cap, but was cast aside by a strategic blow to the chest from his shield. Later in the battle, War Machine became ensnared by a now giant-sized Ant-Man, who tossed War Machine toward a passenger airliner, but he was saved by a well-timed web from Spider-Man. When Cap and the Soldier escaped in a Quinjet to pursue Zemo, War Machine chased them, but was attacked by Falcon. War Machine asked Vision to disable Falcon's flight pack, but when Falcon dodged, a distracted Vision accidentally shot War Machine instead, destroying the armor's power source and leaving War Machine to uncontrollably fall to Earth.

Despite Iron Man and Falcon's efforts to catch him, War Machine impacted with extreme velocity. The crash lacerated Rhodey's spinal cord, leaving him with limited mobility from the waist down. He was initially treated at Columbia Medical but returned to Avengers HQ in upstate New York. Helped by Tony Stark and custom Stark Technology leg braces, Rhodey began his difficult physical therapy, maintaining his sense of humor as he did. ✪

WINTER SOLDIER
UPDATE

FIRST APPEARANCE:
Captain America: The First Avenger [2011]

In 1991, James "Bucky" Barnes was kept in cryo-stasis at a Siberian Hydra base, where he was routinely mind-wiped and reprogrammed with code words kept in a red ledger. On December 16th, the programmed Barnes caused Howard Stark's car to crash on a deserted road and stole five samples of an augmenting serum for Hydra's Winter Soldier program. Barnes' brainwashing compelled him to kill Howard and his wife Maria, then secure a nearby surveillance camera's recording of the incident. Barnes later helped train five newly-created Winter Soldiers until they went rogue and had to be put into stasis.

In the present day, the fugitive Barnes quietly lived in Bucharest until Sokovian terrorist Helmut Zemo, disguised as Barnes, detonated a massive explosion outside a United Nations conference in Vienna, killing Wakanda's King T'Chaka; T'Chaka's son T'Challa vowed vengeance. Concerned for his safety, Barnes' childhood friend Captain America and his ally Falcon located Barnes shortly before German Special Forces attacked, making themselves criminals by disregarding the Sokovia Accords legislation, which required the Avengers to obtain United Nations approval for all superhuman activity. Their escape was intercepted by

T'Challa in his Black Panther identity, and all four were arrested by Special Forces. Barnes was incarcerated in Taskforce Headquarters, where Zemo posed as a psychiatrist, activated Barnes' Hydra programming, and sent him on a rampage. Cap and Falcon escaped custody and captured Barnes, detaining him at an abandoned building until the brainwashing subsided. Upon recovering, Barnes revealed the existence of the five other Winter Soldiers to Cap and hypothesized that Zemo intended to activate them.

While en route to stop Zemo, Barnes, Cap, and other fugitive heroes were confronted by Iron Man's Accords-registered Avengers team. Their allies sacrificed their freedom so Barnes and Cap could go after Zemo, but Barnes believed his past misdeeds made him unworthy of this effort. In Siberia, Barnes and Cap were joined by Iron Man, who had learned of Zemo's machinations. However, Zemo played the surveillance footage of the murder of Iron Man's parents, causing a rage-filled Iron Man to attack Barnes and sever his metal arm. Cap ultimately defeated Iron Man and escaped with Barnes. Now aware Barnes had been framed, T'Challa complied with Barnes' wish to be cryogenically frozen until his Hydra programming could be removed, storing his stasis chamber in Wakanda. ✪

FACT SHEET

▶ THE RUSSIAN WORDS THAT TRIGGERED BARNES' HYDRA PROGRAMMING TRANSLATE INTO ENGLISH AS "LONGING," "RUSTED," "17," "DAYBREAK," "FURNACE," "NINE," "BENIGN," "HOMECOMING," "ONE," AND "FREIGHT CAR."

▶ EN ROUTE TO CONFRONT ZEMO, CAP AND BARNES SHARED STORIES FROM THEIR YOUTH, THE TWO BONDING AGAIN AFTER YEARS OF SEPARATION AND BARNES' BRAINWASHING.

HELMUT ZEMO

FIRST APPEARANCE: *Captain America: Civil War [2016]*

During the battle between the Avengers and Ultron, Col. Helmut Zemo and his EKO Scorpion death squad were called upon to assist in Sokovia's defense. Zemo sent his wife and son to his father's house outside the city for safety, but returned days later to find them dead in the ruins. Consumed with rage, he vengefully plotted to destroy the Avengers. Zemo learned from decrypted documents released during S.H.I.E.L.D.'s collapse that James "Bucky" Barnes had become Hydra's Winter Soldier, and that he had murdered Howard and Maria Stark—the parents of Tony Stark, a.k.a. Iron

Man—in 1991. Zemo killed Hydra operative Vasily Karpov after he refused to divulge details of the incident, but acquired the trigger words capable of compelling Barnes to comply. Disguised as Barnes, Zemo bombed a United Nations summit, resulting in the death of Wakanda's King T'Chaka. When authorities captured Barnes, psychiatrist Theo Broussard was called in to interrogate him. Zemo murdered and impersonated Broussard, triggered an electromagnetic pulse to cause chaos, and then used the codewords to send Barnes on a mindless rampage.

In Siberia, Zemo located a Cold War-era Hydra base housing a squad of Winter Soldiers in stasis. Not wanting more superhumans active in the world, Zemo killed them while they slept and waited. Clues he had left lured Captain America, Barnes, and Iron Man to him. Zemo showed them video of the Starks' murders, resulting in a brutal battle between the heroes. Outside, Zemo attempted

SON OF CAPTAIN AMERICA'S NAZI foe Baron (Heinrich) Zemo, Baron (Helmut) Zemo believes the Zemos were destined to rule mankind, and has often battled Captain America and the Avengers both alone and while leading the Masters of Evil. When Earth's heroes were believed dead, Zemo had the Masters pose as the heroic Thunderbolts to gain the public's trust and make conquering them easier; eventually exposed, Zemo returned to more overt villainy.

FIRST APPEARANCE: *CAPTAIN AMERICA* #168 (1973); (AS BARON ZEMO) *CAPTAIN AMERICA* #275 (1982)

suicide, but Black Panther—son of Wakanda's slain king—prevented him from escaping justice. In captivity, Zemo was pleased his actions had resulted in the Avengers' disintegration. ✪

FACT SHEET

- ▶ ZEMO KEPT THE LAST VOICEMAIL HIS WIFE HAD SENT HIM AND LISTENED TO IT REGULARLY, ONLY DELETING IT WHEN HIS PLAN WAS COMPLETE.

- ▶ WHILE IN VIENNA, ZEMO ORDERED BLACK COFFEE AND BACON FOR BREAKFAST EVERY MORNING.

- ▶ ZEMO WAS PLEASED TO OBSERVE A TRACE OF GREEN IN CAPTAIN AMERICA'S BLUE EYES—A SMALL FLAW IN HIS PHYSICAL PERFECTION.

PEGGY CARTER
UPDATE

FIRST APPEARANCE:
Captain America: The First Avenger [2011]

During a meeting with the Avengers, Captain America received a text message notifying him that Peggy Carter, his longtime friend, World War II ally, and former lover, had passed away in her sleep; Cap immediately left the meeting to weep quietly in private. Funeral services for Carter were held in London, where the enormous church was filled to capacity with the friends, family, and allies she had collected over her long life—testament to the immense respect she'd earned for decades of service to the world. During the funeral, Carter's great-niece Sharon delivered a moving eulogy that detailed some amazing facts about her Aunt Peggy, among them her role as a founder of S.H.I.E.L.D., her meeting with U.S. President John F. Kennedy, and her mastery of diplomacy and espionage in an age before women were given credibility in those fields. Carter once told Sharon she had been able to accomplish so much by compromising where she could and refusing to do so when standing for what was right, even as all others tried to convince her she was wrong. After Carter was laid to rest, Sharon and Cap spent time together, sharing stories of the incredible woman they mutually loved. ✪

FACT SHEET

▶ IN HIS CIVILIAN IDENTITY OF STEVE ROGERS, CAPTAIN AMERICA SERVED AS A PALLBEARER FOR CARTER'S UNION JACK-DRAPED COFFIN; ROGERS WAS TEARY-EYED WHILE CARRYING OUT THIS HONOR.

▶ UNTIL THE FUNERAL, CAP ONLY KNEW OF SHARON AS AGENT 13, LEARNING HER TRUE IDENTITY WHEN SHARON APPROACHED THE PODIUM AT CARTER'S FUNERAL.

▶ A BEAUTIFUL FRAMED PHOTO OF CARTER, TAKEN DURING WWII, STOOD NEAR HER COFFIN DURING THE CEREMONY.

CROSSBONES/ BROCK RUMLOW
UPDATE

FIRST APPEARANCE: *Captain America: The Winter Soldier [2014]*

As Crossbones, Brock Rumlow made headlines worldwide by robbing police stations and selling stolen weapons to terrorists. Hired by an unidentified party to steal a biological weapon, Crossbones led a mercenary group in attacking the Institute for Infectious Diseases (IFID) in Lagos, Nigeria, gaining entry by using a garbage truck as a battering ram. When confronted by the Avengers, Rumlow escaped by nearly killing the Black Widow with a grenade and attacking Captain America with truck-mounted heavy weaponry. Crossbones separated from his mercenaries and battled Captain America to buy them time to flee with the weapon. While the Avengers captured the mercenaries, Crossbones—intending to kill Cap and himself with a suicide bomb—distracted Cap by mentioning Cap's brainwashed friend Bucky. Crossbones triggered the bomb, but the Avengers' telekinetic Scarlet Witch contained the blast and hurled the mercenary into the air. The subsequent explosion killed Rumlow, but inadvertently destroyed a large part of a nearby building, killing civilians. ✪

FACT SHEET

▶ CROSSBONES WAS UNAFFECTED BY BLACK WIDOW'S ELECTRIC SHOCK WEAPONS, APPARENTLY DUE TO SEVERE NERVE DAMAGE, AS WELL AS THICK NECK AND FACIAL SCARRING.

▶ CROSSBONES' MECHANICAL GAUNTLETS ENHANCED THE FORCE OF HIS PUNCHES AND WERE EQUIPPED WITH RETRACTABLE BLADES.

▶ DESPITE HIS MASSIVE DISFIGUREMENT, RUMLOW THOUGHT HE "LOOKED PRETTY GOOD, ALL THINGS CONSIDERED."

MIRIAM

FIRST APPEARANCE:
Captain America: Civil War [2016]

After Tony Stark delivered a speech announcing the donation of millions of dollars to fund the projects of students at the Massachusetts Institute of Technology, he came upon Miriam in a backstage hallway. Miriam praised Stark for the donation, but said some people believe there's a correlation between generosity and guilt. Miriam accused Stark of murdering her son, Charlie Spencer, in Sokovia during the Avengers' battle with Ultron, thrusting Charlie's photo at a stunned Stark. Before walking away, Miriam asked Stark who would avenge her son. Stark learned that Charles had earned a degree in computer engineering with a 3.6 grade point average, and that he had an entry-level position waiting for him when he returned from a summer building affordable housing for Sokovia's poor. Guilt over Charles' accidental death when a building fell on him drove Stark to agree to the United Nations' Sokovia Accords. ✪

IN THE COMICS

MIRIAM SHARPE LOST HER SON, DAMIAN, WHEN HIS elementary school was destroyed during a superhuman battle. She went on to become a vocal proponent of the Superhuman Registration Act. Originally hostile toward superhumans, Sharpe came to begrudgingly respect them due to her interactions with Tony Stark.

FIRST APPEARANCE:
CIVIL WAR #1 (2006)

FACT SHEET

▶ MIRIAM TOLD STARK SHE WORKED IN HUMAN RESOURCES FOR THE STATE DEPARTMENT—A JOB SHE DIDN'T FIND GLAMOROUS, BUT ONE THAT ENABLED HER TO RAISE CHARLES.

▶ MIRIAM SAID SHE WAS PROUD OF THE MAN CHARLES WAS BECOMING.

MAY PARKER

FIRST APPEARANCE:
Captain America: Civil War [2016]

The guardian of her teenage nephew, Peter, May Parker was blissfully unaware he was Spider-Man. When Tony Stark came to visit Peter at their Queens apartment, hoping to recruit Spider-Man to help him apprehend the fugitive Captain America, he told May he was there to present Peter with a scholarship from his September Foundation. Later, when Peter returned from the mission battered and bruised, May tended to his injuries, which he claimed he'd received in a fight with peers. May was pleased to learn he'd landed a few blows himself. ✪

IN THE COMICS

LEFT TO CARE FOR HER YOUNG nephew, Peter, after his parents died, May Parker raised the boy alongside her husband, Ben—only for Ben to die at the hands of a burglar. May's compassion and determination are a constant inspiration to Peter, even when her frail health and dire finances weigh on his mind. Largely unaware of Peter's career as Spider-Man, May has frequently been endangered by his foes. She was recently widowed again when her second husband Jay Jameson died.

FIRST APPEARANCE:
AMAZING FANTASY #15 (1962)

FACT SHEET

▶ MAY SERVED WALNUT DATE LOAF TO STARK, WHICH HE PRETENDED TO ENJOY.

▶ STARK FOUND IT DIFFICULT TO BELIEVE THAT SOMEONE AS ATTRACTIVE AS MAY COULD BE ANYONE'S AUNT, AND REFERRED TO HER AS "AUNT HOTTIE."

▶ WHEN PETER ATTRIBUTED HIS INJURIES TO A FIGHT WITH STEVE, MAY INITIALLY ASSUMED HE MEANT THEIR NEIGHBOR STEVE "WITH THE OVERBITE."

EVERETT K. ROSS

FIRST APPEARANCE:
Captain America: Civil War [2016]

The officious Everett K. Ross served as deputy commander of the Joint Terrorism Task Force. At the Task Force's Berlin headquarters, he oversaw the arrival of Captain America, Falcon, and Black Panther—detained for violating the Sokovia Accords in their pursuit of the Winter Soldier, who was also captured. While he imprisoned the Winter Soldier in a containment cell, Ross sequestered Captain America, Falcon, and Black Panther in offices, ordering them to remain there. Ross called in Dr. Theo Broussard to psychologically evaluate the Winter Soldier, but Broussard had been murdered and replaced by Helmut Zemo, who freed the Winter Soldier to further his plans for revenge against the Avengers. Zemo manipulated the Winter Soldier's brainwashing to provoke a rampage that also resulted in the escape of all of Ross' detainees. Black Panther later captured Zemo and returned him to Ross' custody. ✪

IN THE COMICS

STATE DEPARTMENT EMPLOYEE
Everett K. Ross was assigned as government attaché for Black Panther (T'Challa) during his sojourns in America. Although the two initially disliked and distrusted each other, they eventually became friends. Panther even appointed Ross his regent in Wakanda during one of his absences.

FIRST APPEARANCE: *KA-ZAR #17 (1998)*

FACT SHEET

▶ ROSS SUGGESTED THAT CAPTAIN AMERICA AND FALCON, NOT JUST THE WINTER SOLDIER, SHOULD RECEIVE PSYCHOLOGICAL EVALUATIONS.

▶ ROSS TAUNTED ZEMO FOR HIS FAILURE TO DESTROY THE AVENGERS, BUT ZEMO QUESTIONED WHETHER HIS PLAN HAD, IN FACT, FAILED.

THADDEUS ROSS
UPDATE

FIRST APPEARANCE:
The Incredible Hulk [2008]

After suffering a heart attack that required 13 hours of triple-bypass surgery, Gen. Thaddeus Ross left the military to become secretary of state. Accompanying Tony Stark to the Avengers' upstate compound one month after a mission in Lagos, Nigeria, resulted in civilian casualties, Ross presented the team with the Sokovia Accords—legislation that would place the Avengers under the control of a United Nations panel. Ross suggested that those who refused to sign should retire, and that resistance would be met with force. When Captain America and Falcon pursued the fugitive Winter Soldier in violation of the Accords, Ross wanted all three prosecuted upon their arrest. When they escaped custody, he gave Stark 36 hours to apprehend them. While Captain America and the Winter Soldier evaded capture, their allies were remanded to the Raft. Ross phoned Stark after Captain America breached the facility to liberate them, but Stark placed a frustrated Ross on hold. ✪

FACT SHEET

▶ DURING HIS 40 YEARS OF MILITARY SERVICE, ROSS EARNED A CONGRESSIONAL MEDAL OF HONOR.

▶ WHILE CONFRONTING THE AVENGERS, ROSS COMPARED THE MISSING THOR AND HULK TO TWO MISPLACED 30-MEGATON NUCLEAR WARHEADS.

HOWARD STARK
UPDATE

FIRST APPEARANCE:
Iron Man [2008] [PHOTO];
Iron Man 2 [2010] [FULL APPEARANCE]

On December 16, 1991, Stark Industries CEO Howard Stark and his wife Maria visited with their son Tony, unaware it would be the last time they saw him. Howard teased Tony—home during the holidays from studying abroad—for being a philanderer, despite his own womanizing past. Commenting on Tony's sarcasm, Howard prodded his son to apply himself in his studies. While Howard gathered luggage, Maria told Tony that Howard missed him while he was away, but had a difficult time showing it. Under the guise of taking a week-long trip to the Bahamas, Howard planned to deliver a human enhancement serum—similar to the Super-Soldier serum that had created Captain America—to the Pentagon. En route, the Starks' car was forced off-road by the Winter Soldier, Cap's former WWII ally "Bucky" Barnes, now a brain-washed assassin for Hydra. The Winter Soldier beat Howard to death as Maria called for her husband; the Winter Soldier then strangled Maria, took the serum, and staged the Starks' death to look like a car accident. ✪

FACT SHEET

▶ BEFORE REALIZING HIS CAR CRASH WASN'T AN ACCIDENT, HOWARD ASKED THE WINTER SOLDIER TO HELP MARIA. RECOGNIZING HIS ATTACKER, HOWARD'S LAST WORDS WERE "SGT. BARNES."

▶ FOLLOWING HOWARD'S DEATH, THE WINTER SOLDIER TOOK THE SERUM TO HIS HYDRA MASTERS, WHO USED IT TO CREATE MORE WINTER SOLDIERS.

▶ HOWARD'S FRIEND AND BUSINESS PARTNER OBADIAH STANE BECAME INTERIM CEO OF HOWARD'S COMPANY STARK INDUSTRIES UNTIL TONY TOOK OVER AT AGE 21.

T'CHAKA

FIRST APPEARANCE:
Captain America: Civil War [2016]

King of the reclusive African nation of Wakanda, T'Chaka was one of the chief proponents of the Sokovia Accords, legislation placing the Avengers under United Nations control, due to the Wakandan nationals inadvertently killed by the Scarlet Witch during an Avengers mission in Lagos, Nigeria. T'Chaka was the keynote speaker at the ceremony ratifying the Accords in Vienna, Austria, but a bombing engineered by Sokovian terrorist Helmut Zemo devastated the building, killing T'Chaka and eleven others. T'Chaka's son T'Challa was forced to become Wakanda's new king, but he first sought vengeance for his father's murder in his already established role as Wakanda's guardian, the Black Panther. ✪

IN THE COMICS

T'CHAKA WAS THE CHIEFTAIN OF Wakanda and as such acted as the sworn protector of their people's primary resource, the energy-absorbing mineral Vibranium. He also served as Wakanda's costumed guardian, the Black Panther. T'Chaka was murdered by Dutch scientist Ulysses Klaw when he refused foreign overtures to trade in Vibranium.

FIRST APPEARANCE:
FANTASTIC FOUR #53 (1966);
COVER SHOWN: *BLACK PANTHER #30 (2001)*

FACT SHEET

▶ T'CHAKA PUBLICLY CONDEMNED BOTH THE CRIMINAL ACTIONS THAT LED TO THE CONFLICT IN NIGERIA AND THE AVENGERS' PERCEIVED INDIFFERENCE TOWARDS NONCOMBATANTS. HE NEVERTHELESS ACCEPTED BLACK WIDOW'S APOLOGY AND PRAISED THE AVENGERS FOR SUPPORTING THE ACCORDS. HE ALSO EXPRESSED REGRET OVER CAPTAIN AMERICA'S ABSENCE FROM THE SIGNING CEREMONY, A SENTIMENT ROMANOFF SHARED.

▶ T'CHAKA FELT THAT T'CHALLA EXCELLED AT DIPLOMACY, THOUGH AWARE HIS SON CARED LITTLE FOR IT.

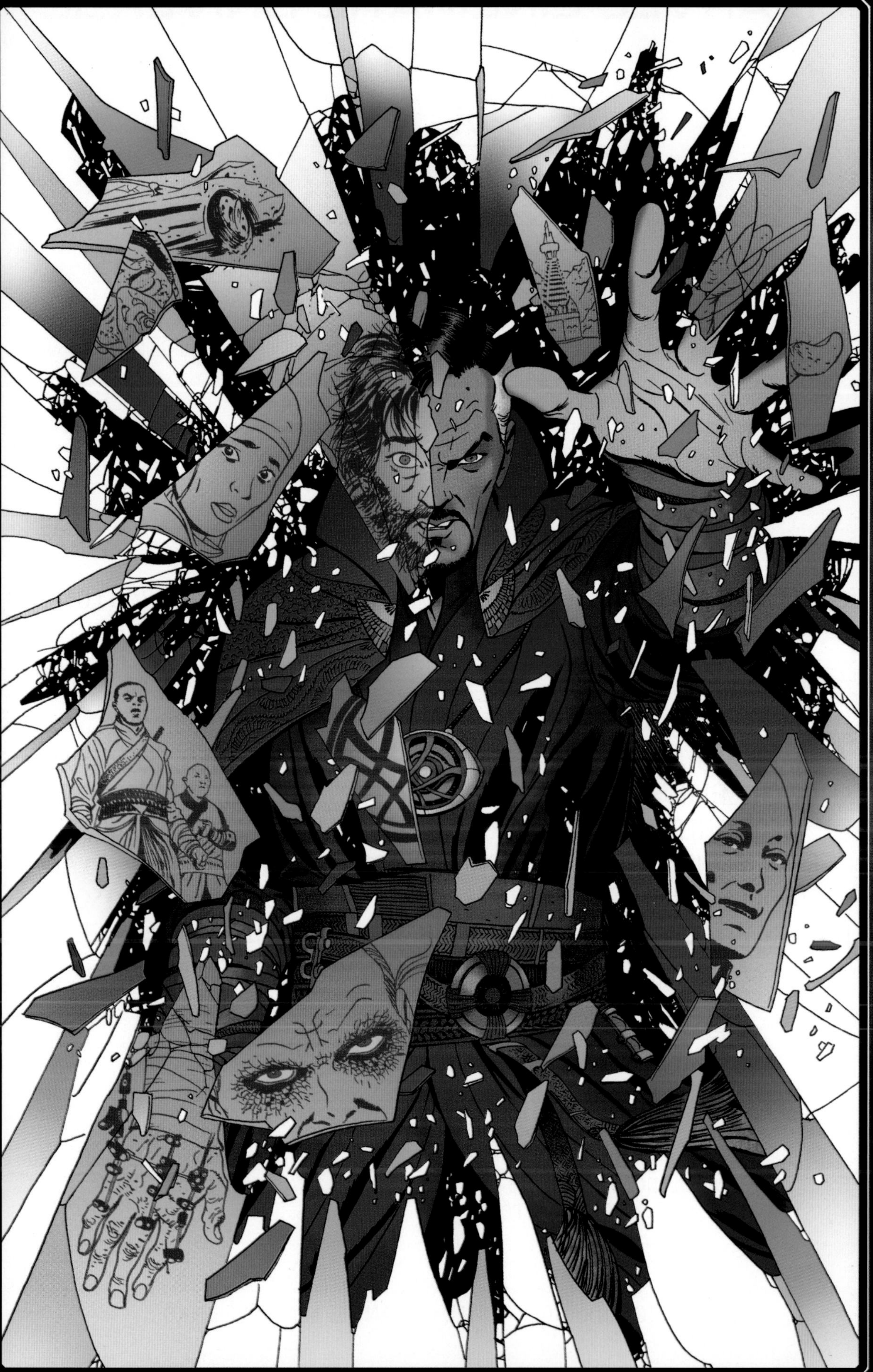

GUIDEBOOK TO THE MARVEL CINEMATIC UNIVERSE

MARVEL STUDIOS PRESENTS BENEDICT CUMBERBATCH "DOCTOR STRANGE" CHIWETEL EJIOFOR RACHEL McADAMS BENEDICT WONG MICHAEL STUHLBARG BENJAMIN BRATT SCOTT ADKINS WITH MADS MIKKELSEN AND TILDA SWINTON CASTING BY SARAH HALLEY FINN, CSA MUSIC SUPERVISOR DAVE JORDAN MUSIC BY MICHAEL GIACCHINO HEAD OF VISUAL DEVELOPMENT RYAN MEINERDING VISUAL EFFECTS SUPERVISOR STEPHANE CERETTI VISUAL EFFECTS AND ANIMATION BY INDUSTRIAL LIGHT & MAGIC COSTUME DESIGNER ALEX BYRNE EDITED BY WYATT SMITH, ACE SABRINA PLISCO, ACE PRODUCTION DESIGNER CHARLES WOOD DIRECTOR OF PHOTOGRAPHY BEN DAVIS, BSC CO-PRODUCER DAVID J. GRANT EXECUTIVE PRODUCER CHARLES NEWIRTH STAN LEE EXECUTIVE PRODUCERS VICTORIA ALONSO STEPHEN BROUSSARD EXECUTIVE PRODUCER LOUIS D'ESPOSITO PRODUCED BY KEVIN FEIGE, p.g.a. WRITTEN BY JON SPAIHTS AND SCOTT DERRICKSON & C. ROBERT CARGILL DIRECTED BY SCOTT DERRICKSON

Collecting information from Marvel's *Doctor Strange* (2016), *Marvel's Doctor Strange Prelude #1-2* (2016), and *Marvel's Doctor Strange Prelude Infinite Comic #1* (2016).

HEAD WRITER/COORDINATOR: MIKE O'SULLIVAN

WRITERS: ANTHONY COTILLETTA, KEVIN GARCIA, DARON JENSEN, ROB LONDON, CHRIS MCCARVER, JACOB ROUGEMONT, AND STUART VANDAL

ARTISTS: ADRIAN ALPHONA, CHRIS BACHALO, ELIOT R. BROWN, FRANK BRUNNER, ROBERTO FERNÁNDEZ CASTRO, JO CHEN, SEAN CHEN, BOB CHESHIRE, STEVE DITKO, BILL EVERETT, TIM HILL, STUART IMMONEN, GEOF ISHERWOOD, JACK KIRBY, MARCOS MARTIN, KEVIN MAGUIRE, RYAN MEINERDING, MIKE MIGNOLA, WIN MORTIMER, KEVIN NOWLAN, GEORGE PÉREZ, SANDY PLUNKETT, CARL POTTS, DARICK ROBERTSON, JOHN ROMITA SR., CHRIS SAMNEE, PAUL SMITH, JIM STARLIN, JIM STERANKO, TOM SUTTON, PETE THOMPSON, AND CHRIS WARNER

COVER ARTIST: MARCOS MARTIN

SPECIAL THANKS TO DAVE ALTHOFF, KAREN BROOKS, SHAWN "KEEBLER" BYERS, JEFF CHRISTIANSEN, JASON DAVIS, MATT DELMANOWSKI, ERIKA DENTON, TIM DILLON, MIKE FICHERA, PERCIVAL LANUZA, CHARLOTTE LEE, CLIFF MCGRADY, AVIA PEREZ, JACQUE PORTE, RYAN POTTER, AND SUSIE SANTOS.

DOCTOR STRANGE CREATED BY STAN LEE AND STEVE DITKO

THE ANCIENT ONE

FIRST APPEARANCE: Marvel's *Doctor Strange* [2016]

Of Celtic descent, The Ancient One was the long-lived Sorcerer Supreme, latest in a long line of mystics dedicated to defending Earth from magical and extradimensional threats. A practitioner of meditation and martial arts, she was the preeminent mage of Kamar-Taj, where she taught numerous students in the mystic arts and worked diligently to help them achieve balance and avoid evil.

When her student Kaecilius' quest to defeat death itself led him to reject her teachings, he murdered the Kamar-Taj librarian and stole pages from the *Book of Cagliostro,* hoping to use a ritual it contained to contact Dormammu, the evil and timeless lord of the Dark Dimension. The Ancient One confronted him in the library and pursued as he and over a dozen of his own followers—the Zealots—fled to London, where she transported them to the Mirror Dimension. In the resulting battle, The Ancient One slew the majority of the Zealots before Kaecilius and a small few escaped through a portal.

When Dr. Stephen Strange arrived at Kamar-Taj seeking healing for his neurologically damaged hands, he was disrespectful of the mystical practices The Ancient One revealed to him. To teach him humility, she briefly separated his astral form from his body and sent him through several other dimensions and universes, revealing the existence of the Multiverse, the system of infinite realities of which their own was only a part. When

he begged her to teach him, she refused, but ultimately relented at Master Mordo's encouragement.

She closely oversaw Strange's training, an investment that paid off when he single-handedly prevented Kaecilius from destroying New York City's Sanctum to weaken the Masters' protective barrier against Dormammu. However, when Strange confronted The Ancient One about Kaecilius' claim that she drew power from Dormammu to prolong her life, she would neither deny nor confirm his suspicions. When Kaecilius subsequently pursued Strange and Mordo into the Mirror Dimension, she followed to help them, but Kaecilius stabbed her and cast her back to Earth, where she fell dozens of floors to the ground. As her body lay dying in the hospital, her astral form visited Strange's, where she admitted hating drawing power from the Dark Dimension, but argued that the greater good sometimes required breaking the rules. She revealed that Strange could return to his previous life by channeling dimensional energy into his hands, but noted that such an effort would preclude him from manifesting other magical abilities, and urged him to use his gifts to continue protecting the world with the Masters. Giving Strange's hand a gentle squeeze, The Ancient One passed away. ✪

THE CENTURIES-OLD ANCIENT ONE was born in Tibet as Yao, and, in his youth, worked as an apprentice doctor. He studied magic in the Himalayan village of Kamar-Taj until another sorcerer, Kaluu, seized control. The Ancient One defeated him and swore to oppose malevolent sorcerers. The Ancient One eventually became Earth's Sorcerer Supreme, and after living several centuries in various dimensions, he returned to the Himalayas, taking Karl Mordo as his disciple. Realizing Mordo was too corrupt to succeed him, Yao took the guise of the High Lama to activate mystic potential in Dr. Anthony Druid, then as the Ancient One taught magic to the ailing surgeon Stephen Strange, who initially sought him out while seeking to heal his injured hands. Even after Strange left to pursue a life of heroic deeds, the Ancient One continued to aid Strange. Though killed battling an extradimensional demon, the Ancient One's astral form continued to appear numerous times after his death.

FIRST APPEARANCE:
(AS THE HIGH LAMA) *AMAZING ADVENTURES #1 (1961)*; (AS THE ANCIENT ONE) *STRANGE TALES #110 (1963)*

TEACHING STRANGE

CLOAK OF LEVITATION

FIRST APPEARANCE:
Marvel's *Doctor Strange* [2016]

AFTER DOCTOR STEPHEN STRANGE defeated Dormammu, the Ancient One (Yao) gifted Strange with the powerful Cloak of Levitation, woven by an unidentified mystical weaver. Strange uses it to fly and can command it to shield him, wrestle foes, or to carry himself and others. It can be transformed into other shapes, such as a scarf, carpet, coat, or kimono. If the Cloak is damaged and repaired incorrectly, it can cause levitational chaos, the full extent of which is unknown.

FIRST APPEARANCE:
STRANGE TALES #127 (1964)

Ahigh-collared garment of unrevealed origin, the Cloak of Levitation is an intelligent, sentient magical item that has been described as "finicky," choosing its own wearer. The Cloak free-floated in a glass case within the New York City Sanctum Sanctorum, where it presumably resided between wearers. The Cloak first encountered Doctor Stephen Strange when he was inadvertently thrown through a portal into the New York City Sanctum by the explosive force released when the traitor Kaecilius destroyed the London Sanctum. While searching the building for other Masters, Strange happened upon the Cloak's case; the Cloak seemed to take a great interest in him, moving within the case while regarding the Master.

When Kaecilius attacked the New York City Sanctum, Strange defended himself. A fierce battle between the two spilled into the Chamber of Relics and destroyed the Cloak's case. As Kaecilius attempted to strike a killing blow against Strange, the Cloak chose to aid Strange against the mad Zealot and blocked it. After saving Strange from a fatal fall, the Cloak then forcibly pulled him toward the Crimson Bands of Cyttorak, rather than the ax Strange was trying to reach, knowing the Bands would restrain Kaecilius and end the battle. When Kaecilius' disciple Lucian attacked Strange and badly wounded him, the Cloak again blocked the killing blow and battled the Zealot while Strange sought medical assistance; Strange ultimately defeated Lucian on the astral plane. The Cloak assisted Strange in a subsequent battle against Kaecilius, and when Strange wept over the death of The Ancient One, the Cloak wiped his tears away, much to Strange's annoyance. When Strange went to Hong Kong to battle Kaecilius, the Cloak continued to aid him, blocking blows and augmenting his maneuverability. Following Strange's defeat of Kaecilius and his corrupt master Dormammu, the Cloak returned to New York City, presumably to wait until Strange needed its help again. ✷

▶ THE CLOAK DEFEATED THE ZEALOT BY WRAPPING ITSELF AROUND HIS HEAD AND JERKING HIS BODY BACK AND FORTH TO DISORIENT HIM. THE CLOAK ALSO REPEATEDLY SLAMMED THE ENEMY TO THE FLOOR DURING THEIR BATTLE.

▶ THE CLOAK APPEARS TO BE VERY RESISTANT TO DAMAGE; THE SOURCE OF THIS POWER HAS NOT BEEN REVEALED.

IN THE COMICS

DESPITE ITS NAME AND LACK OF a visible illumination source, the Dark Dimension is a mostly brightly lit mystic realm, containing islands with their own localized gravity that float within a breathable void, sometimes interconnected by meandering floating paths. Naturally containing pocket dimensions, it has been expanded by the conquest and absorption of other dimensions, both by its former ruler Olnar—last monarch of the G'uranthic Empire who ruled for nearly three millennia—and by his usurper, Dormammu.

FIRST APPEARANCE:
STRANGE TALES #127 (1964)

DARK DIMENSION

FIRST APPEARANCE:
Marvel's *Doctor Strange* [2016]

Existing outside of time itself, the Dark Dimension serves as home for the dreaded Dormammu. The dimension transcends humanity's understanding of physics, and humans perceive it only in abstract psychedelic concepts—free-floating shapes interacting with inexplicable planetoids, colors, and energies from across all identified—and likely even unidentified—spectrums. The realm itself is devoid of light; all illumination within it is apparently from other dimensions that Dormammu has conquered and absorbed into it.

The sorcerer Kaecilius, driven by the loss of his wife and child, came to believe he could defeat death itself by allowing Dormammu to merge Earth's dimension with the Dark Dimension, thus stopping time. To this end, Kaecilius turned against his master and teacher, The Ancient One, and stole a ritual that would allow him to contact Dormammu and gain immense power. After performing this ritual, Kaecilius and his Zealots destroyed the Masters' London Sanctum, one of three repositories of mystical energy that served as anchors for an energy shield protecting Earth from magical and extradimensional threats.

Though the Zealots were prevented from eliminating the New York City Sanctum by Doctor Stephen Strange, they succeeded in destroying the Hong Kong Sanctum, thus weakening the shield. The Dark

Dimension flowed into Hong Kong, amalgamating Earth structures with its own bizarre, esoteric contents. Utilizing the Eye of Agamotto to reverse time, Strange undid the destruction of the Hong Kong Sanctum and trapped Dormammu in a time loop until he agreed to abandon his invasion. ✪

FACT SHEET

▶ A DEFEATED DORMAMMU TRANSFORMED HIS THREE REMAINING ZEALOTS INTO BESTIAL MINDLESS ONES AND BROUGHT THEM TO THE DARK DIMENSION.

▶ THE PLANETOIDS IN THE DARK DIMENSION WERE CONNECTED BY TENDON-LIKE STRANDS. THESE PLANETOIDS AND TENDONS PULSED, AS IF ALIVE.

MERGING WITH HONG KONG

DOCTOR STRANGE

FIRST APPEARANCE:
Captain America: The Winter Soldier [2014] [MENTIONED];
Marvel's *Doctor Strange [2016]* [SEEN]

An acclaimed neurosurgeon at New York City's Metropolitan General Hospital, Dr. Stephen Strange's skills brought him great wealth and prestige, matched only by his pride and ego. A relationship with Emergency Room Doctor Christine Palmer ended badly, and though they remained amicable, Palmer vowed to never date a colleague again. Strange rejected Palmer's offer to be the ER's on-call neurosurgeon, claiming his groundbreaking surgical work—capable of eventually saving thousands of lives—would be wasted in the ER's efforts to save individuals.

Driving too fast to a speaking engagement while checking his text messages, Strange caused an accident that sent his car off a cliff. He spent hours in surgery while 11 stainless steel pins were implanted in his hands, which had suffered multiple broken bones, torn ligaments, and massive nerve damage; the injuries left him unable to continue working as a neurosurgeon. After nearly depleting his entire fortune on seven separate unsuccessful experimental surgeries to restore his hands, the frustrated Strange verbally lashed out at Palmer, who had been acting as a caretaker for him; Palmer subsequently cut all ties with him.

Having exhausted medical options, Strange remembered hearing about Jonathan Pangborn, a miraculously recovered paraplegic, and tracked him down. Pangborn told Strange of Kamar-Taj, a Nepalese temple where he learned to cure himself without conventional medicine. Skeptical, Strange nonetheless spent the last of his money to travel there. Walking through city markets asking for Kamar-Taj, Strange was attacked by bandits, but was saved by Mordo, a Kamar-Taj mystic who had overheard his inquiries. Mordo took him to meet The Ancient One; Strange assumed the title referred to the elderly Hamir, and was shocked to find Kamar-Taj's leader was female, and already knew much about him. When he reacted with angry skepticism to her claim that she could reorient the spirit to heal the body, she cast his astral form from his body and sent him on a brief, rapid tour of the Multiverse—the system of infinite realities of which their own was only a part—to

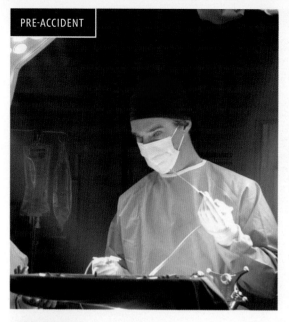

FACT SHEET

- ▶ STRANGE HAS A PHOTOGRAPHIC MEMORY, HELPING HIM EARN HIS MD AND PhD SIMULTANEOUSLY.

- ▶ WELL-VERSED IN MUSICAL TRIVIA, STRANGE OFTEN LISTENED TO MUSIC WHILE OPERATING; HE WOULD ALSO TAP HIS FEET AND DANCE IN PLACE.

- ▶ STRANGE WOULD CHERRY-PICK MEDICAL CASES PRESENTED TO HIM, SELECTING ONLY THOSE HE KNEW WOULD NOT IMPACT HIS SUCCESS-RATE STATUS; ONE OF THE CASES HE REJECTED WAS JONATHAN PANGBORN'S.

- ▶ STRANGE WAS FLATTERED THAT PALMER NAMED HER POLICY AGAINST DATING CO-WORKERS THE "STRANGE POLICY."

- ▶ WHEN TOLD THAT DOCTORS DID THEIR BEST TO SAVE HIS HANDS, STRANGE ARROGANTLY INSISTED HE COULD HAVE DONE BETTER.

- ▶ FOLLOWING HIS ACCIDENT, STRANGE COULD NOT EVEN WRITE HIS NAME LEGIBLY, AND BLAMED HIS INITIAL INABILITY TO CREATE SPELLS ON HIS DAMAGED HANDS, UNTIL HE LEARNED THAT MASTER HAMIR COULD CAST SPELLS DESPITE MISSING HIS LEFT HAND.

- ▶ STRANGE WAS DISTRESSED TO LEARN HE HAD KILLED A ZEALOT IN BATTLE, AGONIZING OVER THE BREAKING OF HIS HIPPOCRATIC OATH.

- ▶ STRANGE REJECTED THE NAME "MASTER STRANGE," INSISTING HE BE CALLED "DOCTOR STRANGE."

- ▶ STRANGE STILL WEARS A WATCH PALMER GAVE HIM, EVEN THOUGH IT WAS BROKEN DURING A FIGHT.

show him how little he truly knew. The shocked Strange asked her to teach him, and though she initially refused, she relented at Mordo's urging after Strange sat at her door for five hours.

During training, Strange learned that "magic" was actually a method of tapping into energies from the Multiverse to create specific results. Strange's rapid assimilation of Kamar-Taj's vast library encouraged its librarian, Wong, to let Strange access books generally reserved for Master-level students. Finding it hard to silence his ego, Strange struggled to use his Sling Ring, a device that could open portals in space for instantaneous travel, until The Ancient One stranded him on Mount Everest, forcing him to quickly open an escape portal to survive. After this success, Strange's mastery rapidly came to fruition. Strange also received martial arts training from Mordo, and Strange's astral form studied whenever his physical body slept, maximizing his study time. Learning humility during his studies, Strange repeatedly emailed Palmer trying to apologize, but she never replied.

Eager to learn more, Strange rashly used the ancient Eye of Agamotto to manipulate time, but was stopped by Masters Mordo and Wong, who warned that misuse of such powerful artifacts could disturb natural law and threaten time itself. Still only ultimately wanting to heal his hands, Strange refused to participate in what he called a "mystic war" when he learned that The Ancient One and the Masters existed to protect Earth from magical threats, much like the superhuman Avengers protected it from physical ones. Before he could leave, the traitorous Master Kaecilius explosively destroyed the London Sanctum to disable the mystic barrier the Sanctums projected to prevent extradimensional invasions, in the hope of allowing his new master Dormammu to claim Earth. The blast transited the portal between London and Kamar-Taj and catapulted Strange through the New York City Sanctum's portal in time to witness Kaecilius arrive there and murder Master Daniel Drumm. Defending himself, Strange ultimately knocked Kaecilius' Zealots through portal doors to remote locations on Earth, then battled Kaecilius in the Chamber of Relics, where they accidentally shattered the case housing the sentient Cloak of Levitation. The Cloak saved Strange's life, then forcibly directed him to use the Crimson Bands of Cyttorak to restrain Kaecilius.

Trying to win Strange over, Kaecilius claimed that merging Earth with Dormammu's Dark Dimension, which existed outside of time, would stop time's passage and so defeat death—adding that The Ancient One herself, despite forbidding others to access Dormammu's energies, was secretly using them to extend her own life. While listening, Strange was stabbed by a returning Zealot, Lucian, but as the Cloak battled Lucian, Strange used a Sling Ring to open a portal to Metropolitan General Hospital, where he sought medical attention from a shocked Palmer. As she operated on his body, Strange's astral form told her what had happened, then battled

Lucian's pursuing astral form. Discovering that Palmer's use of a defibrillator caused his astral form to discharge electricity, Strange's spirit insisted she give him a massive charge, enabling him to destroy Lucian's astral form. After apologizing to Palmer for his past behavior, Strange returned to the Sanctum to find Lucian dead and Kaecilius gone.

The Ancient One and Mordo, who had arrived at the Sanctum during Strange's absence, were surprised to see the fickle Cloak had chosen Strange. Strange confronted The Ancient One about Kaecilius' claim, but she would neither deny nor confirm it; his accusations

angered Mordo, who called Strange a coward for "whining" about killing a Zealot. Before their argument could proceed, Kaecilius returned to destroy the Sanctum, but Strange pulled them into the Mirror Dimension, unaware that Kaecilius' connection to the Dark Dimension made him more powerful there. After being chased through a nightmarish, kaleidoscopic version of New York City, Mordo and Strange were saved by The Ancient One, but in using her power, a scar-like symbol of Dormammu was revealed on her forehead, confirming Strange's suspicions. Kaecilius stabbed The Ancient One and cast her from the Mirror Dimension to fall multiple stories in New York City.

Though Strange enlisted Palmer and other hospital staff, they could not save The Ancient One. As she lay dying, her astral form visited Strange. She revealed that Strange could use the majority of his magical abilities to channel dimensional energy into his hands and thus regain his old life, but argued that he could do more good by protecting the world with the other Masters. Though he believed he was not ready to face Dormammu without her, she reminded him that no one gets to choose their time.

ASTRAL FORM

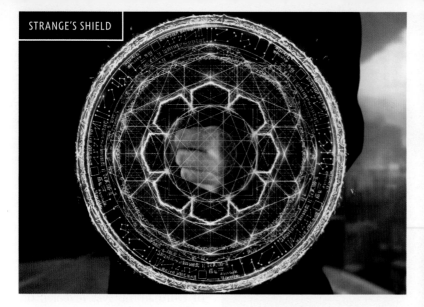

STRANGE'S SHIELD

With that encouragement, The Ancient One's astral form dissipated.

Strange was comforted by Palmer before he left to confront Dormammu, and they acknowledged what she had tried to tell him after his accident: losing his hands was not the end, and there were other ways to save lives. Palmer kissed Strange on the cheek and left. Despite Mordo's anger at The Ancient One's use of forbidden sorcery, Strange convinced him to help defeat Kaecilius, but the two men arrived in Hong Kong to find the Sanctum there already destroyed. Desperate to stop Earth from merging with the Dark Dimension, Strange used the Eye's time manipulation

powers to reverse the destruction, then trapped Dormammu in a time loop to force him to cease his invasion; Strange was prepared to spend eternity in this loop, being repeatedly killed by Dormammu, to ensure Earth remained free.

After Dormammu relented and withdrew the Dark Dimension and his Zealots, Strange returned the Eye to Kamar-Taj and relocated with Wong to New York City to serve as the Sanctum's guardian and prepare to defend Earth once word spread of The Ancient One's death. He later met with the Asgardian Avenger Thor, and agreed to help him locate his missing father Odin, Asgard's king. ⊕

STEPHEN STRANGE WAS AN extremely talented, yet arrogant and materialistic, surgeon until a horrific car accident left his hands with severe and incurable nerve damage. Desperate to regain what he'd lost, Strange traveled to Tibet after hearing rumors of mystical healing performed by the Ancient One (Yao) and was eventually allowed to train with him. While there, Strange discovered the Ancient One's pupil Karl Mordo had secretly allied with the Dark Dimension's evil Dormammu and repeatedly opposed his former teacher. Following years of study, Strange used his mystical abilities to aid other sorcerers and costumed heroes in defending Earth. When the demonic Shuma-Gorath sought to invade Earth through the Ancient One's mind, Strange was forced to kill his mentor and then became the new Sorcerer Supreme.

As Doctor Strange, he has battled evil individually, with his various disciples, alongside his manservant Wong, with both the Defenders and Avengers super-teams, and with his wife Clea, Dormammu's niece; however, the two eventually divorced. Strange also helped form the covert Illuminati with other prominent heroes in an effort to quietly prevent global catastrophic events. Clashes against mystical foes have periodically diminished Strange's power, and he's been replaced as Sorcerer Supreme on occasion. Defeating the Empirikul, extradimensional beings determined to eradicate magic, left Strange weakened and at the mercy of other magic users, especially Mordo, who promised to kill Strange for Dormammu.

FIRST APPEARANCE:
STRANGE TALES #110 (1963)

IN THE DARK DIMENSION

DORMAMMU

FIRST APPEARANCE:
Marvel's *Doctor Strange* [2016]

Also known as the Destroyer of Worlds, the malevolent Dormammu is constantly plotting to conquer all of the infinite realities and dimensions within the Multiverse and absorb them into his home domain, the Dark Dimension. A being of unquenchable hunger and infinite power, Dormammu longs to conquer Earth's reality the most, making him the sworn enemy of Earth's Sorcerer Supreme and the Masters of the Mystic Arts, all of whom are dedicated to protecting Earth from magical and extradimensional threats.

When Master Kaecilius—distraught over losing his loved ones—sought to defeat death, he contacted Dormammu, knowing that Dormammu and his dimension exist outside of time. Dormammu granted Kaecilius and his Zealot followers vast power so they could

KAECILIUS, WITH DORMAMMU'S MARK ON FOREHEAD

destroy the three Sanctums of Kamar-Taj, which projected a protective shield around Earth that prevented Dormammu from invading and merging the timeless Dark Dimenson with

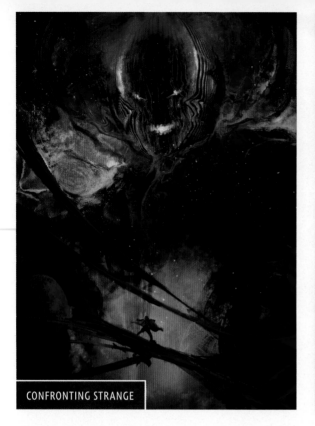

CONFRONTING STRANGE

Earth, which Kaecilius believed would eliminate death by stopping time. The Zealots successfully eliminated the London location, but Doctor Stephen Strange prevented the New York City Sanctum's destruction, though he was unable to stop Kaecilius from killing the Sorcerer Supreme, The Ancient One. Turning their attention to Hong Kong, the Zealots tore down the Sanctum there, weakening the shield enough to allow Dormammu to spread the Dark Dimension onto Earth.

However, Strange accessed the Infinity Stone within the Eye of Agamotto and reversed time, restoring the Hong Kong Sanctum. Strange then journeyed into the Dark Dimension and used the Eye to trap Dormammu in a time loop, constantly repeating a brief confrontation with Strange. Desperate to escape the temporal torture, Dormammu agreed to end his invasion of Earth. He then completed the corruption of Kaecilius and the

Zealots—now the bestial Mindless Ones—and at Strange's insistence, brought them to the Dark Dimension.

FACT SHEET

▶ DORMAMMU APPEARS AS A MASSIVE FLOATING HEAD COMPOSED OF SPACE-TIME, WITH EYES CENTERED WITHIN VERTICAL STRIPS OF CRACKLING, RIPPLING ENERGY.

▶ HE IS ALSO KNOWN AS "THE COSMIC CONQUEROR."

IN THE COMICS

BORN UNTOLD YEARS AGO, DORMAMMU gathered power until he was exiled from his home dimension. While exploring dimensions in human form, he found the Dark Dimension. Decades later, when Dormammu attempted to merge it with the dimension of the bestial Mindless Ones, they rampaged, killing the Dark Dimension's King Olnar and others. Dormammu assumed the throne and merged his essence with the Dark Dimension, becoming enormously powerful. In his quest to conquer Earth, Dormammu repeatedly clashed with Agamotto, Earth's first Sorcerer Supreme, and Doctor Stephen Strange, the current being to hold that title; he also often allies with Baron Karl Mordo and other pawns in his quest to conquer neighboring dimensional realms. Dormammu has occasionally been supplanted as Dark Dimension ruler by his power-hungry sister Umar and his benevolent niece, Clea.

FIRST APPEARANCE:
STRANGE TALES #126 (1964)

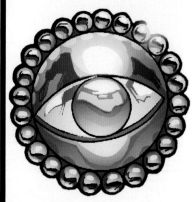

EYE OF AGAMOTTO

FIRST APPEARANCE:
Marvel's *Doctor Strange* [2016]

The Eye of Agamotto was created by the father of the mystic arts, Agamotto, and is an age-old relic that houses an Infinity Stone, an object of vast, nearly unimaginable power. The Eye is generally stored in its own chamber off of the library in Kamar-Taj, where The Ancient One and other Masters use it to remotely observe mystical happenings on Earth. When manifested, the energy produced by the Eye is bright green.

When Doctor Stephen Strange, during his study of the mystic arts, consulted the *Book of Cagliostro* without approval, he read about the Eye and tapped into its immense power to control time. Strange's experiments included manipulating an apple from pristine to half-consumed to a rotting core, and restoring pages to the *Book of Cagliostro* that were torn out by the traitorous Kaecilius. However, Strange used the Eye before reading the warnings of its misuse. When his experiments inadvertently threatened the fabric of time, he was stopped by Masters Mordo and Wong before he could cause irreparable harm.

When Kaecilius destroyed the Hong Kong Sanctum, the Dark Dimension began merging with Earth. Strange used the Eye to undo the damage to the Sanctum and trapped

AN AMULET BESTOWED UPON the Sorcerer Supreme by the ancient mystical entity Agamotto, the Eye of Agamotto can dispel illusions, amplify its wearer's mental powers, and repel creatures of darkness. Recently, Agamotto tried to reclaim the Eye, stating his fellow mystical entities turned against him. Then-Sorcerer Supreme Doctor Voodoo (Jericho Drumm) sacrificed his own life to prevent this. Agamotto later granted Doctor Stephen Strange the Eye again, indicating that the ordeal had all been a test of his worthiness.

FIRST APPEARANCE:
STRANGE TALES #127 (1964)

Dormammu in a time loop until he agreed to end his invasion. Following this, Strange returned the Eye to its chamber in Kamar-Taj. ⊗

FACT SHEET

- ▶ WHEN USED, THE FRONT OF THE METAL EYE OPENS TO REVEAL THE STONE INSIDE.

- ▶ WHILE CASTING TIME-MANIPULATION SPELLS, STRANGE'S FOREARM IS ENCIRCLED BY INTRICATE ENERGY RINGS AND A SHAPE THAT APPEARS LIKE A DIAL IN FRONT OF HIS HAND.

EMPOWERED BY THE GEM

PRE-RITUAL

KAECILIUS

FIRST APPEARANCE:
Marvel's *Doctor Strange* [2016]

Some time after losing a young son in unrevealed circumstances, Kaecilius' wife Adria suddenly collapsed in a marketplace, then died after a months-long coma. After contemplating suicide, the drunken, grieving Kaecilius was eventually approached by an emissary of Kamar-Taj, who offered him help finding his way through the mystic arts. Stubborn, ambitious, and very aggressive in his training, Kaecilius was nonetheless taught by The Ancient One because she felt he was gifted. After becoming a Master, Kaecilius mocked fellow Master Wong's defeat at the hands of an unidentified witch's use of a powerful scepter; when the arrogant Kaecilius was also defeated, he humbly accepted help from Wong and other Masters in defeating the witch, then admitted Wong's Master-level abilities.

At some point, Kaecilius learned that The Ancient One had extended her life using energies from the malevolent Dormammu, despite forbidding others from such practices; after confronting The Ancient One, she still refused to teach him how to manipulate

---

Kaecilius and the Zealots performed the stolen spell and gained power from Dormammu

---

time. After scouring the tomes in Kamar-Taj's library, Kaecilius came to believe death could be defeated by allowing Dormammu to merge his timeless Dark Dimension with Earth's dimension, thereby eliminating death by

stopping time. Kaecilius won other frustrated Apprentices—his Zealots—to his cause. Needing a ritual from the *Book of Cagliostro* to contact Dormammu, Kaecilius and the Zealots invaded the Kamar-Taj library, executed the librarian, then tore out the relevant pages. When The Ancient One appeared and warned Kaecilius the ritual he was stealing would only bring him sorrow, he and the Zealots fled through a portal to London. Pursuing, The Ancient One pulled them into the Mirror Dimension and killed most of them; however, Kaecilius and a few Zealots escaped through another portal.

Kaecilius and the Zealots performed the stolen spell and gained power from Dormammu, which marred their faces with cracking and discoloration around the eyes and scarred their foreheads with Dormammu's symbol.

Now able to forge fractured spacetime into deadly shards, Kaecilius and the Zealots launched an attack on the Masters by destroying the London Sanctum, then swiftly attacked the New York City Sanctum. However, its destruction was prevented by Doctor Stephen Strange, who bound Kaecilius with the Crimson Bands of Cyttorak. While constrained, Kaecilius tried to win Strange over by explaining his plan to defeat death, and informing him of The Ancient One's apparent hypocrisy. When a returning Zealot Lucian distracted Strange, Kaecilius somehow escaped the Bands and fled.

Kaecilius swiftly returned to New York's Sanctum reinforced by additional Zealots, but Strange pulled himself, Mordo, Kaecilius and two Zealots into the Mirror Dimension, unaware Kaecilius' Dark Dimension connection made him more powerful there. He nearly slew Strange and Mordo before The Ancient One intervened, revealing her connection to the Dark Dimension before Kaecilius mortally wounded her and cast her from the Mirror Dimension to fall dozens of stories to the ground. After this, Kaecilius and his remaining two Zealots destroyed the Hong Kong Sanctum, allowing the Dark Dimension to begin merging with Earth.

When Strange arrived, he reversed time to undo the damage and ended the invasion by trapping Dormammu in a time loop until he agreed to stop his attack. A defeated Dormammu turned Kaecilius and his followers into bestial Mindless Ones by letting his energies fully corrupt them; the Mindless Ones were taken to the Dark Dimension by Dormammu at Strange's insistence. ⊕

BARON KARL MORDO'S CHIEF disciple Kaecilius aided his master in his hunt for Doctor Stephen Strange, a quest that took them to the Ancient One's palace, Hong Kong, and England, but the Sorcerer Supreme evaded him at every turn. After Mordo's subsequent defeat, Kaecilius joined forces with fellow Mordo operatives Adria and Demonicus to capture Strange, but he escaped and wiped the trio's memories of magic. They eventually recovered their memories, and united to invade Strange's Sanctum Sanctorum in disguise as a TV crew; Strange saw through their ruse, and exiled them to the inescapable Purple Dimension.

FIRST APPEARANCE:
STRANGE TALES #130 (1965)

BATTLING STRANGE IN THE MIRROR DIMENSION

▶ KAECILIUS FREQUENTLY USES TWO BLADED SCYTHES, WHICH HE STORES ON HIS BACK, UNDERNEATH A FOLD IN HIS TUNIC.

▶ FOLLOWING THE RITUAL, KAECILIUS COULD FOLD SPACE AND MATTER AT WILL, AS IF HE WERE IN THE MIRROR DIMENSION.

▶ KAECILIUS BELIEVED TIME IS THE TRUE ENEMY OF LIFE, AS IT INEVITABLY LEADS TO DEATH.

▶ TO ATTACK THE ANCIENT ONE, KAECILIUS STABBED THROUGH ONE OF HIS OWN ZEALOTS, KILLING HIM AS WELL.

KAMAR-TAJ

FIRST APPEARANCE:
Marvel's *Doctor Strange [2016]*

The temple of Kamar-Taj is located in Kathmandu, Nepal, and serves as both the home of The Ancient One, the Sorcerer Supreme for Earth's dimension, and as the training ground for her students, including novices, apprentices, disciples, and the Masters of the Mystic Arts. There, the students train almost to the brink of ruin, learning discipline of body and mind, striving to obtain enough balance to learn sorcery. The Ancient One also works to help her novices avoid evil and achieve sufficient enlightenment, purpose, and understanding to protect Earth from mystical threats.

The temple grounds house living quarters for all residents, indoor and outdoor training grounds, storage for numerous mystical artifacts, and Wi-Fi for internet access. The walls of the central compound are 20 to 25 feet high, and both inside and outside walls and surfaces are covered with ornate art and intricate designs befitting their mystical setting.

The heart of Kamar-Taj is the library, which houses countless magical tomes that are available to students, and a collection of books that contain practices too powerful for any but the Sorcerer Supreme to use. This special collection resides on honeycomb-like racks that can recess into the library's walls.

A chamber in Kamar-Taj, the Sanctum Rotunda houses three doors that instantly transport a person to one of three Sanctums, in New York, Hong Kong, and London. Part of Kamar-Taj was damaged when the

LIBRARY

THOUGH SEEMINGLY INNOCUOUS, the Himalayan village of Kamar-Taj secretly hid both a potentially humanity-destroying Talisman and "Nine Wise Men" guarding a *Darkhold* scroll containing a vampire-destroying spell. Circa 1450 A.D., two local youths, Kaluu and Yao (later the Ancient One), studied magic, but the ancient vampire Varnae corrupted Kaluu. Taking over the villagers' minds, he turned them into a conquering army; trying to stop Kaluu, Yao inadvertently killed them all. After the Deathwalkers unearthed the Talisman in 1908, Kaluu opposed their attempts to use it, angry at Kamar-Taj's desecration. Some accounts claim a resettled Kamar-Taj is either Wong's home village, the site of the Ancient One's palace, or both.

FIRST APPEARANCE:
(THE ANCIENT ONE'S PALACE, UNNAMED) *STRANGE TALES #110 (1963)*; (VILLAGE, NAMED) *STRANGE TALES #148 (1966)*

disturbed Master Kaecilius destroyed the London Sanctum, intent on shattering the mystic shield keeping the evil Dormammu from Earth. The Ancient One was killed in the subsequent battles between Kaecilius' Zealot forces and the Masters.

Presumably, the Masters repaired Kamar-Taj after the Masters/Zealots war, and a new Sorceror Supreme for Kamar-Taj will be sought. ⊕

FACT SHEET

▶ THE PASSWORD FOR THE TEMPLE'S WI-FI IS SHAMBALLA.

▶ NO KNOWLEDGE IS FORBIDDEN IN KAMAR-TAJ, BUT BOOKS IN THE LIBRARY ARE DIVIDED INTO STAGES, SO THAT STUDENTS LEARN PRACTICES AT PROPER TIMES DURING THEIR TRAINING.

▶ STUDENTS WERE TAUGHT THE SEEMING DICHOTOMY THAT LEARNING CONTROL IN MAGIC REQUIRED GIVING UP CONTROL.

▶ STUDENTS TRAIN BOTH INDOORS AND IN LARGE OUTDOOR PLAZAS.

HONEYCOMB RACKS

MAGICAL RELICS

FIRST APPEARANCE:
Thor [2011] [ODIN'S VAULT];
Marvel's *Doctor Strange* [2016]
[MASTERS' COLLECTION]

As part of their mission to protect Earth from mystical threats, the Masters of the Mystic Arts collect and safeguard relics that sustain power too great for a human body to withstand. Besides mystical tokens known to be kept in Odin's vault in Asgard, other items are housed in Kamar-Taj and the New York Sanctum Sanctorum, including the Cloak of Levitation, the Eye of Agamotto, and the following:

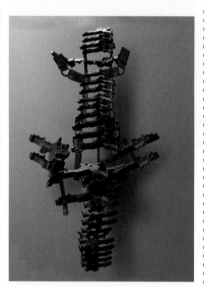

The **BOOK OF CAGLIOSTRO**, a study of time itself, is kept within The Ancient One's private collection due to the immense power within its pages. Before they were stolen by Kaecilius, pages detailed how to contact Dormammu; the ornate decoration on the front cover glows with orange energy.

The **CRIMSON BANDS OF CYTTORAK** are interlocking strips of magical metal and hardware that can close around a subject to constrain them, silence them, and prevent the use of mystical abilities. The Bands are housed in the New York Sanctum's Chamber of Relics and were briefly used to restrain Kaecilius during his assault on the building.

SLING RINGS are jewelry individually crafted for each wearer, enabling the opening of portals for instantaneous travel across Earth and the Multiverse through visualization. Loss of a ring can result in the user being stranded, as portal creation requires a ring. The rings are generally 2"-3" in length and have holes for two fingers.

IN THE COMICS

A BOOK OF SPELLS COMPILED BY THE immortal mystic Cagliostro (O-Bengh), the *Book of Cagliostro* was safeguarded by his followers for generations until Baron Karl Mordo stole it to use its secrets to strike against his former master the Ancient One (Yao).

FIRST APPEARANCE:
MARVEL PREMIERE #12 (1973)

IN THE COMICS

POWERED BY THE MALEVOLENT mystical entity Cyttorak, the nigh-unbreakable Crimson Bands can be called forth to bind all but the strongest of foes in bands of magical energy. On at least one occasion, a mystical circle of energy called the Circle of Cyttorak performed a similar function as the Bands.

FIRST APPEARANCE:
(BANDS MENTIONED) *STRANGE TALES #124 (1964)*;
(CIRCLE) *STRANGE TALES #125 (1964)*;
(BANDS SHOWN) *STRANGE TALES #126 (1964)*

PORTAL TO EVEREST

The **STAFF OF THE LIVING TRIBUNAL** is a wooden staff with handles on both ends that is presumably imbued with the power of the Living Tribunal, the cosmic embodiment of judgment. The staff can be split into segments connected by powerful energy, functioning as a whip.

The **VAULTING BOOTS OF VALTORR** allow the wearer to defy gravity and walk on air. Each step in the air leaves behind a glowing orange disc of energy that fades within seconds. Master Mordo frequently uses these boots, and wore them in battle against the traitor Kaecilius.

The **WAND OF WATOOMB** is a double-horn-headed baton of unrevealed power stored at the Hong Kong Sanctum; it was wielded by Wong in the battle against Kaecilius.

IN THE COMICS

A CONCEPTUAL BEING, THE LIVING Tribunal is the cosmic embodiment of judgment. Not guided by personal motivation, the completely impartial Tribunal determines the greater interests of the universe; it has the power to quarantine sections of the universe or entire timelines deemed too dangerous, and is willing to sacrifice millions of lives for the sake of billions.

FIRST APPEARANCE:
STRANGE TALES #157 (1967)

IN THE COMICS

ONE OF EIGHT COMPETING MYSTIC entities named the Octessence, Valtorr empowers his exemplars with mystic power when they invoke his name.

FIRST APPEARANCE:
DOCTOR STRANGE, SORCERER SUPREME #49 (1993)

IN THE COMICS

A SOURCE OF VAST MYSTICAL POWER, the Wand of Watoomb was coveted by the dark magician Xandu the Unspeakable, who wished to use it to revive his dead lover Melinda Morrison. Doctor Stephen Strange and Spider-Man (Peter Parker) repeatedly kept it away from him.

FIRST APPEARANCE:
AMAZING SPIDER-MAN ANNUAL #2 (1965)

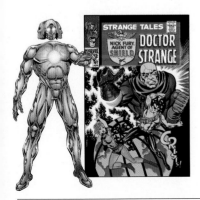

MASTERS OF THE MYSTIC ARTS

FIRST APPEARANCE: Marvel's *Doctor Strange* [2016]

The Masters of the Mystic Arts, also known as People of the Light, are students of The Ancient One—the Sorcerer Supreme of Earth's dimension. They exist to protect the Sanctums, three sanctuaries that project a protective mystical energy shield around Earth, and they live and operate from Kamar-Taj, a compound in Kathmandu, Nepal. They are extensively trained in the use of magical relics (repositories of mystical energy too powerful for the body to withstand), astral projection, and the mystic and martial arts. Known Masters include Doctor Stephen Strange; former Masters Kaecilius and Mordo; and the following:

Master **DANIEL DRUMM** was assigned to guard the New York Sanctum Sanctorum, but was slain by former Master Kaecilius and his Zealots.

IN THE COMICS

DANIEL DRUMM WAS THE deceased brother and disembodied mentor to voodoo practitioner Jericho Drumm (Brother Voodoo). Embittered by Jericho's inability to resurrect him, Daniel bargained with the Hand ninja clan for his own resurrection.

FIRST APPEARANCE:
STRANGE TALES #169 (1973)

Despite having lost his left hand, the silent Master **HAMIR** could cast spells at a Master level and served The Ancient One.

IN THE COMICS

HAMIR WAS THE ANCIENT ONE'S attendant and is Wong's father. After the Ancient One's death, Hamir trained his own pupils.

FIRST APPEARANCE:
STRANGE TALES #111 (1963)

TINA MINORU, the Hong Kong Sanctum's guardian, was presumably killed when the Zealots attacked there, but likely returned to life when Doctor Strange's manipulation of time undid their destruction.

IN THE COMICS

SORCERESS TINA MINORU SERVED the ancient, malevolent Gibborim deities as a member of the criminal Pride organization, which was apparently killed by the Gibborim when they failed to deliver a sacrificial soul.

FIRST APPEARANCE:
RUNAWAYS #1 (2003)

SOL RAMA was appointed the guardian of the London Sanctum, but was killed by a shard of tangible time thrown by former Master Kaecilius.

MORDO

FIRST APPEARANCE:
Marvel's *Doctor Strange* [2016]

Initially coming to Kamar-Taj seeking power to defeat his enemies, Mordo instead learned to hold his personal demons at bay while studying under The Ancient One, and he became a Master of the Mystic Arts. During his training, Mordo became proficient in the martial arts, as well as in the use of mystical relics including the Staff of the Living Tribunal and the Vaulting Boots of Valtorr. When Mordo learned that the Dragon Raiders were using the Bow and Arrow of Apollon to blackmail the citizens of Guizhou, China, he notified The Ancient One; the two defeated the gang and collected the Arrow for safekeeping.

Some time later, while walking through Kathmandu's city markets, Mordo overheard Dr. Stephen Strange asking for directions to Kamar-Taj and followed him. After saving Strange from bandits, Mordo took him to meet The Ancient One. When she refused to teach the disrespectful, skeptical Strange, Mordo convinced her to relent. After Strange was admitted to Kamar-Taj, Mordo assisted in his training, helping teach him martial arts and educating him in the use of mystical relics. When the curious Strange brashly used the Eye of Agamotto to experiment with time manipulation, Mordo and Wong stopped him. They told him of the Masters' history and their purpose: to safeguard Earth against magical and extra-dimensional threats, such as the Dark Dimension's Dormammu.

Mordo was separated from Strange when the Zealots' attack destroyed the London Sanctum. Mordo found him again after Strange prevented Kaecilius from destroying the New York City Sanctum, but became angered when Strange agonized over killing a Zealot in battle and accused The Ancient One of drawing power from Dormammu to prolong her life. The Ancient One soon

FACT SHEET

► MORDO SAID HE ONCE WAS DISRESPECTFUL OF THE MYSTICAL, BUT QUICKLY LEARNED TO FORGET WHAT HE THOUGHT HE KNEW TO STUDY AT KAMAR-TAJ.

► MORDO IS HAUNTED BY HIS PAST, BUT WILL NOT SPEAK OF IT. HE SIMPLY MAINTAINS THAT BECAUSE OF IT, HE IS WILLING TO TAKE DRASTIC MEASURES IN LIFE, INCLUDING KILLING HIS ENEMIES WITHOUT HESITATION.

► THE ANCIENT ONE BELIEVED MORDO'S SOUL WAS RIGID AND UNMOVABLE DUE TO HIS LIFE EXPERIENCES, AND THAT HE AND STRANGE WERE PERFECT COUNTERPARTS FOR EACH OTHER.

revealed her connection to the Dark Dimension during a battle with Kaecilius that resulted in her death.

Though devastated that The Ancient One had participated in practices she had forbidden, and believing she led Kaecilius and the Zealots to Dormammu, Mordo helped Strange fight them in Hong Kong. Strange used the Eye of Agamotto to reverse time to undo the Hong Kong Sanctum's destruction, then trapped Dormammu in a time loop until he agreed to end his invasion. In the aftermath, Mordo declared he would no longer walk the path of the Masters, believing Strange and The Ancient One's repeated violations of natural law could not be justified. Months later, having decided Earth had too many sorcerers, Mordo stripped Jonathan Pangborn of the mystical energy he used to move his crippled body, returning him to paraplegia. ⊕

KARL AMADEUS MORDO, THE son of a Transylvanian baron, succeeded his father after his death. The teenage Baron Mordo was schooled in black magic before traveling to Tibet to study under the Ancient One (Yao), but Mordo was consumed with jealousy upon learning a boy named Stephen Strange was destined to replace the Ancient One as Earth's Sorcerer Supreme. Years later, Mordo allied himself with the Dark Dimension's Dormammu in an attempt to kill both Strange and the Ancient One. He was repeatedly unsuccessful in clashes with Strange, whether alone or employing other mystics to fight with him. When Mordo discovered he had cancer, he sought to atone for past misdeeds, even saving Strange's life before he died. Mordo was resurrected when Strange was forced to manipulate time to save an ally. Again allied with Dormammu, Mordo promised to claim Strange's head for him or sacrifice his own as a replacement.

FIRST APPEARANCE:
STRANGE TALES #111 (1963)

CHRISTINE PALMER

FIRST APPEARANCE:
Marvel's *Doctor Strange* [2016]

Dr. Christine Palmer practices emergency medicine at Metropolitan General Hospital in New York, where she and Dr. Stephen Strange worked together to create new medical techniques. After their romantic relationship ended, Palmer vowed never to become involved with a coworker again. When fellow doctor Nicodemus West declared a gunshot victim brain-dead, Palmer called in Strange, who humiliated West by saving the man's life. Afterward, Palmer repeated her offer for Strange to become the ER's neurosurgeon on call, but Strange refused. Palmer posited that this was because he would not gain fame or accolades working in the emergency room.

After Strange suffered massive damage to his hands in an automobile accident, Palmer was present when he awoke from surgery to tell him what had happened. She remained by his side to assist in his recovery, but in his anger and despair, he dismissed her compassion and care.

Months later, a wounded Strange surprised Palmer by turning up at the hospital seeking her medical help. She quickly came to his aid, but was shocked when the now-mystically powered Strange's astral form appeared to advise her while she was operating on his physical body. Despite damage occurring in the operating room because of a battle between the astral forms of Strange and a Zealot named Lucian, Palmer remained focused on her work to save Strange's body. When it became necessary for Palmer to use defibrillators on Strange, his

FACT SHEET

▶ PALMER NAMED HER WORKPLACE NON-FRATERNIZATION RULE THE "STRANGE POLICY."

▶ WHILE THEY WERE DATING, PALMER GAVE STRANGE A WATCH WITH "TIME WILL TELL HOW MUCH I LOVE YOU ~ CHRISTINE" ENGRAVED ON THE BACK.

▶ WHILE HE WAS EXPLAINING HIS MYSTICAL JOURNEY TO HER, PALMER ACCUSED STRANGE OF JOINING A CULT.

▶ IT WASN'T UNTIL AFTER THE ANCIENT ONE'S DEATH THAT STRANGE REALIZED PALMER HAD BEEN RIGHT WHEN SHE TOLD HIM THERE WERE OTHER WAYS TO SAVE LIVES THAN USING HIS HANDS FOR SURGERY.

astral form channeled the shock as additional power on the astral plane. Strange advised Palmer to shock him again to grant him enough energy to defeat the Zealot, and Palmer reluctantly complied. After reuniting with his body, Strange apologized to a stunned Palmer for the way he'd treated her in the past and explained he'd been studying the mystic arts. Watching him leave through a spatial portal he'd created in a supply closet, she began to believe him.

When The Ancient One was mortally wounded in battle against her traitorous former student Kaecilius, Strange brought her to Palmer for assistance, but they were unable to save her life. Palmer comforted a grieving Strange, and then gave him a kiss on the cheek before he departed to confront Kaecilius. ⊕

CHRISTINE PALMER DEFIED HER wealthy father to become a nurse in order to build her own life. As an employee of New York's Metropolitan General Hospital, Palmer became an assistant to surgeon William Sutton, who persuaded an admiring Palmer to conceal his alcoholism and drug addiction. After Sutton lost a patient by operating on her while inebriated, Palmer confessed Sutton's addictions, which led to his arrest. Ashamed, she left Metro-General and became a private nurse for paralyzed recluse Derek Porter, only to discover he was a drug smuggler faking his paraplegia. Returning to Metro-General, Palmer assisted the X-Man Nightcrawler (Kurt Wagner) as he investigated a mass killing in the hospital's psychiatric ward. A mutual attraction briefly blossomed between the two, but Palmer considered relocating to her mother's home in Tucson, Arizona, after barely surviving an attack by a demon-possessed Wolverine (Logan/ James Howlett). Ultimately, Palmer remained at Metro-General.

FIRST APPEARANCE:
NIGHT NURSE #1 (1972)

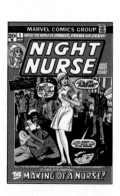

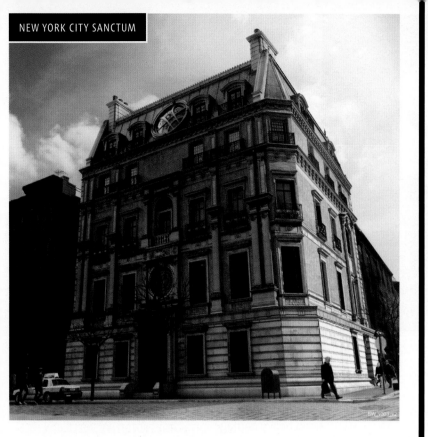

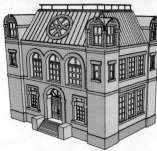

DR. STEPHEN STRANGE'S SANCTUM
Sanctorum, at 177A Bleecker Street in New York City's Greenwich Village, exists on a mystical nexus point that has hosted various sacred rituals and buildings in years past, many of which met tragic ends. The current townhouse is magically alive, allowing Strange to alter room shapes and locations—and even the laws of physics—within; spells have often been cast to protect it and disguise its true nature. Some rooms have remained constant, including the library filled with tomes of eldritch knowledge, a storage area for occult artifacts, and the meditation chamber, which includes a distinctive circular window. Other areas have changed to meet Strange's needs, such as a door to the nexus dimension of Fandazar Foo, and a cellar chamber that housed Strange's pain and suffering. The Sanctum has served as base for the Defenders, the Avengers, and other superhuman gatherings throughout the years.

FIRST APPEARANCE:
STRANGE TALES #110 (1963)

SANCTUMS

FIRST APPEARANCE:
Marvel's *Doctor Strange* [2016]

Seeking to protect Earth from extradimensional and magical threats, Agamotto—the first Sorcerer Supreme and father of the mystic arts—constructed three Sanctums on places of power and mystically connected them to serve as focal points for a supernatural shield around the planet. Over time, these Sanctums came to be surrounded by great cities: New York, Hong Kong, and London. Without these three sacred strongholds of the mystic arts, Earth would become vulnerable to invasion and destruction. Each Sanctum is capped with a large, stylized window bearing a symbol that presumably has arcane meaning. A chamber in Kamar-Taj, home of the Masters of the Mystic Arts, houses three doors providing instant transport to each Sanctum. Located on the top floor of the

New York Sanctum—called the Sanctum Sanctorum—is the Chamber of Relics, where the Masters safeguard magical items from misuse, including the Cloak of Levitation and Crimson Bands of Cyttorak. Three doors in the

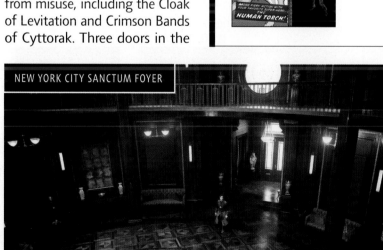

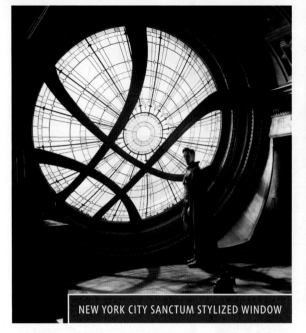

NEW YORK CITY SANCTUM STYLIZED WINDOW

NEW YORK CITY SANCTUM ROTUNDA OF GATEWAYS

Rotunda of Gateways open portals to various locations on Earth, determined by turning a dial on each doorframe. The New York City Sanctum is vast and ornate, larger inside than outside. Perception and reality become skewed within its walls, as it serves as a nexus between realities; presumably these are common traits shared by all three Sanctums. Each Sanctum has a guardian, appointed by The Ancient One, who lives in the building and safeguards it from external threats.

The traitor Kaecilius and his Zealots razed the London Sanctum in their opening salvo to destroy the planet's protective shield. Doctor Strange prevented the Zealots from destroying the New York Sanctum, though it sustained heavy damage during the battle between them. Strange was unable to save the Hong Kong Sanctum, which allowed the merging of Earth's reality with the Dark Dimension to begin in that city. A desperate Strange used the Eye of Agamotto to reverse time and undo the damage to the Sanctum, apparently restoring the shield around Earth.

Subsequently, Doctor Strange was appointed the guardian of the New York Sanctum. ⊕

HONG KONG SANCTUM

LONDON SANCTUM

WONG

FIRST APPEARANCE:
Marvel's *Doctor Strange* [2016]

Wong is a Master of the Mystic Arts who studied under The Ancient One in Nepal's Kamar-Taj sanctuary. After fellow Master Kaecilius turned on The Ancient One and murdered Kamar-Taj's librarian to steal instructions for a ritual to contact the malevolent Dormammu, Wong became the library's new caretaker. When Dr. Stephen Strange began his training under The Ancient One, Wong was resistant to his attempts at levity, making Strange think Wong was cold and humorless. Wong was surprised at how quickly Strange read and allowed him to progress to more advanced texts, but warned him against removing books without approval.

Later, Wong and Master Mordo observed Strange rashly experimenting with the Eye of Agamotto and stopped him before permanent damage was inflicted upon the timestream. The two then revealed the Masters' true purpose: to protect three Sanctums—in London, Hong Kong, and New York City—that collectively produced a shield protecting Earth from extradimensional and magical threats. However, during their explanation, Kaecilius destroyed the London Sanctum; the explosive force struck Kamar-Taj's library through a portal door, separating the men.

After learning The Ancient One died from battling with Kaecilius and his Zealots, Wong gathered a number of Masters to protect the Hong Kong Sanctum from them, but their efforts failed and Wong was killed. However, Strange's use of the Eye reversed the Sanctum's destruction, resurrected Wong, and forced Dormammu to cease the invasion he had begun when the Sanctum fell. Later, Wong accompanied Strange to New York City to help prepare for Earth's defense when word spread of The Ancient One's death. ⊕

ZEALOTS

FIRST APPEARANCE: **Marvel's *Doctor Strange* [2016]**

The Zealots are former Apprentices of the Mystic Arts from Kamar-Taj who chose to follow Kaecilius when he undertook a quest to eliminate death. More than a dozen Zealots accompanied Kaecilius to the Kamar-Taj library and helped him murder the librarian, then watched as he tore pages from the *Book of Cagliostro* that contained a ritual for contacting Dormammu in order to acquire great power. They fled when The Ancient One confronted them, but she pursued and transported them to the Mirror Dimension, where she thinned the Zealots' ranks through direct combat and by manipulating the surrounding landscape. A small number escaped with Kaecilius through a teleportation portal.

Now numbering four, the Zealots helped Kaecilius perform the ritual, believing the merger of Earth with Dormammu's Dark Dimension would grant humanity eternal life. The spell caused Dormammu's brand to appear on their foreheads; mystic corruption formed around their eyes, resembling burnt, charred skin. The Zealots assisted Kaecilius in numerous battles with the Masters, including the destruction of the London Sanctum, but lost Zealot Lucian when Doctor Strange destroyed his astral form. Another Zealot fell when Kaecilius stabbed through him to kill The Ancient One. Only two Zealots remained when Kaecilius attacked the Hong Kong Sanctum. They battled Wong, Strange, and Mordo as a spell cast by Strange rewound time to reverse the Sanctum's destruction. Strange trapped

Dormammu in a time loop until he agreed to end his invasion of Earth. At Strange's insistence, Dormammu completed the corruption of Kaecilius and the Zealots' bodies, transforming them into bestial Mindless Ones and pulling them into the Dark Dimension. ✪

THE MINDLESS ONES ARE A RACE of unintelligent, superhumanly strong, stone-like humanoids that fire energy beams from their eyes. Initially created by the Hell-lord Plokta to destroy his enemies, they were contained by the malevolent sorcerer Dormammu and his sister, Umar. Dormammu often used the Mindless Ones in his efforts to conquer Earth, sending them to battle Sorcerer Supreme Dr. Stephen Strange, the Avengers and Defenders, and other Earth heroes.

FIRST APPEARANCE:
STRANGE TALES #127 (1964)

BECOMING MINDLESS ONES

MIRROR DIMENSION

FIRST APPEARANCE:
Marvel's *Doctor Strange* [2016]

The Mirror Dimension exists within the same dimensional plane as Earth, but those within the Mirror Dimension cannot be perceived by Earthly senses, and no actions taken there can impact Earth. This dimension is frequently used by The Ancient One to survey, imprison threats, and as a training ground for her students, the Masters of the Mystic Arts, as the danger to the corporeal world is negated there. Masters can access the Mirror Dimension through portals that resemble fractured glass. Within this realm, standard rules of physics do not apply, and mystics at the level of The Ancient One can appear to alter reality on a massive scale.

After former Master Kaecilius devoted himself to the service of the evil Dormammu, Doctor Stephen Strange pulled him into the Mirror Dimension, believing this would prevent him from harming Earth. However, thanks to Dormammu, Kaecilius' power had increased drastically, and he could now manipulate the Mirror Dimension as The Ancient One did. He folded entire blocks of New York City upon itself, creating nightmarish, M.C. Escher-like landscapes. In the resulting battle inside the Mirror Dimension, Kaecilius stabbed The Ancient One and pushed her through a portal to the real world, causing her to fatally fall dozens of stories. ⊕

FACT SHEET

▶ WHEN IN THIS DIMENSION, ONE SEES EARTH LOCATIONS AROUND THEM AS IF VIEWED THROUGH A FACETED GEM OR A KALEIDOSCOPE.

▶ ANY SPOKEN WORD HAS AN EERIE ECHO WITHIN THIS REALM, AS IF THE SPEAKER WERE IN A TUNNEL.

JONATHAN PANGBORN

FIRST APPEARANCE:
Marvel's *Doctor Strange* [2016]

A factory accident broke Jonathan Pangborn's back, leaving him fully paralyzed from the chest down and partially paralyzed in both hands. He recovered at Metropolitan General Hospital, where Dr. Stephen Strange practiced neurosurgery. Strange refused to treat Pangborn, believing his hopeless case would mar his success record. Later, while receiving treatment for his own severely damaged hands, Strange learned that his physical therapist had also worked with Pangborn. The therapist told Strange he had seen Pangborn walking down the street a few years after he'd stopped coming for treatment. Desperate, Strange approached Pangborn, who told him he'd given up on his body and chose to elevate his mind instead. After traveling the world—sitting with gurus, holy men, and sacred women—Pangborn learned of Kamar-Taj. After learning how to channel dimensional energy to reverse his paralysis, Pangborn returned to New York City rather than explore deeper mystical secrets. Pangborn warned Strange of the high cost for what he sought, then wished him luck. Months later, Pangborn was stripped of his magic and rendered paraplegic once more by Mordo, who believed Pangborn was using his magic outside the natural order. Mordo stated that to protect Earth, he needed to eliminate its sorcerers. ⊕

FACT SHEET

▶ PANGBORN'S INJURY WAS CLASSIFIED AS C7-C8 LEVEL SPINAL CORD DAMAGE.

▶ BASKETBALL WAS ONE OF PANGBORN'S REGULAR PASTIMES.

THOR
UPDATE

FIRST APPEARANCE:
Thor [2011]

Sometime after battling the malevolent robot Ultron, Thor journeyed to New York City searching for his father, Odin. Consulting with Doctor Strange, he was intrigued to learn that Earth's diverse population now included wizards. Strange offered Thor tea, but transformed the cup into a large glass mug presumably filled with mead when Thor said he didn't drink tea.

As Thor drank, Strange voiced concern that Thor had brought his brother, Loki, to his city, as Loki was on the list Strange was keeping of potential dangers facing Earth. When Strange asked Thor whether he intended to return to Asgard after locating Odin, Thor promised they promptly would. Eager to see Loki far away from Earth, Strange quickly agreed to help Thor accomplish his goal. ⊕

FACT SHEET

- ▶ WHILE CONSULTING WITH STRANGE, THOR WORE HUMAN CLOTHING INSTEAD OF HIS STANDARD ASGARDIAN GARB.

- ▶ THOR DOWNED HIS DRINK RAPIDLY, THEN WATCHED WITH BEMUSEMENT AS THE LARGE MUG MYSTICALLY REFILLED BEFORE HIS EYES.

- ▶ THOR CONFIRMED FOR STRANGE THAT LOKI WAS A WORTHY INCLUSION ON HIS WATCH LIST.

NICODEMUS WEST

FIRST APPEARANCE:
Marvel's *Doctor Strange [2016]*

When a gunshot victim arrived at the Metropolitan General Hospital emergency room, Dr. Nicodemus West declared him brain-dead and was preparing to harvest his organs when Dr. Christine Palmer alerted Dr. Stephen Strange. Recognizing that the patient was being poisoned by the bullet lodged in his brain, Strange skillfully removed it, saving the man's life and humiliating West. When Strange's hands suffered massive damage in a car accident, he insisted on experimental surgeries to recover their use. Despite his disdain for West, Strange allowed him to operate. Later, a humbled Strange brought The Ancient One, mortally wounded, to the hospital for surgery and asked West to perform the operation, but she died nonetheless. ⊕

IN THE COMICS

ONE OF THE SURGEONS WHO TREATED Stephen Strange after the accident that cost him his manual dexterity, Nicodemus West later sought out Strange in a guilt-ridden quest to once again try to heal him, only to encounter the mage named the Ancient One (Yao) and become his student. West thereafter sought to mystically heal the infirm but inadvertently killed a cancer patient with a miscast spell. Later, Timely Pharmaceuticals blackmailed West—who had abandoned magic—into joining their crusade against mystical medicine, making him the firm's C.E.O. West died in combat with Strange, now Earth's Sorcerer Supreme, while trying to steal from him a rare extra-dimensional elixir that could cure any disease.

FIRST APPEARANCE:
(SHADOWED) *DOCTOR STRANGE: THE OATH #1 (2006);*
(FULL) *DOCTOR STRANGE: THE OATH #2 (2006)*

FACT SHEET

- ▶ WEST WAS PALMER'S SECOND CHOICE FOR NEUROSURGEON ON CALL FOR THE EMERGENCY ROOM, AWARDED THE ROLE ONLY AFTER STRANGE TURNED IT DOWN.

- ▶ WEST ENJOYS JALAPEÑO-FLAVORED KETTLE-STYLE POTATO CHIPS.

GUIDEBOOK TO THE MARVEL CINEMATIC UNIVERSE

MARVEL

GUARDIANS OF THE GALAXY VOL. 2

MARVEL STUDIOS PRESENTS A JAMES GUNN FILM "GUARDIANS OF THE GALAXY VOL. 2" CHRIS PRATT ZOE SALDANA DAVE BAUTISTA FEATURING VIN DIESEL AS BABY GROOT BRADLEY COOPER AS ROCKET MICHAEL ROOKER KAREN GILLAN POM KLEMENTIEFF ELIZABETH DEBICKI CHRIS SULLIVAN SEAN GUNN WITH SYLVESTER STALLONE AND KURT RUSSELL CASTING BY SARAH HALLEY FINN, CSA MUSIC SUPERVISOR DAVE JORDAN MUSIC BY TYLER BATES VISUAL DEVELOPMENT SUPERVISOR ANDY PARK VISUAL EFFECTS SUPERVISOR CHRISTOPHER TOWNSEND COSTUME DESIGNER JUDIANNA MAKOVSKY EDITED BY FRED RASKIN, ACE CRAIG WOOD, ACE PRODUCTION DESIGNER SCOTT CHAMBLISS DIRECTOR OF PHOTOGRAPHY HENRY BRAHAM PRODUCER DAVID J. GRANT EXECUTIVE PRODUCERS NIKOLAS KORDA STAN LEE EXECUTIVE PRODUCERS VICTORIA ALONSO JONATHAN SCHWARTZ EXECUTIVE PRODUCER LOUIS D'ESPOSITO PRODUCED BY KEVIN FEIGE, p.g.a. WRITTEN AND DIRECTED BY JAMES GUNN #GOTGVOL2

Collecting information from Marvel's *Guardians of the Galaxy Vol. 2* (2017).

HEAD WRITER/COORDINATOR: MIKE O'SULLIVAN

WRITERS: **ANTHONY COTILLETTA, KEVIN GARCIA, DARON JENSEN, ROB LONDON, CHRIS MCCARVER, JACOB ROUGEMONT,** AND **STUART VANDAL**

ARTISTS: **CARLO BARBERI, DANILO S. BEYRUTH, JOHN BUSCEMA, JOHN BYRNE, GENE COLAN, DON HECK, IAN JOYNER, JACK KIRBY, STEVE MCNIVEN, DAVID NAKAYAMA, TILL NOWAK, GEORGE PÉREZ, GERARDO SANDOVAL, VALERIO SCHITI, JIM VALENTINO, DAVID WENZEL, KEVIN WEST,** AND **RON WILSON**

BOOK DESIGN: **JAY BOWEN**

EDITOR: **SARAH BRUNSTAD**
VP PRODUCTION & SPECIAL PROJECTS: **JEFF YOUNGQUIST**
MANAGER, SPECIAL PROJECTS: **BRIAN OVERTON**
ASSISTANT EDITOR: **CAITLIN O'CONNELL**
ASSOCIATE MANAGING EDITOR: **KATERI WOODY**
EDITOR, SPECIAL PROJECTS: **MARK D. BEAZLEY**
SENIOR EDITOR, SPECIAL PROJECTS: **JENNIFER GRÜNWALD**
SVP PRINT, SALES & MARKETING: **DAVID GABRIEL**

EDITOR IN CHIEF: **AXEL ALONSO**
CHIEF CREATIVE OFFICER: **JOE QUESADA**
PRESIDENT: **DAN BUCKLEY**
EXECUTIVE PRODUCER: **ALAN FINE**

FOR **MARVEL STUDIOS**
CREATIVE DIRECTOR, RESEARCH & DEVELOPMENT:
WILL CORONA PILGRIM
VP PRODUCTION & DEVELOPMENT: **JONATHAN SCHWARTZ**
PRESIDENT: **KEVIN FEIGE**

SPECIAL THANKS TO DAVE ALTHOFF, SARAH BEERS, SHAWN "KEEBLER" BYERS, MATT DELMANOWSKI, ERIKA DENTON, TIM DILLON, GIANNA FICHERA, MIKE FICHERA, ELISSA HUNTER, PERCIVAL LANUZA, AVIA PEREZ, JACQUE PORTE, AND RYAN POTTER

IN LOVING MEMORY OF NICODEMUS JENSEN (2001-2017)

AYESHA

FIRST APPEARANCE:
Guardians of the Galaxy Vol. 2 [2017]

The golden-skinned Ayesha is the high priestess of the Sovereign, a race of humanoids who genetically modify themselves to achieve theoretical perfection. When the monstrous Abilisk threatened to consume their valuable Anulax Batteries, Ayesha hired the Guardians of the Galaxy to prevent the theft. After the successful completion of the mission, the Guardians met with Ayesha and claimed their reward: Gamora's adopted sister, Nebula, who had a high bounty on her head. However, when Ayesha learned that Rocket had stolen some Anulax Batteries for himself, Ayesha sent a Sovereign fleet after the Guardians, not caring if the batteries were destroyed so long as the Guardians were killed for their slight. After the Sovereign fleet was destroyed by the Guardians' Celestial ally Ego, Ayesha hired the Ravagers—led by Star-Lord's foster father Yondu Udonta—to bring the Guardians to her for one million units.

When Yondu's Ravagers faction failed to retrieve the Guardians due to a mutiny, Ayesha sent another Sovereign fleet to Ego's living planet body to kill the Guardians, but the fleet was again destroyed. A furious Ayesha was summoned to meet with a Sovereign council, who she knew were perturbed at the waste of resources resulting from her actions. Ayesha believed the council's wrath would dissipate when they saw her new creation—an upgraded birthing pod containing the next step in Sovereign evolution: a being of vast power and beauty who would be capable of destroying the Guardians. She planned to name the being "Adam." ◈

FACT SHEET

- ▶ AYESHA'S CROWN IS CONNECTED TO HER THRONE.
- ▶ AYESHA IS CONSTANTLY FLANKED BY A GROUP OF FOUR IMPOSING HANDMAIDENS WHO ATTEND TO HER NEEDS.
- ▶ WHEN OFF-PLANET, AYESHA WALKS ON A BLUE CARPET THAT IS ROLLED OUT BEFORE HER BY HER HANDMAIDENS.
- ▶ SHE WAS ESPECIALLY INTERESTED IN STAR-LORD'S MIXED GENEALOGY, FINDING HIS MIX OF HUMAN AND CELESTIAL DNA TO BE "PARTICULARLY RECKLESS."
- ▶ THOUGH THE SOVEREIGN ARE BIRTHED IN PODS, AYESHA OFFERED TO HAVE ARCHAIC MATING RITUALS WITH STAR-LORD FOR WHAT SHE CALLED "ACADEMIC REASONS."

WHEN HUMAN SCIENTISTS CREATED an entity to spawn the perfect race, their creation resisted their efforts and transformed itself into the female Her to procreate with another of the scientists' creations, Adam Warlock. Finding Warlock apparently dead, Her was christened J'Ridia Starduster after saving U'sr'prian aliens, and later allied with another potential mate—the cosmic Earth hero Quasar (Wendell Vaughn)—as Kismet. Later, the scientists remade Kismet into the villainous Ayesha, but she eventually broke their control and aided the universe's heroes against the Mad Titan Thanos.

FIRST APPEARANCE:
(AS HER) *MARVEL TWO-IN-ONE #61 (1980)*

DRAX UPDATE

FIRST APPEARANCE:
Guardians of the Galaxy [2014]

A few months after forming, the Guardians were hired by the Sovereign race to prevent an interdimensional Abilisk from consuming their Anulax Batteries. During the battle, Drax felt the monster's hide was too thick, so he jumped into its gaping maw and began stabbing it from the inside. Unaware Gamora had found a weakness and used her sword to cut the creature open, Drax emerged from the beast believing he had singlehandedly killed it. The Guardians collected their bounty and left, but Rocket had stolen several batteries; a Sovereign fleet pursued and punctured a hole in the *Milano*, destroying its weapons system. Drax attached a safety line to himself, donned a spacesuit, and destroyed a Sovereign craft while being towed in space. When their damaged ship crash-landed on a nearby planet, Gamora held onto the tether, saving Drax from falling to his death, though he collided with many trees during the landing; the super-durable Drax laughed off the experience.

After being taken to the living planet Ego, Star-Lord's long-lost father, Drax met and befriended Ego's servant Mantis, who eventually warned the Guardians of Ego's desire to absorb all life in the universe. When the Guardians' former enemy Nebula wanted to flee the planet, Drax refused to leave anyone behind, declaring the Guardians family. During a subsequent battle against Ego, Drax encouraged Mantis to use her empathic abilities to put Ego to sleep, and when Mantis was knocked unconscious during the struggle, Drax protected her until the Guardians could flee. Following Ego's destruction, Drax held a sleeping infant Groot during the funeral for the Guardians' ally Yondu. ⚡

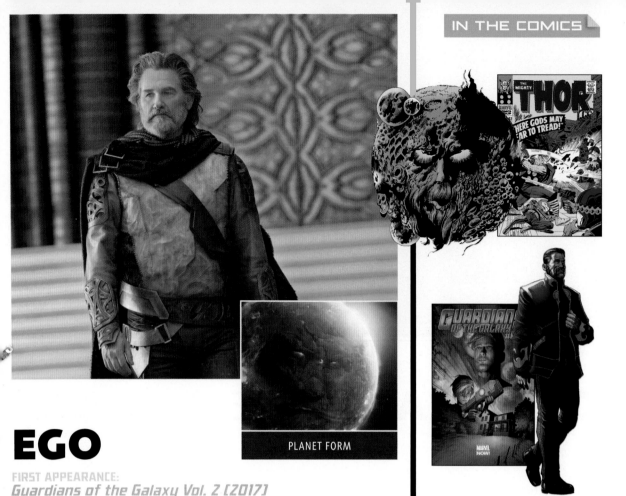

PLANET FORM

EGO

FIRST APPEARANCE:
Guardians of the Galaxy Vol. 2 (2017)

Ego is a millennia-old godlike Celestial who, over millions of years, created a planet around his drifting consciousness. Coming to believe that he should expand his being and consciousness across the universe to properly direct it, Ego

FACT SHEET

▶ EGO CAN CONTROL MOLECULES, CREATING OBJECTS AND BEINGS FROM SPACE MATTER; HIS TRUE FORM IS A COLORFUL, BLISSFUL, ORNATELY DETAILED PLANET THE SIZE OF EARTH'S MOON. FROM SPACE, THE PLANET'S SURFACE RESEMBLES AN ENORMOUS FACE.

▶ EGO'S AVATAR CAN WITHSTAND EXPOSURE TO SPACE, OCCASIONALLY RIDING OUTSIDE HIS OVAL-SHAPED SPACESHIP.

▶ EGO'S AVATAR MIMICKED MOST HUMANOID FUNCTIONS, INCLUDING WASTE PRODUCTION AND PROCREATION; THE AVATAR HAD TO RETURN TO EGO'S PLANET REGULARLY TO AVOID DYING.

▶ THE EMPATHIC MANTIS WAS RAISED BY EGO; HER EMOTION-MANIPULATING POWERS ENABLED HIM TO SLEEP.

formed a humanoid avatar to create countless offspring across galaxies, hoping they would serve as batteries for his "inner Light" and enable his universal expansion. In the early 1980s, Ego fell in love with Earthling Meredith Quill and visited her three times, siring a son. Ego ultimately gave her terminal brain cancer to end the distraction she had become. Years later, Ego hired the Ravager Yondu Udonta to kidnap Quill's son, Peter, but Yondu learned of Ego's intentions and instead kept Peter with the Ravagers until he grew up to be the spacefaring Star-Lord. Years later, after hearing of a human from Earth who had held an Infinity Stone, Ego began searching for him, knowing the human had to be his son. When Ego located Star-Lord and revealed his origins, Quill was initially thrilled to meet his father, but rebelled against him once he

THE CINEMATIC EGO IS DERIVED from two comic characters: Ego the Living Planet is a sentient, planet-sized being that can control its mass, alter its appearance to resemble other worlds, and create humanoid antibodies to fight invaders; it has a breathable atmosphere, can manipulate its weather, trigger tremors on its surface, and can consume beings that land on it. Originating from a region of space dubbed the Black Galaxy, Ego has often clashed with Thor Odinson; J'Son, heir to the Spartax planetary system, fathered a son with Meredith Quill after crashing on Earth, but departed before the child—Peter Quill—was born. As Star-Lord, the adult Peter triggered a rebellion that dethroned his despotic father, prompting J'Son to reinvent himself as interstellar crime lord Mister Knife.

FIRST APPEARANCE:
(EGO) *THOR #132* (1966); (EMPEROR JASON OF SPARTA, REALITY-791) *MARVEL PREVIEW #11* (1977), (KING J'SON OF SPARTAX, REALITY-616) *GUARDIANS OF THE GALAXY #0.1* (2013)

learned Ego had murdered his mother and planned to terra-form the universe. Star-Lord used his Celestial DNA to access Ego's energies to battle him while fellow Guardians Rocket and Groot placed a bomb in Ego's core, destroying Ego when it detonated. ▰

GAMORA UPDATE

FIRST APPEARANCE:
Guardians of the Galaxy [2014]

After the battle on Xandar, the Guardians were hired by the Sovereign race to protect their valuable Anulax Batteries, offering as payment the captive Nebula, Gamora's criminal adopted sister. In the Guardians' custody, Nebula vowed to kill Gamora, but she shrugged it off, telling Nebula she would live out the rest of her life in a Xandarian prison. Learning Rocket had stolen several batteries, a Sovereign fleet attacked the Guardians. While Rocket and Star-Lord argued over who was the better pilot—to Gamora's fury—Drax tethered himself outside the *Milano* to attack Sovereign ships, forcing Gamora to save his life when the *Milano* crash-landed. When the mysterious Ego, who had assisted in their escape from the Sovereign, found the Guardians and identified himself as Star-Lord's father, Gamora encouraged Star-Lord to investigate his claims, but quickly pulled away from Star-Lord when she realized she was

being affectionate, and later threatened him with death if he told anyone that they had danced.

On Ego's living planet true form, Gamora was attacked by Nebula, who was let go by the Ravagers after they captured Rocket, her warden. Though Gamora saved her life from an exploding craft, Nebula still attacked and ultimately won, but decided not to kill Gamora, claiming she finally bested her rival. Gamora was humbled when Nebula admitted that all she had truly wanted through their tumultuous, violent childhoods was a sister. After discovering Ego's malevolent plan to dominate the universe, Nebula and Gamora fought together alongside the Guardians; Nebula even saved Gamora from a lethal fall. When Gamora learned Star-Lord was sacrificing himself to destroy Ego, she attempted to rescue him, but Rocket—unwilling to see another friend die—reluctantly used an electric weapon to knock her out. After

Star-Lord was saved by the sacrifice of his foster father Yondu, Gamora finally admitted there was an "unspoken thing" between them, referencing the unacknowledged feelings between characters on Earth television shows Star-Lord had watched as a youth. The two embraced during Yondu's funeral. ◆

FACT SHEET

- AFTER STAR-LORD INSTINCTIVELY RETURNED THE FLIRTATIOUS ADVANCES OF THE SOVEREIGN HIGH PRIESTESS AYESHA, GAMORA ROLLED HER EYES WHEN STAR-LORD TRIED TO BACKPEDAL.

- EVEN IN THE MIDST OF BATTLE, GAMORA COULD NOT RESIST SMILING AND SAYING "HI" TO A NOW INFANT GROOT WHEN HE WAVED AT HER; GAMORA WAS VERY PROTECTIVE AND AFFECTIONATE TOWARD HIM.

- GAMORA PREFERS TO KEEP HER FEELINGS PRIVATE: SHE THREATENED TO BREAK MANTIS' JAW WHEN SHE HARMLESSLY ATTEMPTED TO DISPLAY HER EMPATHIC POWERS ON GAMORA.

- DURING A LATER STRUGGLE, THE EMOTION-MANIPULATING MANTIS MANIFESTED GAMORA'S FEAR, WHICH TERRIFIED AND CONFUSED HER SINCE SHE HAD NEVER FELT THAT EMOTION BEFORE.

- GAMORA'S KNIFE CAN TELESCOPE TO THE LENGTH OF A SWORD.

GROOT UPDATE

FIRST APPEARANCE:
Guardians of the Galaxy [2014]

Groot grew from a surviving twig to an age resembling a human toddler since his destruction. Simpleminded and naive, "Baby Groot" reacted to beings and situations around him with basic, childlike responses such as anger, fear, sadness, joy, and curiosity. When the Guardians of the Galaxy were forced to flee from a Sovereign fleet—who were pursuing them because Rocket had stolen their valuable Anulax Batteries—Groot was passed between teammates for safekeeping. During the subsequent crash landing, Groot obliviously ate candy. Groot was later captured by the Ravagers, who kept him in a birdcage and tormented him by dressing him in a miniature Ravagers outfit as their mascot, kicking him, and dousing him with alcohol. Released and sadly wandering the Ravagers' ship, Groot happened upon fellow captives Rocket and

Yondu, who asked him to bring Yondu's arrow-controlling fin to help them escape. However, Groot naively brought many objects except the fin, beaming with pride each time. Ravager Kraglin helped Groot find the fin so they could escape; Groot personally killed the Ravager who had abused him the most.

After a harrowing journey to reunite with the other Guardians, Groot proved small enough to fit through holes in the metal protecting the core of Ego, the malevolent living planet. Rocket built a bomb and tried to teach Groot how to activate the timer; Groot had difficulty remembering which button to push, repeatedly pointing to the immediate detonator. As a frustrated Rocket briefly turned his attention, Groot ran away with the bomb. Reaching the core, Groot correctly recalled the sequence and set the bomb; he then located Rocket

and escaped before detonation. Later, Groot shared music with Star-Lord, then reached for Drax, who allowed him to sleep on his shoulder. Some time later, a now teen Groot rebelled when Star-Lord began harping on him for only playing video games and sloppily leaving his vines around the ship. ◆

FACT SHEET

▶ GROOT'S PENCHANT FOR DANCING ENTERTAINED HIM THROUGH THE GUARDIANS' BATTLE AGAINST THE BESTIAL ABILISK.

▶ GROOT HATES HATS BECAUSE HE GETS CONFUSED, THINKING THE HAT IS A PART OF SOMEONE'S HEAD.

▶ GROOT FREQUENTLY PLAYED WITH A TINY BRANCH/LEAF GROWING OFF HIS ARM.

▶ YONDU'S AFFECTIONATE NICKNAME FOR GROOT WAS "TWIG."

▶ GROOT HATED THE RAVAGERS OUTFIT HE WAS FORCED TO WEAR, BUT COULDN'T GET IT OFF.

▶ VINES EXTENDING FROM HIS ARMS HELP GROOT CLIMB, WRANGLE OTHER CREATURES, AND ENSNARE ENEMIES.

▶ WHEN WELCOMING YONDU TO THE TEAM, GROOT SWORE, PROMPTING ROCKET TO PROMISE A LECTURE ABOUT HIS LANGUAGE.

MANTIS

FIRST APPEARANCE:
Guardians of the Galaxy Vol. 2 [2017]

THE DAUGHTER OF GERMAN mercenary Gustav Brandt, A.K.A. the Zodiac cartel's Libra, Mantis learned martial arts and extrasensory abilities from the plantlike Cotati race and the Kree Priests of Pama, who believed Mantis would one day sire a Celestial Messiah. After serving as an Avenger, then wedding the Cotati Supreme Exemplar to fulfill her destiny as the Celestial Madonna, Mantis traveled the universe, later joining the Guardians of the Galaxy and the Knowhere Corps.

FIRST APPEARANCE:
AVENGERS #112 (1973)

After finding an orphaned larva on an unidentified world, the Celestial Ego raised it on his own planet body. The larva became the beautiful, empathic Mantis. Eventually, Mantis began using her abilities to help Ego sleep at times when he was preoccupied with the search for his various offspring.

Mantis accompanied Ego when he set out to locate Star-Lord, whom he believed to be his son. Upon meeting Star-Lord and the Guardians of the Galaxy, Mantis began to mimic the behaviors and expressions of those around her, as she lacked knowledge of societal norms and possessed limited social skills after growing up in isolation. At the Guardians' request, Mantis demonstrated her empathic powers on Star-Lord, inadvertently revealing his attraction to Gamora, which prompted great laughter from Drax. However, the equally socially awkward Drax confused the naive Mantis by repeatedly stating she was ugly and nothing more than a pet.

After the Guardians traveled to Ego's planet to investigate his claim that he was Star-Lord's father, Mantis told them the truth: The very planet they were on was Ego's body; his humanoid form was merely an avatar he sent throughout the cosmos to seek his offspring so they could serve as batteries to power his universal expansion. During the ensuing battle, Mantis assisted the Guardians by forcing the rampaging Ego to sleep until debris knocked her unconscious. After the Guardians destroyed Ego and saved the galaxy, Mantis remained with the team. During Yondu's funeral, Drax finally admitted she was beautiful—on the inside. 🖤

FACT SHEET

▷ MANTIS BELIEVES HER ANTENNAE ARE CONNECTED WITH HER EMPATHIC ABILITIES. THEY GLOW WHEN SHE USES HER POWERS TO EXPERIENCE AND/OR ALTER SOMEONE ELSE'S FEELINGS.

▷ MANTIS CALLED ROCKET A "CRABBY PUPPY" AND SAID HE WAS SO CUTE IT MADE HER "WANT TO DIE."

NEBULA UPDATE

FIRST APPEARANCE:
Guardians of the Galaxy [2014]

After fleeing Xandarian space, Nebula found a claw to replace her severed cybernetic hand and later attempted to steal Anulax Batteries from the Sovereign, but was captured during the theft and imprisoned. When the Abilisk threatened to consume the batteries, the Sovereign offered Nebula to the Guardians of the Galaxy in exchange for their help defeating the interdimensional monster. As her adopted sister, Gamora, secured Nebula in the *Milano*, Nebula vowed to kill her.

Learning Rocket had stolen batteries, the Sovereign attacked the *Milano*. The Guardians and Nebula survived the assault with Ego's help. After the Guardians' ship crash-landed on Berhert, Ego claimed to be Star-Lord's father. Half the team left to investigate Ego's claim, but Nebula remained behind as Rocket's captive while he repaired the *Milano*. When the Sovereign-hired Ravagers attacked, Nebula convinced Groot to free her to help Rocket. Instead, she helped the Ravagers capture Rocket, then fostered a Ravager mutiny by incapacitating Ravager captain Yondu by shooting off his cranial fin then turning him over to the mutineers.

After procuring a ship and a new mechanical arm from the Ravagers, Nebula tracked Gamora to Ego's living planet body and attacked her. Nebula's reckless piloting caused her to crash, but Gamora pulled her from the wreckage moments before it exploded. Nebula again tried to kill Gamora, but relented at the last moment, claiming victory. Nebula reminded Gamora that their father, Thanos, would torture and maim her as a child whenever she lost a sparring match against Gamora. They were bitter rivals, Nebula said, but all she ever wanted was a sister. In a subsequent battle against a Sovereign fleet and Ego, Nebula subjected herself to great pain to power the weapons system of the Guardians' ship, then saved Gamora's life. After Ego's destruction, Gamora admitted to Nebula that she was only trying to keep herself alive by beating Nebula in childhood combat, then offered her a place with the Guardians. When Nebula turned down the invitation, Gamora hugged her and confirmed they would always be sisters. Initially stunned, Nebula slowly returned the hug before departing. ◆

FACT SHEET

▶ AFTER HER ROLE IN DEVASTATING XANDAR, A LARGE BOUNTY WAS PLACED ON NEBULA'S HEAD.

▶ NEBULA SUFFERS PROFOUND AND UNCEASING PAIN FROM THE BODY MODIFICATIONS FORCED ONTO HER BY THANOS.

▶ WHEN GAMORA WAS SURPRISED NEBULA SAVED HER LIFE, NEBULA TOLD HER TO "GET OVER IT."

RAVAGERS UPDATE

FIRST APPEARANCE:
Guardians of the Galaxy [2014]

While partying on the pleasure planet Contraxia, the Ravagers in Yondu's faction observed him arguing with his estranged fellow Ravagers captains over Yondu's exile decades before for breaking the Ravagers code. Taserface voiced his dissatisfaction with Yondu, while others—including Kraglin—defended him.

Hired by Ayesha and the Sovereign to capture the Guardians of the Galaxy, Yondu used a tracker to locate the *Milano*. Thanks to his booby traps, stealth, and close-quarters combat skills, Rocket single-handedly defeated the majority of the Ravagers until Yondu threatened him with his Yaka arrow. When the Ravagers learned Yondu wasn't going to turn the captive Rocket over to the Sovereign for fear of angering the Guardians' Nova Corps allies, Taserface and Kraglin led a mutiny, removing Yondu from leadership once Nebula destroyed his Yaka-controlling cranial fin. A defeated Yondu was forced to watch as Taserface and his followers executed all those loyal to Yondu by sending them out of an air lock to die from exposure. Taserface vowed to take the Ravagers to new heights of glory. However, Yondu's life was spared once Taserface became aware of the hefty bounty the Kree had placed on him.

A reluctant Kraglin—saddened by the murder of his friends—freed Yondu, who used a prototype cranial fin and his Yaka arrow to kill the mutinous Ravagers with the help of fellow captives Rocket and Groot. After Yondu sacrificed himself to help prevent Ego from destroying the universe, Rocket sent word to Yondu's estranged peers. All 99 remaining Ravagers factions attended a full-color funeral for Yondu, posthumously welcoming him back to their ranks. Following the funeral, Stakar Ogord gathered together Charlie-27,

RAVAGERS FUNERAL

CHARLIE-27

A co-founder of Reality-691's Guardians of the Galaxy, Jovian militia captain Charlie-27 acted as the team's pilot. Genetically modified to withstand the high gravity and radiation levels of his homeworld Jupiter, Charlie possesses superhuman strength and durability in Earth-level gravity.

FIRST APPEARANCE:
MARVEL SUPER HEROES #18 (1969)

KRUGARR

An alien Lem from Reality-691's 31st century, Krugarr was trained in the mystic arts by Doctor Strange and became the new Sorcerer Supreme. An ally of the Guardians of the Galaxy, he eventually was named an honorary team member.

FIRST APPEARANCE:
GUARDIANS OF THE GALAXY ANNUAL #1 (1991)

Aleta Ogord, Krugarr, Mainframe, and Martinex, who all agreed it was a shame it took losing Yondu to reconnect and

Taserface and Kraglin led a mutiny, removing Yondu from leadership once Nebula destroyed his Yaka-controlling cranial fin.

that Yondu would be proud they were a team once more. Ogord then declared they should resume their thieving ways. ⚑

MAIN FRAME

The synthezoid Vision discarded his physical form and interfaced with an abandoned world's planet-wide computer after a war with Mars devastated Earth in the future of Reality-691. As a vast source of information called Main Frame, he aided the Guardians of the Galaxy on several missions before joining the Galactic Guardians.

FIRST APPEARANCE:
GUARDIANS OF THE GALAXY #5 (1990)

MARTINEX

Genetically engineered to have a silicon-based organic crystalline body to survive on Pluto in the future of Reality-691, Martinex T'Naga is a scientist turned hero who can project both heat and cold from his hands. He both served with and led the Guardians of the Galaxy, founded the Galactic Guardians, and teamed with two other Guardians incarnations to prevent a Highbreed army from dominating all space and time.

FIRST APPEARANCE:
MARVEL SUPER-HEROES #18 (1969)

ALETA OGORD

31st-century Arcturan adventurer Aleta Ogord was merged with her husband, Stakar, to form the cosmic hero Starhawk, who later joined the Guardians of the Galaxy. Eventually, the two became estranged, and Aleta separated from Stakar, gaining her own body and light-manipulation powers for a time.

FIRST APPEARANCE:
(IMAGE) *DEFENDERS #29 (1975)*;
(PHYSICAL FORM) *MARVEL PRESENTS #4 (1976)*

STARHAWK (STAKAR OGORD)

Lovers and adopted siblings Stakar and Aleta Ogord were merged by a cosmic entity, the Hawk God, to become Starhawk. Doomed to relive his life repeatedly, retaining the memories of each life, Stakar referred to himself as "One Who Knows" when he joined the 31st century's Guardians of the Galaxy in Reality-691.

FIRST APPEARANCE:
DEFENDERS #27 (1975)

inability to allow anyone to get close. To stop Ego from terraforming the entire universe, Rocket rigged a detonator to the Anulax Batteries and instructed Groot—the only Guardian small enough to reach Ego's core—in its use. Rocket and Groot were emotional about leaving Yondu behind to help Star-Lord battle Ego while the team escaped. Rocket prevented Gamora from also staying, not wanting to lose another friend. After Ego's destruction, Rocket learned Yondu had sacrificed his life to save Star-Lord and notified Yondu's estranged fellow Ravagers captains of his selflessness. They responded by posthumously welcoming Yondu back to their ranks and giving him a full-color Ravagers funeral. During the ceremony, Rocket wept.

ROCKET UPDATE

FIRST APPEARANCE:
Guardians of the Galaxy (2014)

Though hired to prevent the interdimensional Abilisk from devouring the Sovereign's Anulax Batteries, Rocket stole some of the valuable power cells, prompting a Sovereign fleet to attack the Guardians of the Galaxy. Navigating a quantum asteroid field while fleeing the Sovereign, Rocket and Star-Lord jockeyed for control of the *Milano*, each believing himself to be the better pilot. Due to their bickering, the damaged *Milano* crash-landed on the nearby planet Berhert. The team split up—half going with Star-Lord's father, the Celestial Ego, while Rocket stayed behind with the now-infant Groot and the captive Nebula to repair the ship. When the Sovereign-hired Ravagers located the *Milano*,

Rocket defeated dozens of them until he was stopped by Yondu. Held captive, Rocket observed a Ravagers mutiny led by Taserface. Rocket's hysterical mockery of Taserface's name quickly spread among the Ravagers, angering Taserface. With the help of Groot and the Ravager Kraglin, Rocket and Yondu escaped their cell and killed all of the mutinous Ravagers.

After learning of Ego's malevolence, Rocket and his allies dangerously journeyed through 700 point-to-point portals to Ego's living planet body to reunite with the other Guardians. Rocket claimed he wanted to save Star-Lord so he could hold it over him forever. Rocket and Yondu reluctantly bonded over their painful pasts and shared

SOVEREIGN HOMEWORLD

THE SOVEREIGN

FIRST APPEARANCE:
Guardians of the Galaxy Vol. 2 (2017)

The Sovereign are a humanoid race whose members are genetically enhanced to be as close to perfection as possible. Their coloring—skin, hair, eyes—is mostly gold, matching their very precise vision of beauty. The race lives on a series of connected planets, also collectively called the Sovereign. High Priestess Ayesha leads the race, though she is accountable to a council populated by an unrevealed number of Sovereign members.

The Sovereign are self-indulgent and easily offended; the cost of offending them is death. The race's highly valuable Anulax Batteries power much of their equipment and their society at large, and, being worth thousands of units apiece, are one of the Sovereign's greatest resources. The Sovereign utilize a fleet of highly maneuverable spacecraft that are remotely piloted by Sovereign members in a massive arcade chamber on their homeworld, ensuring their precious citizens are not harmed in battle.

When an interdimensional Abilisk threatened to consume their batteries, Ayesha hired the Guardians of the Galaxy to prevent the theft, offering Gamora's adopted sister Nebula in exchange. However, after successfully completing their task, Rocket stole a number of the batteries, prompting the Sovereign to pursue the departing Guardians, seeking their deaths. The Guardians evaded much of the fleet thanks to Star-Lord and Rocket's amazing piloting, and with help from the Celestial Ego, the rest of the fleet was destroyed. The Sovereign later tracked the batteries to Ego's living planet body and again attacked the Guardians there, but their fleet was destroyed in battle a second time.

As a result of the repeated insults, the Sovereign have vowed eternal enmity with the Guardians, and Ayesha has taken steps to foster the next step in Sovereign evolution to kill them: the more deadly, more beautiful "Adam." ◈

FACT SHEET

▶ SLIGHTS AGAINST THE SOVEREIGN ARE CONSIDERED TO BE HERESY; THEFT OF THE ANULAX BATTERIES IS THE HIGHEST ORDER OF OFFENSES.

▶ THOUGH THEORETICALLY PERFECT, MEMBERS OF THE SOVEREIGN STILL INSULT EACH OTHER AND BICKER AMONGST THEMSELVES.

▶ PILOTS ARE GREATLY ANGERED WHEN THEIR REMOTELY CONTROLLED SHIPS ARE DEFEATED IN BATTLE.

SOVEREIGN FLEET

STAR-LORD
UPDATE

FIRST APPEARANCE:
Guardians of the Galaxy [2014]

After the Guardians of the Galaxy successfully stopped the Abilisk monster from devouring the Sovereign's valuable Anulax Batteries, Sovereign High Priestess Ayesha offered to have sex with Star-Lord to research archaic procreation methods; Star-Lord instinctively flirted back until he remembered Gamora was watching and quickly backpedaled. After Rocket stole batteries, a Sovereign fleet attacked the departing *Milano*. To escape, Star-Lord steered into a dangerous quantum asteroid field, but Rocket repeatedly stole the controls, believing himself the better pilot. However, the mysterious Ego destroyed the fleet, saving the group. Later, on planet Berhert, Ego claimed to be Star-Lord's father; Gamora encouraged Star-Lord to investigate, promising to kill Ego if necessary.

On Ego's home planet, Star-Lord learned Ego was a millennia-old Celestial who had formed his own planet body and sent a humanoid avatar throughout the universe to sire children, including Star-Lord. Ego taught Star-Lord how to access Celestial energy (the Light), and the two played catch with an energy sphere, fulfilling Star-Lord's long-held childhood fantasy. Later, Ego told Star-Lord he was immortal so long as the Light burned, then temporarily bestowed cosmic awareness on

humanoid avatar wither, Star-Lord was prepared to die when Ego's planet body dissolved, but using a Guardians Aero-Rig, Yondu flew Star-Lord into space and put the sole remaining space-suit on him. Yondu told Star-Lord that he considered him his son before dying from exposure.

During Yondu's funeral, a grieving Star-Lord recognized the similarities between Yondu and the TV personalities he idolized in his youth, realizing that he had the father he longed for all along. While watching the Ravagers' funeral for Yondu, Gamora admitted the long-denied "unspoken thing" between them, and embraced Star-Lord. ◆

Star-Lord, expanding his awareness reality-wide. When Ego admitted that he killed Meredith Quill—Star-Lord's mother—to prevent the continued distraction she was to his goal of universal expansion, Star-Lord attacked him. Ego skewered Star-Lord with energy, turning him into the living battery he needed to power his expansion. The Guardians gathered, freed Star-Lord and journeyed into Ego's caverns to destroy his core.

During the subsequent fight, Star-Lord learned his foster father, the Ravager Yondu—who was aiding the Guardians against Ego—was hired by Ego to kidnap Star-Lord from Earth, but Yondu never delivered him, having learned Ego killed his other progeny. While the Guardians attempted to access Ego's core, a Sovereign fleet attacked them again; while the team battled the Sovereign, Rocket and Groot planted a bomb on Ego's core as Ego's servant Mantis—who had become friends with the Guardians—empathically forced Ego to sleep. After Yondu helped destroy the Sovereign fleet, Mantis was knocked unconscious by falling debris. Yondu coached Star-Lord to use Ego's power; tapping into his most cherished life memories, Star-Lord used the Light to battle the raging Ego until Rocket's bomb detonated, ending Ego's expansion. After watching Ego's

YONDU UPDATE

FIRST APPEARANCE:
Guardians of the Galaxy [2014]

When Yondu Udonta encountered fellow Ravagers captain Stakar Ogord for the first time in decades, the two argued about Yondu's exile from the Ravagers for trafficking in children for the enigmatic Celestial Ego. Ogord said Yondu broke the Ravagers' hearts by what he had done and refused to reconcile, even after Yondu admitted his greed kept him from knowing the full details of the job. When approached by the Sovereign, Yondu agreed to capture the Guardians of the Galaxy for them. However, after catching Rocket, Yondu chose not to complete the job for fear of earning the enmity of the Guardians' allies, the Nova Corps. Believing him weak, Ravagers led by Taserface opposed Yondu, and he was overthrown as captain when his cranial fin was destroyed. Taserface executed Yondu's loyalists but left Yondu alive so he could claim a Kree bounty.

Later, with the help of Groot and a remorseful Kraglin, Yondu escaped captivity and slew the Ravagers using a prototype fin to control his Yaka Arrow. He then followed Star-Lord to Ego, who planned to use his offspring to power his conquest of the universe. During the subsequent battle against both vengeful Sovereign and a power-mad Ego, Yondu coached Star-Lord to tap into Ego's power to occupy him while the Guardians set a bomb to destroy the living planet. After Ego's destruction, Yondu sacrificed himself by giving Star-Lord the only spacesuit and told Star-Lord that he considered him his son. Believing him redeemed through his sacrifice and stopping Ego, the Ravagers posthumously welcomed Yondu back to the fold and honored him with a beautiful Ravagers funeral ceremony. ◆

FACT SHEET

▶ YONDU'S OWN PARENTS SOLD HIM INTO SLAVERY AS A BABY; ROCKET AND YONDU BONDED OVER THEIR PAINFUL PASTS AND REFUSAL TO LET ANYONE GET CLOSE.

▶ YONDU CLAIMED HIS CONSTANT THREATS AND ABUSE OF STAR-LORD AS A CHILD TOUGHENED THE BOY TO SURVIVE.

▶ YONDU COULD CAUSE HIS YAKA ARROW TO BURST INTO FLAMES AT WILL.

▶ WHEN USING THE YAKA ARROW TO FLOAT DOWN FROM A SPACECRAFT, STAR-LORD COMPARED HIM TO MARY POPPINS; YONDU EMBRACED THE COMPARISON, UNAWARE IT WAS SAID MOCKINGLY.

▶ STAR-LORD, KRAGLIN AND THE GUARDIANS CREMATED YONDU WITH THE TRINKETS AND POSSESSIONS HE CHERISHED MOST; WHEN RELEASED IN SPACE, YONDU'S ASHES TOOK THE FORM OF AN ARROW AS THEY DRIFTED AWAY.

KRAGLIN

FIRST APPEARANCE:
Guardians of the Galaxy [2014]

A long-standing member of Yondu's Ravagers faction, Kraglin helped raise young Earthling Peter Quill when Yondu, ordered to kidnap him for the Celestial Ego, instead kept the boy after learning of Ego's malevolent plans for him. Kraglin stood by Yondu when he was exiled from the Ravagers for dealing in children and later when an adult Quill betrayed them. After the Ravagers and the Guardians of the Galaxy helped prevent Ronan from destroying the planet Xandar, the Ravagers were hired by the Sovereign race to pursue the Guardians for stealing valuable batteries; when Yondu told his crew he intended to take the batteries and leave Quill alive, Kraglin defended him against disgruntled Ravagers who felt Yondu had put Quill's well-being ahead of his crew too many times, but then sided against him during a resulting mutiny. After the Ravager Taserface executed all Yondu loyalists, a guilty Kraglin helped free Yondu, who slaughtered the mutineers. Later, after Yondu sacrificed himself to save Quill while they stopped Ego from destroying the universe, a mournful Kraglin was ecstatic to see Yondu receive an honorable Ravagers funeral from the 99 Ravagers factions that had exiled him years before. Kraglin remains with the Guardians, with Quill as his captain, learning how to wield the Yaka arrow using Yondu's control fin. 🜲

TASERFACE

FIRST APPEARANCE:
Guardians of the Galaxy Vol. 2 [2017]

A member of Yondu's faction of Ravagers, Taserface came to feel Yondu was becoming soft and pathetic after seeing other Ravagers captains disrespect him. When Yondu decided not to turn the captive Rocket over to the Sovereign as hired, Taserface staged a mutiny, killing Yondu loyalists. The Kree bounty for Yondu stayed his execution. When Rocket mocked Taserface's name, the Ravagers snickered quietly before exploding in laughter. With Rocket and Groot, Yondu escaped and slaughtered the Ravagers. Caught in a massive explosion and gravely wounded, Taserface contacted the Sovereign with Yondu's coordinates. When he asked the Sovereign to tell Yondu it was Taserface who had sealed his fate, she laughed hysterically at his name. Taserface apparently died when the *Eclector* exploded. 🜲

IN THE COMICS

IN REALITY-691, TASERFACE could shoot electromagnetic energy from his face, but was defeated by the 31st-century Guardians of the Galaxy and rechristened the Nameless One in defeat. Taserface's own Iron Man-worshiping Stark race rebuilt him as Overkill, but the Guardians defeated him again.

FIRST APPEARANCE:
(AS TASERFACE) *GUARDIANS OF THE GALAXY* #1 (1990); (AS OVERKILL) *GUARDIANS OF THE GALAXY* #10 (1991)

AS OVERKILL

HOWARD THE DUCK
UPDATE
Guardians of the Galaxy [2014]

AFTER being freed from the Collector's collection, Howard left Knowhere and journeyed to Contraxia—a snowy planet of pleasures that is considered to be the red-light district of its galaxy. Howard located a former industrial city in the tundra filled with neon signs, bars, back rooms, and hedonistic pleasures, and visited the Iron Lotus brothel, which utilized Love Bots, feminine robots created for pleasure. He sipped his drinks in a plush lounge chair while he socialized with a humanoid woman, making her laugh with his motto "you're out of luck until you've gone duck."

FACT SHEET

▶ DESPITE THE IRON LOTUS' BAR SETTING, HOWARD WORE A THREE-PIECE SUIT AND A TIE.

▶ HOWARD DOES NOT WEAR SHOES, ALLOWING HIS WEBBED FEET TO REMAIN UNCONSTRAINED.

MEREDITH QUILL UPDATE
Guardians of the Galaxy [2014]

IN EARLY 1980s Missouri, Meredith Quill fell in love with a "spaceman" who visited her three times; she became pregnant during one visit. When he showed her an alien flower that he claimed would spread across the universe, she told him she didn't understand what he was saying, but liked how he said it. Meredith was unaware the being was Ego, a Celestial who intended to absorb the universe into himself, or that he had placed a tumor in her brain to prevent her from distracting him from his mission. Meredith's son, Peter, and others dismissed tales of her "spaceman" as delusions brought on by the brain cancer that eventually killed her. Peter later became the spacefaring Star-Lord and helped kill Ego to avenge Meredith and stop his expansion.

FACT SHEET

▶ EGO'S NICKNAME FOR MEREDITH QUILL WAS "RIVER LILY."

▶ MEREDITH SHARED HER LOVE OF POPULAR MUSIC WITH EGO, SINGING ALONG TO HER FAVORITE SONGS.

▶ EGO SHOWED PETER QUILL A MASSIVE STATUE OF MEREDITH ON HIS PLANET.

THE WATCHERS
Guardians of the Galaxy Vol. 2 [2017]

WHILE traversing through space portals, a ship carrying some of the Guardians of the Galaxy passed over a barren landscape where three large, enigmatic Watchers listened to stories told by a space traveler. The silent beings briefly watched the ship before returning their attention to the traveler. After a time, the Watchers turned and left the distraught, stranded being to fend for himself.

FACT SHEET

▶ THE WATCHERS WEAR LONG, DARK, FLOWING ROBES ADORNED WITH A CHEST MEDALLION AND A MATCHING COWL BEHIND THEIR HEADS.

▶ EACH WATCHER IS BALD AND HAS GLOWING, PUPIL-LESS EYES.

IN THE COMICS

IN THE COMICS Billions of years ago, a technologically advanced alien culture benevolently gave atomic energy to a planet that ultimately used it to create nuclear weapons and destroy themselves. Horrified, the culture vowed to never again interfere, choosing to solely gain knowledge by omnisciently observing the Multiverse as the Watchers. *FANTASTIC FOUR #13 (1963).*

COVER GALLERY

MARVEL'S AVENGERS: AGE OF ULTRON COVER SKETCHES BY MIKE DEL MUNDO